Data Protection and Privacy in Healthcare

Data Protection and Privacy in Healthcare
Research and Innovations

Edited by
Ahmed Elngar, Ambika Pawar, and
Prathamesh Churi

CRC Press
Taylor & Francis Group
Boca Raton London New York

CRC Press is an imprint of the
Taylor & Francis Group, an **informa** business

First edition published 2021
by CRC Press
6000 Broken Sound Parkway NW, Suite 300, Boca Raton, FL 33487-2742

and by CRC Press
2 Park Square, Milton Park, Abingdon, Oxon, OX14 4RN

© 2021 Taylor & Francis Group, LLC
CRC Press is an imprint of Taylor & Francis Group, LLC

The right of Ahmed Elngar, Ambika Pawar, and Prathamesh Churi to be identified as the authors of the editorial material, and of the authors for their individual chapters, has been asserted in accordance with sections 77 and 78 of the Copyright, Designs and Patents Act 1988.

Reasonable efforts have been made to publish reliable data and information, but the author and publisher cannot assume responsibility for the validity of all materials or the consequences of their use. The authors and publishers have attempted to trace the copyright holders of all material reproduced in this publication and apologize to copyright holders if permission to publish in this form has not been obtained. If any copyright material has not been acknowledged please write and let us know so we may rectify in any future reprint.

Except as permitted under U.S. Copyright Law, no part of this book may be reprinted, reproduced, transmitted, or utilized in any form by any electronic, mechanical, or other means, now known or hereafter invented, including photocopying, microfilming, and recording, or in any information storage or retrieval system, without written permission from the publishers.

For permission to photocopy or use material electronically from this work, access www.copyright.com or contact the Copyright Clearance Center, Inc. (CCC), 222 Rosewood Drive, Danvers, MA 01923, 978-750-8400. For works that are not available on CCC please contact mpkbookspermissions@tandf.co.uk

Trademark notice: Product or corporate names may be trademarks or registered trademarks and are used only for identification and explanation without intent to infringe.

Library of Congress Cataloging-in-Publication Data

Names: Elngar, Ahmed A., editor. | Pawar, Ambika, editor. | Churi, Prathamesh, editor.
Title: Data protection and privacy in healthcare : research and innovations / edited by Ahmed Elngar, Ambika Pawar, and Prathamesh Churi.
Description: Boca Raton, FL : CRC Press, 2021. | Includes bibliographical references and index.
Identifiers: LCCN 2020041976 (print) | LCCN 2020041977 (ebook) | ISBN 9780367501082 (hardback) | ISBN 9781003048848 (ebook)
Subjects: LCSH: Medical care--Data processing. | Data protection.
Classification: LCC R858 .D3778 2021 (print) | LCC R858 (ebook) | DDC 610.285--dc23 LC record available at https://lccn.loc.gov/2020041976LC ebook record available at https://lccn.loc.gov/2020041977

ISBN: 978-0-367-50108-2 (hbk)
ISBN: 978-1-003-04884-8 (ebk)

Typeset in Times
by Deanta Global Publishing Services, Chennai, India

This book is dedicated to all the teachers, students and researchers in data privacy in the healthcare field.

Contents

Preface ix
Acknowledgements xiii
Editor Biographies xv
List of Contributors xvii

Chapter 1 An Overview of Data Privacy in Healthcare in the Current Age 1

Reinaldo Padilha França, Ana Carolina Borges Monteiro, Rangel Arthur and Yuzo Iano

Chapter 2 Privacy in Cloud Healthcare Data 21

Disha Garg

Chapter 3 Privacy-Preserving Authentication and Key-Management Protocol for Health Information Systems 37

Mukesh Soni and Dileep Kumar Singh

Chapter 4 Privacy Issues in Medical Image Analysis 51

Prachi Natu, Shachi Natu and Upasana Agrawal

Chapter 5 Privacy in Internet of Healthcare Things 65

Mohammad Wazid and Ashok Kumar Das

Chapter 6 Heath Device Security and Privacy: A Comparative Analysis of Fitbit, Jawbone, Google Glass and Samsung Galaxy Watch 91

A B M Kamrul Islam Riad, Hossain Shahriar, Chi Zhang and Farhat Lamia Barsha

Chapter 7 Privacy-Preserving Infrastructure for Health Information Systems 109

Sheikh Mohammad Idrees, Mariusz Nowostawski, Roshan Jameel and Ashish Kumar Mourya

Chapter 8 Health Sector at the Crossroads: Divergence vis-à-vis Convergence in the Emergence of New Trends 131

Arindam Chakrabarty, Uday Sankar Das and Saket Kushwaha

Chapter 9 ITreatU: An Effective Privacy and Security Solution for Healthcare Data Using the R3 Corda Platform of Blockchain Technology 165

Priyank Hajela, Ambika Pawar and Shraddha Phansalkar

Chapter 10 Personalized Medicine and a Data Revolution: Hope and Peril 179

Subhajit Basu and Adekemi Omotubora

Chapter 11 Legislation Comparison in the Sphere of Health Protection in Selected European Countries 199

Yuriy Yu. Shvets

Chapter 12 Challenges of Implementing Privacy Policies Across the Globe 211

Tanvi Garg and Navid Kagalwalla

Chapter 13 The Role of Law in Protecting Medical Data in India 229

S. P. Chakrabarty, S. Mukherjee and A. Rodricks

Index 245

Preface

The security and privacy concerns of any type of data are a major issue in today's technology-driven world. The term privacy is defined as an action where the data are kept hidden from either anonymous users or the server to avoid the misuse of the data. In the world of distributed computing environments, the processing and storage of such multidimensional data are also done dynamically and at different dynamic locations keeping various transparencies in mind. In such a scenario, the privacy of data is an important concern. Primarily, there are a number of privacy techniques such as anonymization, generalization, perturbation, role-based access control, encryption, etc. Typically, according to researchers, data have different phases during their lifecycle: The storage of data, transition of data, transfer of data and processing of data. Existing privacy-preserving techniques are still in the maturing stages, and strong privacy protection is still an open research problem. There is research happening in maintaining the privacy of healthcare in various areas, viz. IoT-privacy-based healthcare systems, machine learning in healthcare data with privacy, maintaining the privacy of healthcare big data, privacy-preserving cloud storage of healthcare data, etc.

Various new technologies have been used in the healthcare domain: Machine learning algorithms for the prediction of certain health parameters/data/diseases/behaviour, IoT-based healthcare systems, data analytics in healthcare, blockchain implementation in healthcare, cloud-based healthcare systems, etc. Wearable technology in healthcare is used for continuous patient monitoring, data streaming and sharing and the use of data analysis to provide certain health services to the patients. Additionally, it uses patients' past records, treatment given by healthcare experts/doctors, prescriptions, allergic details of a patient, etc.

The healthcare industry is one of the largest and most rapidly developing industries. According to IBM Global Business Services, Executive Report, 2012, the overall healthcare management is changing from disease-centric to patient-centric. While on one side, the analysis of healthcare data plays an important role in healthcare management, on the other side the privacy of patients' records must be of equal concern. Preserving the privacy of medical data is not only an ethical but also a legal requirement, posed by several data sharing regulations and policies worldwide, such as the Privacy Rule of the Health Insurance Portability and Accountability Act, and the Data Protection Act, etc. Also, we are witnessing a wealth of approaches for preserving privacy in many phases of the healthcare information life cycle, including data collection, communication and sharing, as well as the knowledge management of healthcare information. To achieve privacy goals, these approaches employ various techniques, such as cryptography, access control and data anonymization, generalization and perturbation.

The edited book aims to present research in data protection and privacy in healthcare and addresses the issues of privacy in newer technologies. The book will provide a forum for enthusiastic researchers on all topics related to data privacy technologies, policies and breaches in privacy, considering healthcare as a multidisciplinary domain.

The book also explores other timely aspects of privacy in areas such as usable security, the Internet of Things, cloud computing, cryptography and big data only within the context of the healthcare field. Other popular topics include privacy-enhancing technologies, privacy-preserving healthcare data analytics, privacy-aware wireless/mobile and embedded security and privacy policies.

The edited book consists of 13 chapters from 34 authors from 8 different countries. A short description of each chapter is given below.

Chapter 1 aims to provide an updated review of privacy of physicians' data, and the technologies that use such data, such as big data and cloud computing, discussing their successful relationship, with a concise bibliographic background, categorizing and synthesizing the potential of both technologies.

Chapter 2 emphasizes the core concepts of maintaining data privacy in a cloud environment—the data life cycle (from the inception of data to the destruction of data), the key privacy concerns or challenges faced by cloud users, the importance of data privacy in the healthcare sector, the various stakeholders responsible for maintaining data privacy and the techniques adopted to prevent data disclosure and a comparison of various privacy attacks over the years and the possible techniques to prevent them.

Chapter 3 proposes a privacy-preserving key-agreement protocol for health information systems. This protocol is responsible for transmitting health data securely and on-time in a public environment. Further, the proposed system prevents unauthorized access to health data. The protocol also has a performance analysis of the proposed scheme to check its implementation efficiency based on different performance measures.

Chapter 4 is about the patient's data privacy which is an essential factor for current applications in E-healthcare services frameworks. With the emergence of medical IoT devices, the variety, veracity and volumes of images have altogether expanded. While delivering medical images for remote analysis, the assurance of the protection of patient's data is critical. For the diagnosis of diseases and improving the treatment efficiency, the retrieval of medical images is very important. Medical images also contain the patient's demographics or protected health information (PHI). This PHI should be known to concerned doctors and not to the general public like researchers and learners. The chapter briefly lists the privacy issues in medical image processing.

Chapter 5 contains the details of various types of architectures associated with the Internet of Healthcare Things (IoHT) environment and their various advantages. Next, important applications of IoHT, such as remote monitoring of patients, hospital operations management and remote surgery, are discussed. Moreover, privacy issues and threat models related to the IoHT environment are also discussed. Different types of attacks that are possible in the IoHT environment are highlighted. Finally, a comparative analysis of privacy-preserving security protocols related to the IoHT environment is provided.

Chapter 6 examines the significant security and privacy features of four health tracker devices: Fitbit, Jawbone, Google Glass and Samsung Galaxy Watch. It also analyses the devices' strength and how the devices communicate via their Bluetooth pairing processes with mobile devices.

Chapter 7 focusses on the utilization of blockchain-distributed frameworks in healthcare transactions to and from the cloud, which provides the users with real-time access to the data securely and transparently. Blockchain technology has gained in popularity in numerous sectors including finance, education, manufacturing, etc., and is attracting continuous attention in the healthcare sector as well, because it can resolve the complications mentioned above and deliver a system that is transparent and traceable without any intermediaries. It facilitates a decentralized structure and distributed environment that does not require any central authority to control the system. Blockchain technology exploits the principle of cryptography to keep the transactions safe and secure.

Chapter 8 has attempted to understand the current technological state and the healthcare perspectives along with its convergence as well as divergence in the emerging trends. The chapter has tried to look at the power of analytics to provide appropriate healthcare solutions, i.e., from disease determination and diagnostics to smart and sophisticated treatment. The chapter is based on secondary data and literature from available reliable sources. The chapter has attempted to understand the present problems and suggests primary models and solutions for the health industry.

Chapter 9 explores the application of blockchain in the healthcare sector for storing patient treatment history and develops a proof of concept on the Corda blockchain platform, developed by R3 Consortium. In the wake of significant information penetration episodes, blockchain can strengthen systems that successfully meet regulations of the patient and medicinal services information insurance. R3 Corda is an open-source blockchain platform with the potential to promise strict privacy to healthcare transactions between trusted parties like healthcare providers and patients with smart contracts and a bilateral ledger.

Chapter 10 argues that the future of personalized medicine will depend upon how we address relevant legal and ethical issues arising from both challenges and limitations concerning data. We must be mindful of the rights of patients to access their data and control their use and distribution, particularly respecting and enforcing these rights—including the right to privacy. This chapter examines the challenges posed by the technological breakthroughs, including the complexity of data, and the role to be given to consent that would provide transparency and foster patients' trust in the development of personalized medicine.

Chapter 11 focusses on human rights and the protection of medical data in the European context. Protection of human rights and citizen rights is an essential aspect of public life. Speaking of the most important tasks of the state, it should not be limited to protecting citizens solely to improve the quality of daily life, which is the goal of most health systems.

Chapter 12 discusses various privacy policies in both developing and underdeveloped countries. This chapter discusses the various challenges present in developing countries that inhibit them from establishing a secure privacy system. It also discusses the monetization of the various developing countries in the healthcare plans to make data accessing secure. It then goes on to explore the privacy policies currently present in major developing countries. Finally, it points out possible solutions for implementing a privacy system which has been devised keeping in mind reliability, availability, accessibility, scalability and cost-effectiveness.

Chapter 13 presents research on the socio-economic condition of people living in developing jurisdictions, like India, regarding medical privacy. This research shall unravel whether the law protects the individual's right to privacy, or permits taking advantage of the data available to private service providers for potential economic exploitation in the biggest market of the world. A comparative analysis of the laws relating to medical data protection unveils the existence of specific grey areas like broad consent, commercialization of samples and country-based consent, which demand sincere retrospection to mitigate the vulnerability prevailing in these jurisdictions.

This book has an integrated approach to delivering the concept of privacy through two aspects, viz. technology and law. We hope that this book will create interest among the researchers who are working in similar fields.

- Dr Ahmed A. Elngar, Assistant Professor, Faculty of Computer Science and Artificial Intelligence Beni-Suef University, Egypt
- Dr Ambika Pawar, Associate Professor, Symbiosis Institute of Technology, Symbiosis International Deemed University, Pune, India
- Prof. Prathamesh Churi, Assistant Professor, School of Technology Management and Engineering, NMIMS University, Mumbai, India

Acknowledgements

First and foremost, praises and thanks to God, the Almighty, for His showers of blessings throughout our work to complete the book *Data Protection and Privacy in Healthcare: Research and Innovations* (DPPHRI) successfully.

The authors are the real motivation for this book. We thank them all for considering and trusting our book for publishing their valuable work. We also thank all authors for their kind co-operation extended during the various stages of processing of the book in CRC Press, Taylor & Francis.

For the success of any edited book, reviewers are an essential part, and hence reviewers merit sincere appreciation. The inputs of reviewers are used in improving the quality of submitted book chapters. The reviewing of a book chapter is essential to assure the quality of the chapter published in any book. We thank the following reviewers for their excellent contributions during the review process.

- Dr Utku Kose, *Associate Professor, Department of Computer Engineering, Suleyman Demirel University, Faculty of Engineering, Turkey*
- Prof. Rashi Kohli, *Senior Member, IEEE (USA)*
- Mr. Yash Joshi, *Manager, Alliances and Strategy, Jio Creative Labs, India*
- Prof. Mukesh Soni, *Department of Computer Engineering, Smt S. R. Patel Engineering College, India*
- Prof. Manisha Tiwari, *Department of Computer Engineering, School of Technology Management and Engineering, NMIMS University, India*
- Prof. Krishna Samdani, *Department of Computer Engineering, School of Technology Management and Engineering, NMIMS University, India*
- Prof. Kamal Mistry, *Department of Computer Engineering, School of Technology Management and Engineering, NMIMS University, India*
- Prof. Artika Singh, *Department of Computer Engineering, School of Technology Management and Engineering, NMIMS University, India*
- Prof. Ameyaa Biwalkar, *Department of Computer Engineering, School of Technology Management and Engineering, NMIMS University, India*

The overwhelming responses from the authors across the world have been a real motivation and support in taking forward this book in the area of data protection and privacy in the healthcare field. Last but not least, we would like to thank Ms. Cindy Renee Carelli (Executive Editor—Engineering, CRC Press, Taylor & Francis) and Ms. Erin Harris (Senior Editorial Assistant—Engineering, CRC Press, Taylor & Francis) for their valuable support in the book-editing process.

Editor Biographies

Ahmed Elngar

Dr Elngar is the founder and Head of the Scientific Innovation Research Group (SIRG) and Assistant Professor of Computer Science at the Faculty of Computers and Information, Beni-Suef University. Dr Elngar is a Director of the Technological and Informatics Studies Center (TISC), Faculty of Computers and Information, Beni-Suef University, Egypt. He is a Managing Editor of the *Journal of Cybersecurity and Information Management* (JCIM). Dr Elngar has more than 25 scientific research papers published in prestigious international journals and over 5 books covering such diverse topics as data mining, intelligent systems, social networks and smart environment. He is a member of the Egyptian Mathematical Society (EMS) and International Rough Set Society (IRSS). His other research areas include the Internet of Things (IoT), network security, machine learning and artificial intelligence. He is an editor and reviewer of many international journals around the world. Dr Elngar has won several awards including the *Young Researcher Award in Computer Science Engineering* from Global Outreach Education Summit and Awards 2019. He is also a recipient of *the Best Young Researcher Award (Male) (Below 40 years)* from Global Education and Corporate Leadership Awards (GECL-2018). Dr Elngar takes part in many activities in the community and the environment service including organizing 12 workshops hosted by a large number of universities in almost all governorates of Egypt.

Ambika Pawar

Dr Ambika Pawar is Associate Professor in the Computer Science and Information Technology Department at Symbiosis International (Deemed University). She has published more than 30 papers in the areas of cloud computing, data privacy and algorithms. She has experience of 10+ years in teaching as well as in research. She has been a conference programme committee member and reviewer at various international conferences.

Prathamesh Churi

Prathamesh Churi is an Assistant Professor in the School of Technology Management and Engineering, NMIMS University, India. He is currently an Associate Editor of the *International Journal of Advances in Intelligent Informatics* and Editorial Board Member of *Inderscience International Journal of Forensic Software Engineering*. He is actively involved in the peer-review process of reputed IEEE and Springer journals. He has been a keynote speaker, chair and convener in the reputed international conferences. He is a recipient of *the "Best Young Researcher Award"* by the GISR Foundation for his research contribution in the field of data privacy and security, education technology. He is an active leader, coach and mentor in many non-profit organizations. He is also involved as a board of study member in many universities for curriculum development and educational transformations. He has over 50+ research papers in international journals and conferences. His passion lies in transforming the higher education sector in India. You can follow him on his LinkedIn account: https://www.linkedin.com/in/prathameshchuri/.

List of Contributors

Upasana Agrawal
Northeastern University
College of Professional Studies
Boston, MA

Rangel Arthur
Faculty of Technology
State University of Campinas
  (UNICAMP)
Limeira, São Paulo, Brazil

Subhajit Basu
School of Law
University of Leeds
Leeds, United Kingdom

Ana Carolina Borges Monteiro
School of Electrical Engineering and
  Computing
State University of Campinas
  (UNICAMP)
Campinas, São Paulo, Brazil

Arindam Chakrabarty
Department of Management
Rajiv Gandhi University (Central
  University)
Doimukh, India

Disha Garg
Department of Computer Science
J C Bose University of Science and
  Technology
Faridabad, India

Tanvi Garg
Department of Computer Engineering
Mukesh Patel School of Technology
  Management and Engineering
Mumbai, India

Priyank Hajela
Symbiosis Institute of Technology
Symbiosis International (Deemed
  University)
Maharashtra, India

Yuzo Iano
School of Electrical Engineering and
  Computing
State University of Campinas
  (UNICAMP)
Campinas, São Paulo, Brazil

Sheikh Mohammad Idrees
Department of Computer Science
Norwegian University of Science and
  Technology
Gjøvik, Norway

Roshan Jameel
Department of Computer Science
Jamia Hamdard University
New Delhi, India

Navid Kagalwalla
Department of Computer Engineering
Mukesh Patel School of Technology
  Management and Engineering
Mumbai, India

A. B. M. Kamrul Islam Riad
Department of Information Technology
Kennesaw State University
Kennesaw, GA

Ashok Kumar Das
Center for Security, Theory and
  Algorithmic Research
International Institute of Information
  Technology
Hyderabad, India

Ashish Kumar Mourya
Department of Computer Science
Jamia Hamdard
New Delhi, India

Dileep Kumar Singh
Department of Computer Engineering
Jagran Lakecity University
Bhopal, India

Saket Kushwaha
Banaras Hindu University
Varanasi, India
and
Rajiv Gandhi University (Central University)
Doimukh, India

Farhat Lamia Barsha
Department of Computer Science and Engineering
Military Institute of Science and Technology
Dhaka, Bangladesh

S. Mukherjee
The West Bengal National University of Juridical Sciences
Kolkata, India

Prachi Natu
Computer Engineering Department
MPSTME, NMIMS University
Mumbai, India

Shachi Natu
Information Technology Department
Thadomal Shahani Engineering College
Mumbai, India

Mariusz Nowostawski
Department of Computer Science
Norwegian University of Science and Technology
Gjøvik, Norway

Adekemi Omotubora
Department of Commercial and Industrial Law
University of Lagos
Lagos, Nigeria

Reinaldo Padilha França
School of Electrical Engineering and Computing
State University of Campinas (UNICAMP)
Campinas, São Paulo, Brazil

Ambika Pawar
Department of Computer Science and Information Technology
Symbiosis Institute of Technology
Symbiosis International (Deemed University)
Maharashtra, India

Shraddha Phansalkar
Department of Computer Science and Information Technology
Symbiosis Institute of Technology
Symbiosis International (Deemed University)
Maharashtra, India

Shambhu Prasad Chakrabarty
Centre for Regularly Studies Governance and Public Policy
The West Bengal National University of Juridical Sciences
Kolkata, India

A. Rodricks
Amity Law School
Noida, India

Uday Sankar Das
Department of Management & Humanities
National Institute of Technology Arunachal Pradesh
Yupia, India

List of Contributors

Hossain Shahriar
Associate Professor of Information
  Technology
Kennesaw State University
Kennesaw, GA

Yuriy Shvets
Institute of Problems of Management of
  V.A. Trapeznikov
RAS Financial University
Moscow, Russia

Mukesh Soni
Department of Computer Engineering
Jagran Lakecity University
Bhopal, India

Mohammad Wazid
Department of Computer Science and
  Engineering
Graphic Era Deemed to be University
Dehradun, India

Chi Zhang
Associate Professor of Information
  Technology
Kennesaw State University
Kennesaw, GA

1 An Overview of Data Privacy in Healthcare in the Current Age

Reinaldo Padilha França, Ana Carolina Borges Monteiro, Rangel Arthur and Yuzo Iano

CONTENTS

1.1 Introduction 1
1.2 Data Privacy Relevance and Healthcare Need 2
    1.2.1 The e-Health Benefits of Data Sharing 4
    1.2.2 Types of Medical Data 4
    1.2.3 Anonymization as a Form of Patient Privacy 6
    1.2.4 Data Anonymization Techniques 6
    1.2.5 Privacy Protection with Encryption 7
1.3 The Importance of Digital Management in Healthcare 8
    1.3.1 Challenges in Health Data Privacy 9
    1.3.2 Components for Data Access Control 10
1.4 Importance of Digital Data Security in Health 10
1.5 Discussion 13
1.6 Trends 14
1.7 Conclusions 15
References 16

1.1 INTRODUCTION

Healthcare big data refers to collecting, analysing and leveraging consumer, patient, physical and clinical data that are too vast or complex to be understood by traditional means of data processing. Instead, big data are often processed by machine learning algorithms and data scientists. The importance of big data in health is immense, but it is not only about the amount of data that an institution has, but what each one extracts from them [1].

The concept of big data refers to the daily generation of a huge and very diverse amount of data, which can no longer be analysed only by humans. These data reach institutions through numerous sources, such as social networks, public and private information banks and internal files, among others [2].

The rise of healthcare big data comes in response to the digitization of healthcare information and the rise of value-based care, which has encouraged the industry to use data analytics to make strategic business decisions. Faced with the challenges of healthcare data such as volume, velocity, variety and veracity, health systems need to adopt technology capable of collecting, storing and analysing this information to produce actionable insights. In the case of health, the main providers of information today are applications and devices for monitoring personal activities, electronic medical records, exams and online reports sent remotely and digital files provided by healthcare institutions, such as clinics, among others [3].

Examples of what is generated and what can be captured in the health area are personal data regarding personal document identification number, gender, name, date of birth, affiliation, place of residence; clinical data regarding risk habits, diagnoses, medications taken, vaccinations, allergies; exam data for image exams, electrocardiogram, electroencephalography, blood tests, oximetry and spirometry, among others; and data on procedures such as hospitalizations, interventions received, surgeries and length of stay in the ICU, among others [4].

Institutions must guarantee data protection through firewalls and access controls, and encourage a culture of security in the company, among other actions. The exchange of information online between supplier and pickup systems also needs end-to-end encryption, in addition to anonymizing data before making it public, which concerns the ability for IT professionals to filter, for example, removing information that can identify patients, but leaving clinical information. In this sense, using big data in health requires security. Privacy and information security are even more delicate factors when it comes to medical records about patients [5].

Therefore, this chapter aims to provide an updated overview of the privacy of medical data, showing its successful relationship with other technologies, with a bibliographic background, refining and sharpening the potential of applied technology in health.

1.2 DATA PRIVACY RELEVANCE AND HEALTHCARE NEED

Technologies applied to health are essential for the provision of care to patients, based on observance of the relevance of certain information to public health and the need to identify the bearer of that information; in a way all this digital innovation presents digital risks [6, 7].

If these threats are not properly managed, they result in disruptions to healthcare operations, costly data breaches and damage to patients. In this regard, the management of digital certificates should be discussed concerning the security of data on the medical care of patients due to other security priorities, based on the legal premise related to the protection of life and the physical safety of third parties. What to do with this aspect should be considered to make data publicly accessible through clear identification of interest [6, 7].

Through digital signature using cryptographic methods, digital certificates and critical metadata belonging to an electronic signature, a "fingerprint" of the data is created, guaranteeing the authenticity of the patient's data, and thereby reaching higher levels of privacy of these data, providing responsibility, the confidentiality of the data and avoiding undue tampering [8–10].

Still reflecting on the technological aspects of digital signatures, encryption and authentication, and electronic signatures offer health and medical care institutions valid and manageable digital certificates. This impacts data protection and privacy, given the growing significant concern regarding the use of personal data in the health area and its privacy [8–10].

In the same sense as dealing with digital privacy in the age of current technology, it is essential to understand and know the fate of data in the world outside the domain of an individual, whether they are users or even specifically patients. This is combined with the premise that health and medical care institutions are responsible for what they do regarding patient data, and the patients also need to have greater digital responsibility for what is their property, i.e., data and personal digital information [8–10].

The circumstance and opportunity that the digital age offers and provides, open up several possibilities for the handling of patients' personal digital information, ranging from new types of treatment to even concerning new forms of disease dignity. However, it is necessary and important that a protocol is followed, in order to avoid violation of the fundamental rights of patients, which, in general, is present in the general data protection laws, specific to each country [11, 12].

Based on the understanding that medical data are sensitive, it is necessary to review the use and manipulation of data, since situations such as the protection of life, health and sometimes the public interest provide a legal basis for this treatment. From the premise on the use of patients' data, the logic of the individualization of modern society is related, be it in behaviour change, in the digital aspect and even related to the creation of laws on the protection of personal data [13].

The perspective of forming codes that can guarantee public rights in data "transactions" must be established, and in the opposite direction of the premise of exchanging digital privacy for connection as a way for users to be connected easily and dynamically. The use of personal data, as in a health environment, concerning the patient, is linked to the logic of individualization of being, which also relates to the individual right to exist (an exclusive right as a natural person), concerning their personal information such as name, identity or identification document [14, 15].

It is necessary to understand what data are being collected, processed and becoming intelligence for the whole society, just as there must be a separation between the crucial information for public health, which must be preserved and managed, and the personal information of each patient, which must be processed anonymously, considering a legal basis for the treatment of these medical data, even without the patient's consent document [14, 15].

Digital privacy is an ethical perspective of data privacy. The general data laws, exclusive to each country, make it mandatory to share data essential to the identification of infected people between public administration bodies and entities, with the sole purpose of preventing spread in the case of a pandemic (such as COVID-19). However, in this respect, it is important to understand where the data go and how they converge in this larger system, concerning digital privacy, since in addition to the dissemination of information to the private sector keeping the data public and up-to-date, it is necessary to safeguard the right to confidential personal information. Classifying that it is in the public interest means, however, that the personal data can be disclosed, as long as they are anonymized [14–16].

1.2.1 THE e-HEALTH BENEFITS OF DATA SHARING

The impacts of digital transformation on health include understanding how professionals in the field and patients are affected, concerning the benefits justifying investment in digital technology, both from a digital and a human point of view, since the use of digital devices as a more active tool in medical treatment generates financial savings and health costs, opening the possibility for more people to have access to quality healthcare [17].

The technology innovation in health presents a universe of possibilities, which impact the way in which the ability to provide the best possible treatments through data sharing is seen. These range from genetic studies, cancer and chronic disease records, even substance abuse, and population health management, still assessing the character of large-scale analyses, epidemiology and disease tracking, to interoperability for routine emergency patient care [18].

In addition to clinical and patient-oriented use cases, data exchange is essential to ensure that best practices can be shared between healthcare organizations. As diagnostic conditions improve, inevitably, patients will also feel the positive impact on waiting times in medical care lines, access to reliable diagnostics coupled with care and prevention that increase patient safety, and access to surgery, among many other aspects. However, a greater commitment to data protection and privacy is valid, so that incidents of internal or cyber threats, such as ransomware attacks, can be avoided [19].

Promoting the sharing of health information can help with incident reporting and potentially prevent future cybersecurity incidents from occurring. This is allied to the digital technological revolution in health in the use of digital solutions for the diagnosis and treatment of patients with various types of diseases, directly reflecting on cost control and patient care [20].

1.2.2 TYPES OF MEDICAL DATA

Health information is more valuable than just financial information like credit card numbers or other financial data. With the improper possession of this medical information, cybercriminals can have access to prescription drugs, or even access the financial data of people or health institutions [21].

The rules contained in the data protection and privacy laws, unique to each country, require appropriate safeguards to protect patient information. At the same time, it is essential that health institutions maintain the patient's history, knowing what types of information exist in medical records and other documents used in care procedures for possible future medical care and treatment [22].

The most common patient data are names, phone numbers, e-mail addresses, geographic location identifiers, medical record numbers; biometric identifiers such as fingerprint or retinal scan, full-face photos, health insurance numbers, credit card numbers or any financial document, among others; and information concerning racial origins, data relating to sexual life, genetic data and digital medical examinations performed, among others [22–23].

And through these data, it is worth highlighting the concern with the protection and privacy of information that is applied to medical records in all formats, both electronic health records and paper ones. It is up to health institutions to take appropriate measures when collecting, processing, storing and even discarding any medical record in order to ensure patient compliance and privacy [23].

In addition to taking care of the security offered by the systems used and adapting the technologies already used, health professionals need to review security in the exchange of information in some usual processes, since it is common for medical clinics to send patient data to hospitals in cases of hospitalization, just as it is common for information to be exchanged between laboratories and the hospital or clinic. Given this scenario, hospitals and other health institutions must guarantee the protection of their patients' medical information during the entire service life cycle and the necessary storage period, which define the requirements for the proper management of medical records [23, 24].

Concerning the medical record, this document is owned by the patient, who has full rights of access and can request a copy of this document whenever he deems necessary. The protection of these health data in procedures performed by health professionals, and the interaction between doctors and patient are protected by law and can only be collected, processed and stored for certain purposes, with the patient's consent and authorization [24].

This is true for medical records, or any health information transaction, not necessarily only for the electronic part, including data recorded on paper, in which medical clinics that have already obtained data from patients will have to follow up with patients already registered in the system to seek authorization. That is, there should be greater care on the part of health institutions about informing patients about the reason for the collection of their information, to whom these data may be passed and for what purpose. Applying to a vast number of situations, such as telemedicine, charging for health services via exchange of information on supplementary health related to the standard monitoring by the operators of private healthcare plans, unified health systems, exchange of information between different bodies and regarding requests for laboratory tests, among others [25].

It is important to note that the system created and implemented in Brazil is a single health system, whose main function is to provide low-, intermediate- and high-complexity medical care to the entire Brazilian population. This service receives financial transfers from the government, with access to health, medical consultations, surgeries and treatments free to its population [26].

Although the exchange of messages via applications or social networks is not prohibited, health professionals should be aware and take due care, in order to mitigate the risks taken to remain within the established requirements regarding privacy and regarding messages containing clinical patient information sent incorrectly to another person, or even patient information shared with another user without authorization [27].

The digital age of medical technology can mitigate the damage to privacy caused by messages exchanged between doctors and patients. But with the need for encryption, mailboxes with messages must also be protected, since, in general, they contain the patient's identification [27, 28].

Patients have the right to know their data are in the system and for what purpose this information will be used. For those institutions with greater technological resources, access to information and treatment of their data, and even the process must be available for the patient to understand its purpose, form and duration. In the same sense as the medical data of children or adolescents, they can only be used with specific consent by the parents or legal guardians [28].

Thus, patient data, such as medical reports, must be clear about the need for and treatment of data. Like all information transmissions in the system, they must be encrypted, have protection against fraud and even undergo procedures related to the security and privacy of personal health data, and after fulfilling the objective, they must be erased [28].

1.2.3 Anonymization as a Form of Patient Privacy

Data anonymization (data anonymity) aims to protect the privacy of the individual; it is the use of one or more techniques designed to make it impossible, or at least more difficult, to identify a particular individual (patient) from related stored data, thus making data sharing safe and legal [29].

Anonymization methods rely on the main information techniques including encryption, hashing and pseudonymization among them. The main benefit is to allow health institutions to make better use of this information, enabling use for data analysis and sharing in a way that is conscious of protection of privacy [30].

It is generally a standard for data to be anonymized and confidential before sharing, thus protecting the privacy of patients and data subjects (in the case of parents as well as children and adolescents). Most health institutions carry out these processes by classifying, encrypting, using tokens or hashing on information considered sensitive according to data protection and privacy requirements [30, 31].

The responsibility for the protection of privacy of patient data rests with everyone, concerning the impact on patients' digital privacy, healthcare professionals, and the technical management of the IT infrastructure. They are responsible for protecting their patients' data, regardless of where the data services are hosted, locally, via a data centre or even in the cloud [30, 31].

1.2.4 Data Anonymization Techniques

Employing a **substitution** method involves the modification of the name of the people included in the health data, maintaining consistency between the values. **Scrambling** techniques involve mixing or obfuscating letters, where bits are scrambled before encoding to avoid generating repetitive strings of identical bit characters, making patient data illegible [32].

Even a **masking** technique may be used, allowing part of the data to be hidden with random characters or other data. In practice, this creates a version similar to the original data in terms of structure, but without revealing their true information. **Personalized anonymization** techniques that allow the user to use their own anonymization technique may be used, which can be done using scripts or an application. **Data defocusing** techniques use an approximation of the data values to make it impossible to identify patients [32, 33].

Although no method is perfect, the methods and techniques used to protect the privacy of the information, including encryption, anonymization, masking and tokenization, need to be evaluated frequently in order to not damage the implemented digital structure. The implementation of digital certificates can even limit exposure to the health professional and his institution, if a security breach occurs [32, 33].

1.2.5 Privacy Protection with Encryption

Health information is a gold mine that should be accessible only to doctors and patients themselves, in order to develop new developments in digital medicine; however concerns about data related to the patient's identity remain at the centre. In this scenario, there are ways to protect a document that contains confidential information against digital intruders who could possibly misuse patient data. One way is to protect all terminals that reach the patient, so that the data are not accessible to unauthorized third parties. Another is to encrypt the data, so that, even though unauthorized third parties can reach the document, they are unable to read the content [34].

The variety of threats that currently exist affects all digital users, even patients, doctors, researchers and other health professionals. The growth of advanced threats of the type of invasion of applications and systems should be analysed. In this scenario, more appropriate, administrative security practices and controls should be applied, in line with technical policies and procedures, through digital technology, which manages access to medical data and is integrated into the normal workflows around those data [34–36].

In short, given the difficult and complex operating environment in which medical professionals work, encryption of healthcare data is, by a wide margin, the most powerful tool for protecting the privacy of patient data, regarding the end-to-end encryption that covers "data at rest" in storage units, and still considering "data in motion" during file transfer, offering more complete protection for a document throughout its cycle of life within a health system [34–36].

Data encryption applied to healthcare is a powerful and reliable way to guarantee privacy. This encryption process can be automated and can be implemented with confidence, even for users (healthcare professionals) who are not used to digital security. However, as a positive characteristic, from the user's point of view, how transparent the system is will be how much that user "does not know" and needs to know the implementation of the internal functioning of this system [34–36].

the ultimate goal is to achieve and obtain a high level of trust concerning the security and privacy of health data, and also when it comes to the management of digital technologies, which help to progress towards the digital privacy of patients [34–36].

1.3 THE IMPORTANCE OF DIGITAL MANAGEMENT IN HEALTHCARE

With the technological renewal in the area, the reality of medical institutions has completely changed; after all, patients will be able to receive medical care and treatment without leaving home. There are many identifiable benefits in the use of electronic medical record systems, considering the possibility of accessing online records, while still evaluating the provision to patients of access to their health records [37].

Handwritten documents are subject to spelling errors and illegible writing, which in general is typical of doctors. Health records are migrating to digital formats as technology evolves. These problems can be avoided through electronic medical record systems, minimizing errors in medical records and providing a way to eliminate inconsistencies, while patient care becomes more agile, as they also standardize patient histories. Similar benefits may be seen through the centralization of health information, practices and services free from tracing by paper records. However, strong cybersecurity measures are needed, which require appropriate administrative, physical and technical protections, to maintain and guarantee the protection, privacy, confidentiality, integrity and security of data and health records in all formats. These electronic medical record systems give health professionals the ability to share information instantly with other health professionals [38].

Besides, it is currently common for health organizations to think about the security of their data, still reflecting on the horizon of medical care crossing barriers and expanding outside health institutions such as hospitals, laboratories, operators and clinics. It is worth assessing that electronic systems create a safer way to store medical records, since digital security needs to keep pace with digital transformations. These data are sensitive, targeted by cybercriminals, and in this type of context cyber governance is not simple if there is no use of a digital solution that helps in protection and digital privacy [38, 39].

One of the main aspects of health data sharing is ensuring that this is done securely, with solutions such as digital signature, encryption of data at rest (stored data) and derivatives and a platform that helps in the governance of that information, and that does not compromise patient information. Concerning data encryption, it is obtained using some algorithmic process to transform data in order to decrease the probability of giving meaning to that information, without using a specific process or a confidential key [40].

Moving data are information sent from one individual (patient) or private device to another via direct messages, e-mail or other means of exchanging data and messages. In that respect, that unencrypted data can be intercepted while moving from one location to another. Data at rest refers to that information stored somewhere, and not transported, i.e., being stored on hard disk, a removable disk, pen drive, on a local server or even mobile devices, such as notebooks, tablets and smartphones. Even so, the privacy and integrity of health data must be protected not only against external threats, but also against unauthorized access attempts (human attacks) from within the health institution's network or digital ecosystem [41].

1.3.1 Challenges in Health Data Privacy

Cybersecurity is about building a safe environment with the use of technology, to protect against digital threats that grow in volume, intensity and sophistication. Traditionally, cybersecurity has focused on preventing intrusions, and protecting information stored on computers and various computing devices, which they transmit through communication networks. It is the digital protection of systems connected to the Internet, including hardware, software and data, from cyber-attacks, as well as the defence with the use of firewalls, in monitoring ports and the like, including the defensive controls that are necessary to deal with the threat of digital cyberspace [41–51].

In this context, ransomware attacks and healthcare data breaches are the top concerns of healthcare institutions of all sizes. These occur when some external unauthorized users gain access to the network of a healthcare institution, and the files are encrypted or stolen. This type is specifically considered to be of high digital risk, since health institutions are in charge of medical care for patients; if this information is locked or inaccessible, then consequently, medical care will be affected. Other types of cyber-attacks such as leaks or modifications of data, intentional and/or unintentional, should also be assessed [41–51].

Thus, digital reliability and privacy require activities and operations built around security, surveillance and digital resiliency. Involving these three principles reflects the need for a more dynamic strategy that ensures data privacy and that can guarantee the reduction and prevention of threats and vulnerabilities, rapid response to incidents and even a quick recovery in case of such incidents; and even the implementation of data and information protection policies, through intelligence operations related to cyberspace security [41–51].

As this number and the frequency of projected cyber threats increase, the importance of the human factor in managing information security cannot be underestimated, both positively and negatively. Social engineering is the use of techniques for manipulating individuals, in order to disclose confidential or private medical information of patients, for later use for fraudulent purposes [41–51].

In this panorama of combating cyber-attacks that exploit human factors in the data protection chain, it is essential to recognize digital security in response to advanced threats, developing a solid structure for risk management and the application of new detection standards, which reduce risks to health information that occur due to vulnerabilities related to professional health users, since this aspect goes far beyond simply testing digital health systems for vulnerabilities [41–51].

The transition from printed records to electronic media containing information related to patients' medical history, allergies and previous treatments should raise important questions regarding the determination of who can have access to patients' medical information and how to control the data protection and privacy of each patient throughout their care cycle [41–51].

Assuming that these files include patient care information, regardless of the origin of the person collecting it and where that information will be stored, affecting storage inside or outside the country, online or offline, all requirements must be met to guarantee the safety of sensitive information. This concerns digital anonymization, data protection in hybrid infrastructure environments, control of access to sensitive data and monitoring and records of data access, still reflecting on aspects of centralized and/or decentralized secure authentication [41–51].

1.3.2 Components for Data Access Control

Digital certificates, credentials and cryptographic keys are means used to authenticate the **identification**, a component consisting of a mechanism that ensures the veracity of the user's identity. While a system searches for a user's identity during the login procedure, a valid digital certificate or credential is provided [41–51].

Based on the sharing and management of access to information in the health system, the existence of **authentication** is essential, to authorize, for example, the user's access to the file after going through an identity confirmation process. A process is achieved through the use of certificates and digital signatures in compliance with the main security standards, such as public key infrastructure (PKI) [41–51].

Authorization is the process that occurs after authentication has been validated, concerning the privileges that are granted to a particular user when using a health application, for example, regarding permission to use, execute resources or manipulate data in electronic medical records, in order to provide a better quality of care to patients, as well as the best possible experience during treatments [41–51].

Additionally, it is still possible to use Secure Socket Layer (SSL) digital certificates to protect data traffic on the hospital, laboratory or clinic network, to ensure that all data transmitted are confidential and secure. Alternatively, Transport Layer Security (TLS) digital certificates can be used that guarantee the exchange of sensitive information on the Internet [41–51].

1.4 IMPORTANCE OF DIGITAL DATA SECURITY IN HEALTH

Big data is the technological instrument that deals with data, processing high volumes, which are the most valuable input that an institution, whatever the area in which it operates, may have. After all, most organizations are guided through this processing of data volumes, guiding their business, according to the information collected from users (patients) [41–51].

In this sense, data processing is understood as any and all procedures whose digital processing involves the use of the patient's data, whether for collection, classification, manipulation, use, processing, storage, sharing, transfer, disposal or other activities. However, it is a priority that there be digital privacy, digital data security and the consent and authorization of the use, sharing and even manipulation of those data. It is necessary to create digital awareness in patients that these data are not the property of health institutions, but their own [51, 52].

The fact is that more and more technology is used to make life easier for digital users, especially through mobile devices and technology. We are faced with so many options and ease of communication, sharing, entertainment, digital transportation, banking, and financial services, and even health services, among many others. This technological focus, applied in health, will increase the amount of sensitive data existing and in transit between devices connected to the Internet, throughout the implanted cybernetic structure. In this sense, it is essential that information security is part of all aspects of the digital structure of healthcare institutions, and technology for data privacy is also employed. If implementation is weak, cyber risk will be associated with the violation of privacy, enabling easy access to stored information regarding patients and interactions between doctors [51–55].

In this context, another technology used on data, to extract information, is machine learning, an aspect of artificial intelligence. In addition to processing and generating data insights, it is also used in virtual assistants that provide patient care. Assessing the use of small snippets of conversations between patients and virtual assistants makes it possible to develop new features in medical equipment. However, this context is becoming more and more delicate, due to technological evolution being increasingly present inside the home, through the various connected objects which end up collecting and investigating the details of the users' own private lives [51–55].

We can still reflect on the growing use of mobile devices, as well as the subsequent collection of patient data, assessing the health area, bringing a new emphasis to the importance of certificate management, public and private key infrastructures, and digital privacy property. Many different gadgets are used, including smartwatches measuring vital signs, or ingestible sensors, or digital pacemakers, among other state-of-the-art devices, collecting data, generating and extracting information and using techniques that can improve people's lifestyles. However, the continuous effort for interoperability, i.e., the ability of different systems, devices, applications or digital solutions to connect and communicate in a coordinated manner, without the end user's effort (transparency), has helped to drive the growth of data sharing in the health field [51–55].

Although data collection has its risks, the benefits for patients are undeniable, through faster and more efficient assistance in situations of low or medium complexity, reducing the number of readmissions and fraud, avoiding medication errors, reducing duplicate tests or even talking to a digital attendant, as explained above. Even so, in the face of all the imaginable advantages, healthcare institutions need to consider the rules of data protection legislation, exclusive to each country, and privacy rules related to the sharing of sensitive information [51–56].

In protecting the privacy of health information, in the face of increasing numbers and the impact of data breaches, the security of medical records must be one of the main priorities of the health sector. Regarding ownership of their personal data and their own experience, both patients and digital users should not be sceptical about the non-transparent methods that institutions use to provide the many benefits of personalization of care, due to control and/or manipulation of algorithms with the commercial use of personal data [55–57].

Today's personalization methods, based on robust data collection and analysis, are failing to provide transparency for users and patients. In this sense, in order to customize services, they need to be increasingly transparent, protecting and giving greater power, confidence and stability over the use of their data and information. The most common and general practice to ensure the safety of patient data is to make them anonymous. This is one of the ways in which the balance between technology and privacy is achieved. In this sense, calls, medical records and other types of interaction with patients are stored in their systems without the identification of users [55–58].

The digital certificates used in the health area are similar to those used in other market segments, which include a public key, stored in your certificate, and published in a secure repository, and a private key, stored on the computer of the health professional, or in a personal hardware token (device model or smartcard), or even in a digital cloud technology structure [55–59].

Given this scenario, the data transmitted between the systems of the health institutions themselves, between clinics and hospitals, laboratories or health operators, or even others, must be treated more rigorously in the face of countless cases reported around the world concerning data leakage worldwide, whether due to failures in the security systems of health institutions, or even the improper use and provision of patient information. In addition to the need for authorization by patients, sharing of this information can only be done if the messages are encrypted (encrypted) [55–59].

A healthcare institution should be aware that the integration of digital signatures, electronic signatures and digital certificates through the encryption of these keys and credentials is essential and of fundamental importance. They authenticate all informed and in-transit procedures, ensuring that the files are safe and verifiable, protecting the privacy of patient data during medical and administrative procedures [55–59].

However, it is worth considering the main security flaws associated with the management of certificates and private keys, such as not changing private keys and passwords when an administrator leaves the institution, not changing KeyStore passwords regularly, incorrect use of the same password in several KeyStores (key repository), private keys distributed among groups of employees without adequate control or even high quantities and complexity in the management of keys and occurrence of failures in the process of managing keys and digital certificates [55–59].

Based on fundamentals such as respect for privacy; informative self-determination; the non-abuse of data; freedom of expression, information, communication and opinion; the improper treatment of data; the inviolability of intimacy, confidentiality and the privacy of patient data; technological development and medical innovation; and even the defence of human rights concerning the freedom and dignity of the patient. It is essential to adopt the best practices to perform the management of certificates, private keys and credentials that create an inventory of certificates, carrying out analysis based on compliance and with the institution's policies; monitoring digital audio data transmission tracks and validating digital accesses; optimizing and protecting the provision of proprietary information for each certificate and/or key; in addition to raising the awareness of interested parties (health professionals) about the risks involved [55–59].

In addition to these technological complexities, the interoperability of several certification authorities presents challenges. In this sense, trust in the infrastructure depends on knowledge about the appropriate measures to link a patient's healthcare credentials to his identity, aiming to mitigate the risks related to human and machine failures, enabling technologies to be developed in an environment of security and privacy, included in the certificate policy of each institution [55–59].

Finally, patient data have become a bargaining chip converted into opportunities for healthcare institutions, which feeds a market for personal data for commercial purposes without patient authorization, such as the sale of that personal information initially collected for another purpose to companies selling health plans or even medicines. Even so, data on the health of patients are considered sensitive, and it is necessary that institutions in the health sector have double care related to digital security, investing in technology to anonymize patient data, so that unauthorized third parties are unable to gain access. After all, the data must be made anonymous as soon as they enter the digital system of the health institution, so that, throughout the patient's journey, their data are protected and private [55–59].

1.5 DISCUSSION

It is possible to make a brief analysis regarding the privacy of medical data in the panorama of the current coronavirus pandemic, which has caused a spread of true and false information. This diffusion has perhaps been faster than that of the disease itself, concerning numbers, measures, care and medical guidance. This is the result of modern technological interconnectivity.

However, what was seen was also a lot of this information involving the private data of patients, sensitive data related to the health of famous people. So, it should be brought to light in the scope of the privacy of medical data, personal information and public interest. This is related to the premise of containing an epidemic, clashing with the right to privacy of information involving famous individuals.

This scenario opens up complications in developing countries like Brazil, or even those countries that do not yet have a specific data protection law in place, making actions and interpretations more difficult. What about the clinical picture of people with great importance for public life, or even those patients zero, considered the precursors of contamination? The cases of famous patients who voluntarily disclose their diagnosis on social networks are the opposite of those patients who have their clinical information revealed against their will, i.e., unauthorized leakages, constituting a violation of privacy, and medical ethics and laws.

In developed countries, such as in Europe, there are governments that have guidelines for responsible health professionals on how to deal with coronavirus pandemic data, concerning patient privacy. Respect for privacy must be maintained, given the occurrence of the leakage of health data for other purposes, through messages by chat applications to friends or a group of contacts.

It is okay to disclose data and information on the circumstances of transmission as long as patients are not identified. Since there is no patient identification, this serves to make the population aware of the seriousness of the pandemic and the forms of contagion.

The use of personal data has to bring benefits to the population, through information beneficial to public health, such as the exclusive exploitation of data to prevent the spread of COVID-19, as well as highlighting those situations in which data privacy violations may occur, by hospitals, clinics and other health institutions.

We may also reflect on other violations that result in security errors and lack of privacy committed by health institutions, concerning the theft of backup tapes, optical discs and mobile devices with medical information from unencrypted patients. It is in this event that the use of cryptographic keys is mandatory. Still reflecting on this context, the management of cryptographic keys has brought more security and data privacy to healthcare institutions. This technology is capable of protecting access to medical documents and records such as medical reports, exams, diagnoses and medical records of patients.

A large part of the management of non-digital medical records, aligned with the premise of minimizing the risk of breach of confidential medical data, is in the destruction and elimination of documents from these files, or even the transition to electronic health records using shredding due to the large volume of paper that needs to be eliminated after a digitization process. Human failures regarding the disposal of this information in dumps accessed by unauthorized people, or even failures when moving patient data to publicly accessible servers should be prevented.

Successful compliance with laws, regulations and policies for the protection and privacy of patient data requires strategies that assess and address the risks of regularly protected electronic health information, such as the disclosure of patient information to third parties without protection or restrictions (digital signatures and certificates in digital administrative procedures) or even the display of patient data in online application databases. This includes continuous improvement in security processes and standards, analysis of systems in search of unpatched vulnerabilities and unsupported software and investment in technological digital infrastructure preventing patients' information from being susceptible to malware, ransomware and other cyber risks.

1.6 TRENDS

The future of medical security is in the electronic data available without losing sight of the importance of the security and privacy of the exchange of health information, when it comes to sharing information between systems with varying levels of privacy. Since all information will be stored electronically, old physical files will no longer exist, and this "digital collection" will increasingly gain potential for data breach and identity theft [60].

The protection of medical records can range from biometrics and two-step authentication to algorithms with blockchain technology, which allows digital information to be distributed, but not copied. Other techniques include the adoption of multiple cloud usage strategies and information protection, drive data security and privacy strategies through cloud encryption [61].

The new encryption standards highlight data protection and privacy, and allow sensitive data to be encrypted until a recipient with a private key can unlock the information. The use of hardware security modules (HSMs) provides a rigid and tamper-resistant environment, with higher levels of trust, integrity and control for medical data and applications, and big data encryption code signing [62].

Symmetric encryption ciphers, such as Advanced Encryption Standard (AES), are used to encrypt application data and decrypt text ciphers. This encryption technology combined with others, such as cipher block chaining (CBC) or Galois/Counter Mode (GCM), has the properties of providing authenticity and confidentiality that prevent attempts to steal data in transit, yet affecting the performance of the encrypted transfer rate [63].

As the world becomes more digital, security, privacy and identity have become critical for healthcare institutions and patients. It is essential that institutions offer high security and continuous access, protecting data, information and critical medical applications, implementing data security and privacy technologies that guarantee the integrity and reliability of data and applications [64].

1.7 CONCLUSIONS

Evidently, the digital technological evolution has brought several benefits to the lives of both health professionals and patients. However, it is important to be aware of all aspects that derive from privacy, concerning demographic personal health information, medical histories, test and laboratory results, mental health conditions, medical insurance information or even the financial information of each patient and other data that a healthcare professional collects to identify and determine appropriate care.

This same detailed information about patient health is also a digital product in an area that generates large amounts of sensitive data, and the good management of this information is crucial to meet legal requirements and the expectations of the health market. In addition to the use of digital privacy technology for patients and health professionals, these data are valuable for clinical and scientific researchers and needs to be anonymized.

Digital privacy in health is a topic of wide debate, for health institutions such as hospitals, laboratories, clinics and systems in the area, in general, that deal with extremely confidential data, which by nature require even greater care in the protection of patient information transmitted between systems. These data must be protected from being improperly stolen and sold elsewhere, or even hijacked through ransomware until the medical institution pays the financial value of the digital ransom.

These data are a digital treasure, comprising personal information of patients allowing the unification of the information, offering a system that stores data in an optimized way. Thus, these data provide a broader basis for the professional to carry out the diagnosis, i.e., the doctor, even if he has not monitored the patient's health condition, can easily access data from previous consultations, such as exam results and medical history.

Apart from the benefits, data protection and privacy, security and efforts to respond to breaches should always be a priority; due to the nature of the sector, healthcare institutions handle confidential patient details. As this information includes sensitive data for each patient, any attitude different to this puts patients at digital privacy risk.

When ensuring data security, whether in paper records or an electronic registration system, it is important to pay attention to whether the chosen system has a certification that attests that it meets the established requirements. Provided personal health information describes a patient's medical history, thus including illnesses, treatments and results.

However, there is still a long way to go to reach the appropriate level of maturity regarding the use of technologies, in order to obtain a more accurate diagnosis and monitor the patient's condition through continuous digital monitoring. On the positive side, health institutions that decide to invest in digital health practices, adding technology to their processes, differentiate themselves in the market, by tracking this information during the life of a patient, offering the doctor the context of the patient's health, making it easier to make better treatment decisions.

And while recording personal health information appropriately, it can be stored without identifying features and added with anonymous features to large databases of patient information. This contributes to health management and care programmes based on the higher value.

Although privacy requires security measures, to maintain the patient's trust in digital treatment of this information, it is essential to have security restrictions that fully protect private information. Many data breaches could have been avoided with the adoption of digital signatures and the correct privacy policies in health institutions.

In this sense, it is clear that the exposure of patients' data not only threatens to expose them to identity theft, but also reveals their medical conditions. Since privacy must be more than a digital product offered, and not a mere commercial exchange, and it must be a matter of maintaining confidentiality.

REFERENCES

1. Mehta, N., & Pandit, A. (2018). Concurrence of big data analytics and healthcare: A systematic review. *International Journal of Medical Informatics*, 114, 57–65.
2. França, R. P., Iano, Y., Monteiro, A. C. B., & Arthur, R. (2020). A review on the technological and literary background of multimedia compression. In *Handbook of Research on Multimedia Cyber Security* (pp. 1–20). Hershey, PA: IGI Global.
3. Waschkau, A., Götz, K., & Steinhäuser, J. (2020). Fit for the future: Development of a seminar on aspects of digitization of healthcare as a contribution of medical sociology. *Zeitschrift für Evidenz, Fortbildung und Qualität im Gesundheitswesen*, 155, 48–53.
4. Li, H., Zhu, L., Shen, M., Gao, F., Tao, X., & Liu, S. (2018). Blockchain-based data preservation system for medical data. *Journal of Medical Systems*, 42(8), 141.
5. Abouelmehdi, K., Beni-Hssane, A., Khaloufi, H., & Saadi, M. (2017). Big data security and privacy in healthcare: A Review. *Procedia Computer Science*, 113, 73–80.

6. Cruz-Cunha, M. M. (Ed.). (2016). *Encyclopedia of E-health and Telemedicine*. Hershey, PA: IGI Global.
7. Guha, M. (2017). Review e-health. *Journal of Mental Health*, 26, 390–392.
8. Ardy, R. D., Indriani, O. R., Sari, C. A., & Rachmawanto, E. H. (2017). Digital image signature using triple protection cryptosystem (RSA, Vigenere, and MD5). In International Conference on Smart Cities, Automation & Intelligent Computing Systems (ICON-SONICS) (pp. 87–92). IEEE.
9. Barker, E. (2016). Guideline for using cryptographic standards in the federal government: Cryptographic mechanisms (No. NIST Special Publication (SP) 800-175B (Draft)). National Institute of Standards and Technology.
10. Buldas, A., Firsov, D., Laanoja, R., Lakk, H., & Truu, A. (2019). A new approach to constructing digital signature schemes. In International Workshop on Security (pp. 363–373). Cham: Springer.
11. Shahid, F., & Khan, A. (2020). Smart digital signatures (SDS): A post-quantum digital signature scheme for distributed ledgers. *Future Generation Computer Systems*, 111, 241–253.
12. Venot, A., Burgun, A., & Quantin, C. (2016). *Medical Informatics, e-Health*. Cham: Springer.
13. Md, I. P., Lau, R. Y., Md, A. K. A., Md, S. H., Md, K. H., & Karmaker, B. K. (2020). Healthcare informatics and analytics in big data. *Expert Systems with Applications*, 113388.
14. Vora, J., Italiya, P., Tanwar, S., Tyagi, S., Kumar, N., Obaidat, M. S., & Hsiao, K. F. (2018). Ensuring privacy and security in E-health records. In 2018 International Conference on Computer, Information, and Telecommunication Systems (CITS) (pp. 1–5). IEEE.
15. Pussewalage, H. S. G., & Oleshchuk, V. A. (2016). Privacy-preserving mechanisms for enforcing security and privacy requirements in E-health solutions. *International Journal of Information Management*, 36(6), 1161–1173.
16. Shrestha, N. M., Alsadoon, A., Prasad, P. W. C., Hourany, L., & Elchouemi, A. (2016). Enhanced e-health framework for security and privacy in healthcare system. In 6th International Conference on Digital Information Processing and Communications (ICDIPC) (pp. 75–79). IEEE.
17. Wootton, R., Craig, J., & Patterson, V. (2017). *Introduction to Telemedicine*. Boca Raton, FL: CRC Press.
18. Calton, B., Abedini, N., & Fratkin, M. (2020). Telemedicine in the time of coronavirus. *Journal of Pain and Symptom Management*. Retrieved from https://www.jpsmjournal.com/article/S0885-3924(20)30170-6/fulltext
19. Hassibian, M. R., & Hassibian, S. (2016). Telemedicine acceptance and implementation in developing countries: Benefits, categories, and barriers. *Razavi International Journal of Medicine*, 4(3). Retrieved from http://eprints.mums.ac.ir/13030/1/50008420 160303.pdf
20. Ehrenfeld, J. M. (2017). Wannacry, cybersecurity and health information technology: A time to act. *Journal of Medical Systems*, 41(7), 104.
21. Magnuson, J. A., & Dixon, B. E. (Eds.). (2020). *Public Health Informatics and Information Systems*. London: Springer Nature.
22. Davis, N. A. (2019). *Foundations of Health Information Management-E-Book*. Amsterdam, The Netherlands: Elsevier Health Sciences.
23. Nelson, R., & Staggers, N. (2016). *Health Informatics-E-Book: An Interprofessional Approach*. Amsterdam, The Netherlands: Elsevier Health Sciences.
24. Yang, C. G., & Lee, H. J. (2016). A study on the antecedents of healthcare information protection intention. *Information Systems Frontiers*, 18(2), 253–263.

25. Andrade, N., Neto, P. L. D. O. C., de Mello Torres, J. G., Júnior, I. G., Scheidt, C. G., & Gazel, W. (2019). E-Health: A framework proposal for interoperability and health data sharing. A Brazilian Case. In IFIP International Conference on Advances in Production Management Systems (pp. 625–630). Cham: Springer.
26. Rodrigues, C. F. M., Rodrigues, V. S., Neres, J. C. I., Guimarães, A. P. M., Neres, L. L. F. G., & Carvalho, A. V. (2017). Desafios da saúde pública no Brasil: relação entre zoonoses e saneamento. *Scire Salutis*, 7(1), 27–37.
27. Esteva, A., Robicquet, A., Ramsundar, B., Kuleshov, V., DePristo, M., Chou, K., & Dean, J. (2019). A guide to deep learning in healthcare. *Nature Medicine*, 25(1), 24–29.
28. Knoppers, B. M., & Thorogood, A. M. (2017). Ethics and big data in health. *Current Opinion in Systems Biology*, 4, 53–57.
29. Jayabalan, M., & Rana, M. E. (2018). Anonymizing healthcare records: A study of privacy-preserving data publishing techniques. *Advanced Science Letters*, 24(3), 1694–1697.
30. Majeed, A. (2019). Attribute-centric anonymization scheme for improving user privacy and utility of publishing e-health data. *Journal of King Saud University-Computer and Information Sciences*, 31(4), 426–435.
31. Bild, R., Kuhn, K. A., & Prasser, F. (2018). Safepub: A truthful data anonymization algorithm with strong privacy guarantees. *Proceedings on Privacy Enhancing Technologies*, 2018(1), 67–87.
32. Lee, H., Kim, S., Kim, J. W., & Chung, Y. D. (2017). Utility-preserving anonymization for health data publishing. *BMC Medical Informatics and Decision Making*, 17(1), 104.
33. Ali, O., & Ouda, A. (2016). A classification module in data masking framework for business intelligence platform in healthcare. In IEEE 7th Annual Information Technology, Electronics and Mobile Communication Conference (IEMCON) (pp. 1–8). IEEE.
34. Lin, C., Song, Z., Song, H., Zhou, Y., Wang, Y., & Wu, G. (2016). Differential privacy-preserving in big data analytics for connected health. *Journal of Medical Systems*, 40(4), 97.
35. Tang, W., Ren, J., Zhang, K., Zhang, D., Zhang, Y., & Shen, X. (2019). Efficient and privacy-preserving fog-assisted health data sharing scheme. *ACM Transactions on Intelligent Systems and Technology (TIST)*, 10(6), 1–23.
36. Abouelmehdi, K., Beni-Hessane, A., & Khaloufi, H. (2018). Big healthcare data: Preserving security and privacy. *Journal of Big Data*, 5(1), 1.
37. Laurenza, E., Quintano, M., Schiavone, F., & Vrontis, D. (2018). The effect of digital technologies adoption in healthcare industry: A case-based analysis. *Business Process Management Journal*. Retrieved from https://www.emerald.com/insight/content/doi/1 0.1108/BPMJ-04-2017-0084/full/html
38. Singh, K., Meyer, S. R., & Westfall, J. M. (2019). Consumer-facing data, information, and tools: Self-management of health in the digital age. *Health Affairs*, 38(3), 352–358.
39. Biggs, J. S., Willcocks, A., Burger, M., & Makeham, M. A. (2019). Digital health benefits evaluation frameworks: Building the evidence to support Australia's national digital health strategy. *Medical Journal of Australia*, 210(6 Suppl) Suppl 6, S9–S12.
40. Zheng, X., Mukkamala, R. R., Vatrapu, R., & Ordieres-Mere, J. (2018). Blockchain-based personal health data sharing system using cloud storage. In IEEE 20th International Conference on e-Health Networking, Applications and Services (Healthcom) (pp. 1–6). IEEE.
41. Riso, B., Tupasela, A., Vears, D. F., Felzmann, H., Cockbain, J., Loi, M., & Rakic, V. (2017). Ethical sharing of health data in online platforms–which values should be considered? *Life Sciences, Society, and Policy*, 13(1), 12.

42. Hartmann, M., Hashmi, U. S., & Imran, A. (2019). Edge computing in smart health care systems: Review, challenges, and research directions. *Transactions on Emerging Telecommunications Technologies*, e3710.
43. França, R. P., Iano, Y., Monteiro, A. C. B., & Arthur, R. (2020). A proposal of improvement for transmission channels in cloud environments using the CBEDE methodology. In *Modern Principles, Practices, and Algorithms for Cloud Security* (pp. 184–202). Hershey, PA: IGI Global.
44. Siyal, A. A., Junejo, A. Z., Zawish, M., Ahmed, K., Khalil, A., & Soursou, G. (2019). Applications of blockchain technology in medicine and healthcare: Challenges and future perspectives. *Cryptography*, 3(1), 3.
45. Sun, W., Cai, Z., Li, Y., Liu, F., Fang, S., & Wang, G. (2018). Security and privacy in the medical internet of things: A review. *Security and Communication Networks*, 2018. Retrieved from https://www.hindawi.com/journals/scn/2018/5978636/
46. Chowdhury, M., Jahan, S., Islam, R., & Gao, J. (2018, August). Malware detection for healthcare data security. In International Conference on Security and Privacy in Communication Systems (pp. 407–416). Springer, Cham.
47. Cusick, T. W., & Stanica, P. (2017). *Cryptographic Boolean Functions and Applications*. London: Academic Press.
48. Breier, J., Hou, X., & Bhasin, S. (Eds.). (2019). *Automated Methods in Cryptographic Fault Analysis*. Cham: Springer.
49. Kim, H., & Lee, E. A. (2017). Authentication and authorization for the internet of things. *IT Professional*, 19(5), 27–33.
50. Tschofenig, H., & Fossati, T. (2016). Transport layer security (TLS)/datagram transport layer security (DTLS) profiles for the internet of things. In RFC 7925. Internet Engineering Task Force.
51. França, R. P., Iano, Y., Monteiro, A. C. B., & Arthur, R. (2020). Improvement of the transmission of information for ICT techniques through CBEDE methodology. In *Utilizing Educational Data Mining Techniques for Improved Learning: Emerging Research and Opportunities* (pp. 13–34). Hershey, PA: IGI Global.
52. Padilha, R. F. (2018). Proposta de um método complementar de compressão de dados por meio da metodologia de eventos discretos aplicada em um baixo nível de abstração= Proposal of a complementary method of data compression by discrete event methodology applied at a low level of abstraction. (118 p.). Dissertation (master's degree). State University of Campinas, Faculty of Electrical and Computer Engineering, Campinas, SP. Retrieved from http://www.repositorio.unicamp.br/handle/REPOSIP/331342
53. França, R. P., Iano, Y., Monteiro, A. C. B., & Arthur, R. A methodology for improving efficiency in data transmission in healthcare. In Internet of Things for Healthcare Technologies (p. 49). Springer, Singapore.
54. França, R. P., Iano, Y., Monteiro, A. C. B., & Arthur, R. (2020). Potential proposal to improve data transmission in healthcare systems. In *Deep Learning Techniques for Biomedical and Health Informatics* (pp. 267–283). London: Academic Press.
55. Monteiro, A. C. B., Iano, Y., França, R. P., & Arthur, R. (2020). Development of a laboratory medical algorithm for simultaneous detection and counting of erythrocytes and leukocytes in digital images of a blood smear. In *Deep Learning Techniques for Biomedical and Health Informatics* (pp. 165–186). London: Academic Press.
56. França, R. P., Iano, Y., Monteiro, A. C. B., Arthur, R., Estrela, V. V., Assumpção, S. L. D. L., & Razmjooy, N. (2019). Potential model for improvement of the data transmission in healthcare systems. ARCA: Fiocruz Institutional Repository.
57. Simplicio, M. A., Cominetti, E. L., PATIL, H. K., Fernandez, J. E. R., & Silva, M. V. M. (2020). Cryptographic methods and systems for managing digital certificates. U.S. Patent Application No. 16/702,356.

58. Gueron, S., Feghali, W. K., Gopal, V., Makaram, R., Dixon, M. G., Chennupaty, S., & Kounavis, M. E. (2020). Flexible architecture and instruction for advanced encryption standard (AES). U.S. Patent No. 10,554,386. Washington, DC: U.S. Patent and Trademark Office.
59. Popoveniuc, S., Ripton, D., Ukrainchik, A., Kam, Y. C. E., Denisenko, M., Fitzgerald, R. E., ... & Eckstein, T. (2020). Digital certificates with distributed usage information. U.S. Patent Application No. 16/659,074.
60. Kim, Y. M., & Delen, D. (2018). Medical informatics research trend analysis: A text mining approach. *Health Informatics Journal*, 24(4), 432–452.
61. Menvielle, L., Audrain-Pontevia, A. F., & Menvielle, W. (Eds.). (2017). *The Digitization of Healthcare: New Challenges and Opportunities*. Cham: Springer.
62. Yellepeddy, K. K., Peck, J. T., Hazlewood, K. M., & Morganti, J. A. (2017). Optimizing use of hardware security modules. U.S. Patent No. 9,794,063. Washington, DC: U.S. Patent and Trademark Office.
63. Abdullah, A. (2017). Advanced encryption standard (AES) algorithm to encrypt and decrypt data. *Cryptography and Network Security*, 16. Retrieved from https://www.researchgate.net/profile/Ako_Abdullah/publication/317615794_Advanced_Encryption_Standard_AES_Algorithm_to_Encrypt_and_Decrypt_Data/links/59437cd8a6fdccb93ab28a48/Advanced-Encryption-Standard-AES-Algorithm-to-Encrypt-and-Decrypt-Data.pdf
64. Tariq, N., Qamar, A., Asim, M., & Khan, F. A. (2020). Blockchain and smart healthcare security: A survey. *Procedia Computer Science*, 175, 615–620.

2 Privacy in Cloud Healthcare Data

Disha Garg

CONTENTS

2.1 Introduction 21
    2.1.1 Cloud Computing in the Healthcare Sector..22
        2.1.1.1 Pay as You Use..23
        2.1.1.2 Massive Scalability 23
        2.1.1.3 Resource Sharing...23
        2.1.1.4 Elasticity 23
        2.1.1.5 Large Storage Space 23
    2.1.2 Cloud Infrastructure 23
    2.1.3 Data Life Cycle..24
2.2 Major Data Privacy Challenges/Concerns...26
    2.2.1 Scalable Privacy Preserving Data Mining and Analysis....................26
    2.2.2 Granular Access Control 28
    2.2.3 Cryptographically Enforced Data-Centric Security............................29
    2.2.4 Balancing between Data Provenance and Security............................29
2.3 Importance of Data Privacy in Healthcare..30
    2.3.1 Maintaining Trust in a Doctor–Patient Relationship..........................30
    2.3.2 Better Data Quality...30
    2.3.3 Improved Balance and Integrity in Current Industry Data Monopolies..30
    2.3.4 Protecting the Basic Human Rights..31
2.4 Who Is Responsible for Data Security?..31
2.5 Comparison of Various Privacy Attacks over the Years and Possible Techniques to Contain Them..32
References..33

2.1 INTRODUCTION

Data privacy refers to the rightful ownership of one's personal information from the time the datawere generated till they are destroyed. In today's rapidly evolving era of medical science,the privacy and security of EHRs are given the most importance since digital data, which are preferably stored in a cloud environment, attract various hackers and intruders [1]. Medical data involve a wide area of data owners such as mobile applications tracking a person's diabetes level or blood pressure, meditation apps to help relieve people's stress, menstrual cycle apps for women to track their menstruation timetable, reminders on phones for taking a particular medicine, water intake reminders and the list is not limited [2]. From getting up in the morning to going to bed at night, trillions of bytes of medical data are generated and processed by an individual, which need to be given privacy from the outside world, since they contain highly sensitive and personal information [3]. According to Padmaja et al. [4], attacks on the healthcare domain take approximately 11 hours to mitigate, and cost an average of $2800. Snooping attacks constitute the major area of invasion of privacy of the personal data of users.

Healthcare data include various digital health records as mentioned in Figure 2.1, and is not limited to these domains. Since healthcare data are stored in cloud servers, let us briefly discuss the cloud computing paradigm with its advantages and disadvantages [5].

2.1.1 Cloud Computing in the Healthcare Sector

Cloud computing is a network of systems/servers that are connected together by means of the Internet to provide five major characteristics to its users: Pay as you use, massive scalability, resource sharing, elasticity and large storage space [6].

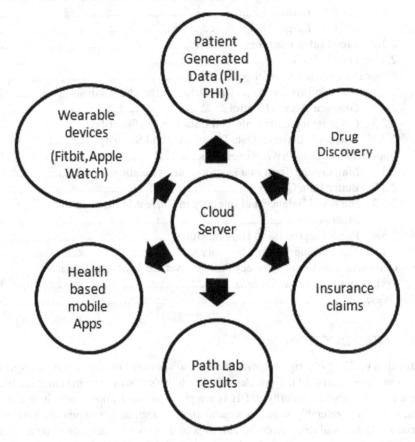

FIGURE 2.1 The healthcare domain in a cloud environment.

2.1.1.1 Pay as You Use

The major benefit given to the users of a cloud is "pay as long as you use the service." The users have the liberty to pay only for those resources which are required for a given period of time, without being worried about the extra incurred cost for underutilized resources [6, 7].

2.1.1.2 Massive Scalability

Since the user of a cloud service can be an individual or an organization with thousands of employees, the cloud environment can scale up/down its services to cater to the needs of the users in any situation [7]. It can provide the necessary network bandwidth along with large storage space as required.

2.1.1.3 Resource Sharing

Also termed *multitenancy*,cloud computing offers the sharing of resources among different users at the same time:At the network level, host level and the application level [4, 8].

2.1.1.4 Elasticity

Cloud service users have the provision to release their claimed resources when no longer needed, to make them available for other users [9].

2.1.1.5 Large Storage Space

Users can ask for TBs of storage space from cloud service providers and pay on a per-use basis [9].

2.1.2 CLOUD INFRASTRUCTURE

Cloud computing is based on the concept of *virtualization* where computing resources, storage and the network are virtualized to provide the benefits of optimized utilization of IT infrastructure, decreased management complexity and deployment time of services.

The cloud infrastructure is shown in Figure 2.2.

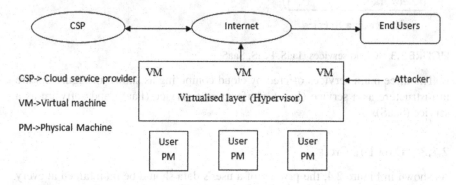

FIGURE 2.2 Cloud infrastructure.

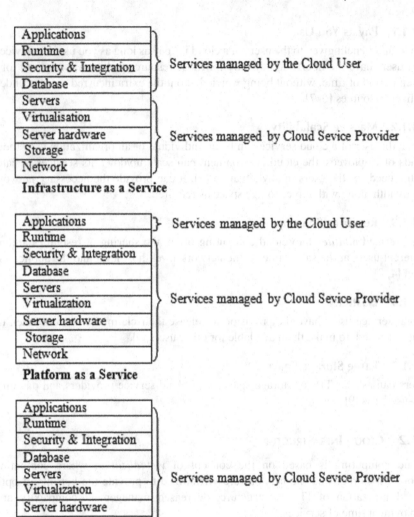

FIGURE 2.3 Cloud services (IaaS, PaaS, SaaS).

The three main services offered by cloud computing as shown in Figure 2.3 are infrastructure as a service (IaaS), platform as a service (PaaS) and software as a service (SaaS).

2.1.3 Data Life Cycle

As shown in Figure 2.4, the privacy of a user's data should be maintained at every stage of the data life cycle, that is, from the point of creation of the data till their

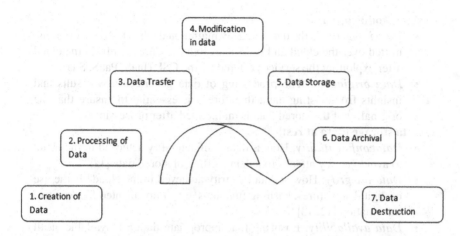

FIGURE 2.4 Data life cycle.

destruction phase [10, 11]. Each phase consists of various components which need to be addressed to ensure the sustaining of data privacy. Let's discuss these components briefly with respect to healthcare organizations.

a. **Creation of data:**
   - *Data possession*: Who is the owner of the sensitive information in the organization and after it is sharedover the cloud servers?
   - *Data categorization*: How are data classified in the organization to determine which data need to be sent to the cloud in contrast to sensitive information (e.g., personally identifiable information) which needs to be kept inside the organization?
b. **Processing of data:**
   - *Data authentication*: Are proper authentication techniques used to ensure rightful access to organization data (e.g.,company's verified login credentials/biometrics/OTPs, etc.)?
   - *Data relevance*: To ensure whether the data are being used for the purpose for which they were created and are notmisused after being deployed over the cloud.
   - *Inter or intra data usage*: Whether the data are used solely by the organization that created the dataor are being used by other organizations via a public cloud (e.g.,insurance companies, private pathology labs).
c. **Transfer of data:**
   - *Cryptographic mechanism*: When data travel from the organization server to the cloud server and vice-versa, are the data protected using any encryption mechanism to avoid any intruder attack?
   - *Use of the private/public network*: Does the organization use a public or private network to transfer the sensitive data over the cloud?

d. **Data modification**:
   - *Data integrity*: Is the data integrity maintained when the data are transmitted over the cloud and users start to access the data from the cloud after exploiting the services offered by the CSP (IaaS, PaaS, SaaS)?
   - *Data originality*: The processing of data generates new results and insights from existing data; therefore it is essential to ensure that the originality of the stored data is maintained after processing.
e. **Data storage (data at rest)**:
   - *Dataconfidentiality*: How is data confidentiality achieved in the cloud to avoid privacy attacks like data sniffing of stored data [12]?
   - *Data integrity*: How is data integrity achieved in the cloud? Is the use of digital signatures, hashing functions, etc., implemented for sensitive information [12, 13]?
   - *Data availability*: Ensuring that appropriate data are available at all times to the authentic users of the organization [12].
   - *Data authorization*: To ensure that only authorized users can gain access to the system and appropriate access controls(right to read, update, edit, etc.) be issued to every employee to limit the unauthorized access [14].
f. **Data archival**:
   - *Time period*: To determine the time period for which the data need to be archived in cloud storage
   - *Future use of data*: To determine if the stored data will be useful in the near future, and to determine the worthiness of archived data in terms of storage cost and maintenance cost.
g. **Data destruction**:
   - *Complete*: To ensure that the complete destruction of data is achieved and to determine whether the data can be recovered in case of mistaken destruction of data.
   - *Data remanence*: To ensure that the residual data do not pose any threat to the existing data and are kept in safe storage [6].

2.2 MAJOR DATA PRIVACY CHALLENGES/CONCERNS

The privacy challenges faced in a cloud environment are broadly classified into four groups:Let us discuss each of the challenges in detail [15, 16].

2.2.1 SCALABLE PRIVACY PRESERVING DATA MINING AND ANALYSIS

With the advent of big data, legacy systems were unable to handle the storage and analysis of TBs of data. This called for powerful servers, which can help the processing of data analytics of big data in large organizations for better decision making, market research, increased data consumption, analysing and predicting profits or losses, etc. [17, 18].

In the healthcare sector, data analytics and market research are used by insurance agencies to study the pattern of claims submitted by customers or to study demographics of people (smoking habits, older age, large families, etc.) to acquire new and more customers [18, 19]. Pharmaceutical companies use analytics to predictdisease outbreaks in the future, to invent vaccinations for pandemics, etc.

Healthcare agencies possess personally identifiable information (PII) and protected healthcare information (PHI) of doctors, patients, nurses and other stakeholders [18]. Using extensive market research on the data can lead to privacy invasions and breaches of data security, which are the two major concerns related to sensitive information [20]. The attacker or malicious intruder can gain access to PII data which can result in serious threats to privacy. Keeping the data anonymous does not help in the healthcare sector.

Hence the major scenarios responsible for invasions of privacy include:

a) An organization using third parties for market research needs to release critical information which may lead to the possibility of an attack by an outsider and the misuse of private information of persons [21].
b) Organizations using a cloud server for remote storage and analysis are at greater risk since the ownership lies in the hands of the cloud service provider (CSP), which is prone to disclosure of data [21, 22].
c) An insider employee of an organization can also be a potential attacker, who can misuse his access rights to gain access to sensitive information of clients for personal benefit.

Many solutions have been proposed to face these challenges such as:

- *Differential privacy*: Using this technique, the organization shares the information about a particular dataset publicly, by making groups of data and sharing patterns. However, the organizations do not disclose the PII information and keep them secure. This is shown in Figure 2.5.
- *Homomorphic encryption*: Using this technique, the organization shares the information with analytics agencies in encrypted form. The data analytics are performed on the ciphertext only and the results are sent back to the organization in encrypted form as shown in Figure 2.6.

Patient Id	Name	Contact No.	Blood Group	Age	Diabetes
1	ABC	12345	A+	12	N
12	XYZ	67892	B+	50	Y
123	MNO	11223	O+	24	N
1234	RST	54321	AB+	42	Y

PII held by organization Information stored for data Analytics

FIGURE 2.5 Differential privacy.

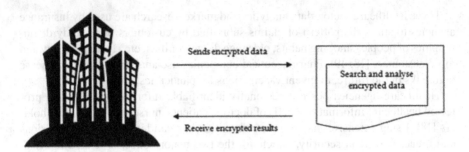

FIGURE 2.6 Homomorphic encryption.

2.2.2 GRANULAR ACCESS CONTROL

Granular access control corresponds to the allocating of access rights to the organization'semployees for each and every part of the system and also stating "what" can be done using those access rights [23]. However, issuingthe access rights for each employee as well as for each part of the system is a difficult and time-consuming task.

Granting access control can be discussed using the four Ws of the process.

- "Who"
  - This refers to the identification of each employee's role and granting them appropriate access control, which requires a great deal of time and effort. For example, a system administrator should be given the rights to access the database of the company; however a web designer need not be given these rights [24].
  - Giving controls for each part of the systeminvites challenges for the roles distributor,since an organization contains diverse data with respect to structural aspects of data or varying security concerns linked to each type of data.
- "What"
  The 'What' of the process refers to what kind of access controls are to be allocated to each person in a company.
  - For instance, in an insurance-based company, read, write and access rights [23] are given to the claims department for analysing the claims submitted by the customers, while the marketing department is given only the reading right for the same.
  - However, giving such explicit rights to each individual is a challenging task.
- "Where"
  - The granting of access rights to individuals and for each part of the system is not sufficient; rather the location from which an employee accesses the company resources plays an important role.

- Employees logging into the system from a remote location can be a major threat to privacy and a breach in security. Hence, access rights should be given to only on-site employees and, if needed, may be granted for the locations which are in close proximity to the employee's residence [25].
- **"When"**
  - It is very crucial to decide the "time duration" for which the rights are given to the individuals. For instance, a full-time employee will require the rights from 9 am to 8 pm every working day, while a part-time employee will require rights for only 3–4 hours daily as long as the contract stays valid [26].
  - Any employee who wishes to access the system outside of his working hours can be considered as a possible threat to the company. However, under special conditions, the issuing of access rights can be granted, which must be terminated after the job is completed.

2.2.3 Cryptographically Enforced Data-Centric Security

In order to maintain privacy of cloud users' data, there are two main approaches used. One is to minimize the visibility of the cloud servers bylimiting the access control rights, and the other is a data-centric approach, which focuses on **encrypting the data** from end to end at the storage level and during transmission in a network.

The first approach is simpler to execute; however it is prone to security attack by malicious users, who can misuse the unprotected data.

The second approach limits the attack area, but is still prone to attacks by adversaries [27].

Since healthcare data are highly confidential and vast in nature, users often store them in a cloud in encrypted form. As soon as the data are stored in the cloud, they are not in the sole control of the users. In order to perform any processing of the data, they need to be decrypted first, which causes the main loophole for the attackers to gain access to the data.

Data encryption alone cannot protect the data since there is always a risk of data modification and data leakage by mistrusted users in the network [17, 28]. Man-in-the-middle attacks, data sniffingand spoofing of data need to be dealt with and therefore,maintaining the confidentiality and integrity of data are the main concerns which need to be addressed for the data stored in a cloud server.

2.2.4 Balancing between Data Provenance and Security

Data provenance or data lineage, put in simple words, means "metadata" which describes the data about the data.It contains all the information about the data: Origin/source of data, travel history of data, who accessed the data, what changes have been made to the data from their inception till date and who is responsible for making the changes.

The provenance of data is critical to organizations where data integrity and confidentiality are of prime concern [17]. Insurance-based companies, the healthcare sector, supply chains and departments focusing on scientific research and development are deeply dependent on historical data records. In the absence of such records, serious security threats can hamper these types of companies.

Many companies are now aware of the importance of evaluating their data provenance through the process of backtracking. When an unexpected error occurs in a system, the general rule is to backtrack to the origin of the error, what caused it and what can be done to erase the problem from its root. This methodology is also practiced by the organizations to gather the provenance of data [24, 29].

Since this metadata contains all the important information about the company's data, it is prone to insider and outsider attacks. An insider of a company can manipulate, delete or forge the provenance records for personal benefit, thus invading the privacy of the user's data. Similarly an outsider can gain unauthorized access to the company's system to delete or change the records and can access the user's personal records [30].

2.3 IMPORTANCE OF DATA PRIVACY IN HEALTHCARE

2.3.1 Maintaining Trust in a Doctor–Patient Relationship

It is vital for the healthcare professionals to build trust with their patients by keeping the patient's data safeand protecting them from any kind of unauthorized disclosure. If a patient believes that the highly sensitive information (PII, name, age, date of birth, medical history, insurance claims, etc.) provided by them to their doctors is not protected, then the patient will be reluctant to provide their complete details for their own health and well-being, hence taking risksin their own lives [3].

2.3.2 Better Data Quality

A transparent system, where a patient can have full access to his own details, can provide higher quality and ultimately provides better healthcare for the patients.

In an electronic health system, the healthcare data are prone to errors. However, if a patient can access their personal records after the required authorization, it can help in increased transparency and better quality in healthcare data [19].

2.3.3 Improved Balance and Integrity in Current Industry Data Monopolies

In today's world where data are considered as "gold," industries misuse the confidential data of patients and outsource them to untrusted parties for personal profits and

Privacy in Cloud Healthcare Data

benefits. The complete picture of a patient's PII and PHI, including finances, insurance and medical history, is prone to data breach. The data privacy laws are essential in seeking answers to questions such as:Who owns the complete picture of the user? What risks are associated with situations of massive data leaks [31]?

2.3.4 Protecting the Basic Human Rights

The UN declared the "right to privacy" as a basic human right, which gives users the right to have privacy for their critical information. Suitable action takes place in case the law is not practised and the privacy of an individual is harmed [22].

Under the Health Insurance Portability and Accountability Act (HIPAA) privacy rule, patients have a number of rights including:

- The right to receive notice of the privacy practices of any healthcare provider
- The right to view their protected health information and receive a copy
- The right to request changes to their records to correct errors or add information
- The right to have a list of the parties to whom their protected healthcare information has been disclosed to
- The right to request confidential communication
- The right to complain

2.4 WHO IS RESPONSIBLE FOR DATA SECURITY?

To date, there is not unanimous consent on the sole stakeholder responsible for protecting the user's data privacy.

Some organizations feel that it is the responsibility of each individual to protect his/her own sensitive data by themselves; while some feel that it is the responsibility of the organization that is collecting the user's data. Others feel that the government should set appropriate standards for the organization for protecting users' data and monitor their activities [32, 33].

The Gigya report showed the distribution of privacy responsibility in 2017 as shown in Figure 2.7.

In the year 2020, many big companies such as Google and Facebook do value their profitsmore than protecting their users' privacy. They sell their customers' sensitive data to advertisement companies for monetary gain. Although these companies give the users the right to decide to use or to not use their particular service by signing the "Terms and Conditions," the users agree to the conditions without thoroughly going through them. This leads to the misuse or disclosureof personal information of the users and makes the service prone to security attacks [32].

In an effort to strengthen the process of protecting the users' privacy, the EU introduced a piece of legislation called the **General Data Protection Regulation (GDPR)** in 2019. It was an attempt to give control of data to the users rather than the

Stakeholders responsible for protecting user's data

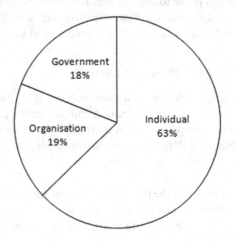

FIGURE 2.7 Responsibility distribution for protecting data privacy.

companies. However, companies like Google and Facebook didn't agree to follow it and faced billion-dollar fines.

Some of the key privacy and data protection requirements of the GDPR include:

- Requiring the consent of subjects for data processing
- Anonymizing collected data to protect privacy
- Providing data breach notifications
- Safely handling the transfer of data across borders
- Requiring certain companies to appoint a data protection officer to oversee GDPR compliance

In order to control the privacy breaches of users' data, California, USA, also came up with a bill called the **California Consumer Privacy Act (CCPA) bill** on January 1, 2020.

To date, the privacy issues still exist since no stringent controls are in place to protect users' sensitive data, especially in the healthcare sector, and privacy continues to be an important domain for discussion and further research.

2.5 COMPARISON OF VARIOUS PRIVACY ATTACKS OVER THE YEARS AND POSSIBLE TECHNIQUES TO CONTAIN THEM

Table 2.1

TABLE 2.1
Privacy Attacks and Techniques for Protecting Privacy

Year	Attacks/Vulnerabilities	Techniques
Tabrizchi et al. (2020) [1]	• Eavesdropping • Masquerade attack • Man-in-the-middle attack	Attribute-based file encryption mechanism from the cloud (ERFC)
Padmaja et al. (2019) [4]	• Data integrity loss • Data segregation authentication • Data breaches	Searchable encryption and proxy re-encryption method
Marwan et al. (2018) [10]	• Unauthorized disclosure of information by intruders	Segmentation approach for healthcare images
Shomrani et al. (2018) [7]	• Encryption of "all" available data on the network	Proper segregation of data, for example, patients' personal details and illness, to decrease encryption time and to encrypt only the sensitive data
Hamid et al. (2017) [19]	• Challenges faced while transporting data from utility to storage server in the cloud	Edge/fog computing is suggested which keeps the processing and storage of data closer to the user
Singh & Singh (2017) [15]	• User data privacy • Audibility • Access control	Blockchain technology is used to prepare a decentralized framework for the sharing of information
Li et al. (2016) [34]	• Loss of confidentiality • Loss of integrity	Key-based auditing
Liang et al. (2016) [29]	• Loss of confidentiality • No data minimization	Encryption using regular language
Zhang et al. (2016) [35]	• Loss of confidentiality	Multi keyword search
Anitha et al. (2014) [18]	• Loss of confidentiality • Loss of isolation of computing resources in a public cloud	Authentication, authorization and auditing (AAA) are used and encryption of data is performed using Secure Socket Layer 3.0
Yu et al. (2010) [23]	• Loss of accessibility	Exception-based access control solution

REFERENCES

1. Tabrizchi, H., & Rafsanjani, K. (2020). A survey on security challenges in cloud computing: issues, threats, and solutions. *The Journal of Supercomputing*, 76, 9493–9532, Issue. 12/2020. doi: 10.1007/s11227-020-03213-1
2. Deepa, N., & Pandiaraja, P. (2020). E health care data privacy preserving efficient file retrieval from the cloud service provider using attribute based file encryption. *Journal of Ambient Intelligence and Humanized Computing*. doi: 10.1007/s12652-020-01911-5.
3. Jathanna, R., & Jagli, D. (2017). Cloud computing and security issues. *International Journal of Engineering Research and Application*, 7(6), 31–38.
4. Padmaja, K., & Seshadri, R. (2019). Analytics on real time security attacks in healthcare, retail and banking applications in the cloud. *Evolutionary Intelligence*. doi: 10.1007/s12065-019-00337-z.

5. Boss, G., Malladi, P., Quan, D., Legregni, L., & Hall, H. (2007). Cloud Computing. IBM White Paper, Version 1.0, October 2007.
6. V. Chang, & Wills, G. (2016). A model to compare cloud and non-cloud storage of big data. *Future Generation Computer Systems*, 57, 56–76. http://eprints.soton.ac.uk/382709/.
7. Al-Shomrani, A., Eassa, F., & Jambi, K. (2018). Big data security and privacy challenges. *International Journal of Engineering Development and Research*, 6, 894–900.
8. Kumar, P. R., Herbert Rajb, P., & Jelciana, P. (2018). Exploring data security issues and solutions in cloud computing, 6th International Conference on Smart Computing and Communications, ICSCC 2017, 7–8 December 2017, Kurukshetra, India. *Procedia Computer Science*, 125, 691–697.
9. Mahesh U. Shankarwar, Ambika V. Pawar (2015). Security and privacy in cloud computing: A Survey. In Proceedings of the 3rd International Conference on Frontiers of Intelligent Computing (FICTA) 2014, Vol. 2, Advances in Intelligent Systems and Computing (p. 328). DOI: 10.1007/978-3-319-12012-6_1.
10. Marwan, M., Kartit, A., & Ouahmane, H. (2018). Security enhancement in healthcare cloud using machine learning. The First International Conference on Intelligent Computing in Data Sciences. *Procedia Computer Science*, 127, 388–397.
11. Ramachandra, G., Iftikhar, M., & Khan, F. A. (2017). A comprehensive survey on security in cloud computing. The 3rd International Workshop on Cyber Security and Digital Investigation (CSDI 2017). *Procedia Computer Science* 110, 465–472.
12. L. D. Dhinesh Babu, P. Venkata Krishna, A. Mohammed Zayan, & Vijayant Panda. (2011). An analysis of security related issues in cloud computing. In International Conference on Contemporary Computing (pp. 180–190). Berlin Heidelberg: Springer.
13. Pardeep Sharma, Sandeep K. Sood, and Sumeet Kaur. (2011). Security issues in cloud computing. In International Conference on High Performance Architecture and Grid Computing (HPAGC) (pp. 36–45). Berlin Heidelberg: Springer.
14. K. S. Wong, M. H. Kim. (2012). Secure biometric-based authentication for cloud computing. In International Conference on Cloud Computing and Services Science (vol. 28, pp. 86–101).
15. Singh, N., & Singh, A., (2017). Data privacy protection mechanisms in cloud. *Data Science and Engineering*, 3, 24–39. DOI: 10.1007/s41019-017-0046-0.
16. Big Data Working Group: Expanded Top Ten Big Data Security and privacy Challenges. (2013). By CSA (Cloud Security Alliance).Link: https://downloads.cloudsecurityalliance.org/initiatives/bdwg/Expanded_Top_Ten_Big_Data_Security_and_Privacy_Challenges.pdf
17. Privacy and Security in Personal Data Clouds, Report. (2016). European Union Agency for Network and Information Security. ISBN: 978-92-9204-182-3, DOI: 10.2824/24216
18. R. Anitha, Saswati Mukherjee. (2014). Data security in cloud for health care applications. In H.-Y. Jeong, et al. (eds.), *Advances in Computer Science and Its Applications, Lecture Notes in Electrical Engineering* (p. 279). DOI: 10.1007/978-3-642-41674-3_167. Berlin Heidelberg: Springer.
19. Al Hamid, H. A., Rahman, S. M. M., Hossain, M. S., Almogren, A., & Alamri, A. (2017). A security model for preserving the privacy of medical big data in a healthcare cloud using a fog computing facility with pairing-based cryptography. *IEEE Access*, 5, 22313–22328.
20. Amandeep Verma, Sakshi Kaushal (2011). Cloud computing security issues and challenges: A survey. In International Conference on Advances in Computing and Communications (ACC) (pp. 445–454). Berlin Heidelberg: Springer.
21. Q., Zhang, L., Cheng, R., Boutaba. (2010). Cloud computing: State-of-the-art and research challenges. *Journal of Internet Services and Applications*, 1(1), 7–18.

22. Tim Mather, Subra Kumaraswamy, Shahed Latif. (2009). *Cloud Security and Privacy*.Gravenstein Highway North, Sebastopol, CA: O'Reilly Media, Inc.
23. S. Yu, C. Wang, K. Ren, W. Lou. (2010). Achieving secure, scalable, and fine-grained data access control in cloud computing. In Proceedings IEEE INFOCOM, San Diego, CA (pp. 1–9). DOI: 10.1109/INFCOM.2010.5462174.
24. V. Chang, M. Ramachandran. (2016). Towards achieving data security with the cloud computing adoption framework. *IEEE Transactions on Services Computing*, 9(1), 138–151.
25. W. Itani, A. Kayssi, A. Chehab. (2009). Privacy as a service: Privacy-aware data storage and processing in cloud computing architectures. In 8th IEEE International Conference on Dependable, Autonomic and Secure Computing, Chengdu (pp. 711–716). DOI: 10.1109/DASC.2009.139.
26. Dr. Ragesh, G. K., & Dr. Baskaran, K. (2016). Cryptographically enforced data access control in personal health record systems, global colloquium in recent advancement and effectual researches in engineering, science and technology (RAEREST 2016). *Procedia Technology*, 25, 473–480.
27. H. Takabi, J. B. Joshi, & G. J. Ahn. (2010). Securecloud: Towards a comprehensive security framework for cloud computing environments. In IEEE 34th Annual Confererence.
28. Elisa Bertino, Robert H. Deng, Xinyi Huang, Jianying Zhou. (2015). Security and privacy of electronic health information systems. *International Journal of Information Security*, 14, 485–486. DOI 10.1007/s10207-015-0303-z.
29. Liang, K., Huang, X., Guo, F., & Liu, J. K. (2016). Privacy-preserving and regular language search over encrypted cloud data. *IEEE Transactions on Information Forensics and Security*, 11(10), 2365–2376.
30. J. J. Cebula, L. R. Young. (2010). A taxonomy of operational cyber security. Technical Note: CMU/SEI-2010-TN-028. Software Engineering Institute, USA.
31. X., Zhang, M., Nakae, M. J., Covington, & R., Sandhu, (2008), "Toward a usage-based security framework for collaborative computing systems", *ACM Transactions on Information and System Security (TISSEC)*, 11(1), 3.
32. Weblink: https://www.pwc.com/us/en/library/risk-regulatory/strategic-policy/top-policy-trends/data-privacy.html.
33. Weblink: https://thenextweb.com/podium/2020/01/25/its-2020-and-we-still-have-a-data-privacy-problem/.
34. Li, Y., et al. (2016). Privacy preserving cloud data auditing with efficient key update. *Future Generation Computer Systems* 78: 789–798.
35. Zhang, W., et al. (2016). Privacy preserving ranked multi-keyword search for multiple data owners in cloud computing. *IEEE Transactions on Computers*, 65(5), 1566–1578.

3 Privacy-Preserving Authentication and Key-Management Protocol for Health Information Systems

Mukesh Soni and Dileep Kumar Singh

CONTENTS

3.1 Introduction 37
    3.1.1 Challenges in Traditional Healthcare Systems 38
    3.1.2 Smart Healthcare 38
    3.1.3 Challenges in Smart Healthcare 39
3.2 Literature Survey of Authentication and Key-Management Protocol in a Health Information System 41
3.3 The Proposed Scheme of Authentication and Key-Management Protocol 42
    3.3.1 The Proposed Registration Phase 42
    3.3.2 The Proposed Authentication Phase 44
3.4 Experimental Analysis and Performance Measurement 45
    3.4.1 Performance Measures 46
3.5 Conclusion 47
References 48

3.1 INTRODUCTION

The term 'smart city' refers to the advancement in people's lifestyles, where traditional systems and facilities are enhanced for further effectuality, sustainability and flexibility with the help of technologies and diverse categories of Internet of things (IoT) sensors to gather tremendous data from different devices. These collected data are analysed to manage assets, resources and services efficiently to improve the city's operations, such as the administration of movement and carriage systems, infrastructure, healthcare systems and crime detection. This increases the protection, efficiency, throughput and superiority of life for the advantage of its populations. So, smart cities are better than normal cities as they are safer [1].

Smart city components include streetlights, traffic management, infrastructure, grid sector, healthcare and so on. These apparatuses make the municipalities smart and effectual by improving the quality of services, such as remote data storage/access/transmission, while reducing overall costs. Healthcare refers to the maintenance or improvement of the health of people by the prevention or avoidance, detection, treatment, recovery or cure of any kind of physical and mental problems in any way possible. There are health professionals who provide different healthcare treatments for various problems. The smart healthcare component of smart cities has been introduced because traditional healthcare systems are facing diverse challenges [2].

3.1.1 Challenges in Traditional Healthcare Systems

Traditional healthcare systems face major challenges in providing low-cost and quality healthcare facilities. These difficulties are also intensified by the growing aged population, which leads to a mass of long-lasting diseases, increasing the need for healthcare facilities [3]. It is tough to get appropriate healthcare amenities in remote areas due to limited resources, such as an insufficient number of physicians to meet the needs of the citizens [4]. Moreover, hospitals may sometimes make errors while supervising infectious diseases, and even sometimes patients are given the incorrect medication. Due to these challenges, the existing healthcare structure must change into a modern healthcare system which is intelligent, sustainable and efficient. The smart healthcare concept involves various entities and technologies like sensors and wearable components while using information and communications technology (ICT).

3.1.2 Smart Healthcare

Smart healthcare is defined as the technology that provides better diagnostic tools, devices, efficient resources and services. Hence, it leads to improved treatment for patients and advances the quality of life for anyone and everyone. With quick and productive innovation in transmission technology and semiconductor tools, IoT-based smart healthcare is not an idea, but real-life experience. Sensing devices collect clients' important data and transmit them via diverse channels to the cloud level for managing, storage space and judgement-making or information mining [5].

Elements of smart healthcare are on-body sensors, hospitals and emergency response groups. A smart healthcare system revolves around, but is not limited to, sensors that are installed close to the patient's body area or in the adjacent ecosystem to know the location, motion and variations in critical signals of patients. Distinct body sensors obtain various biological symptoms like blood pressure, heart rate, blood sugar, pulse rate, brain activity and temperature, while sensors deployed in the environment, such as the home and clothes, are utilized to examine the patient's movements or behaviours. These sensors are conceived to be very portable and even run in situations that may have limited processing infrastructure support. Analysing the output data obtained from such sensors gives an estimate of certain kinds of

Privacy-Preserving Authentication

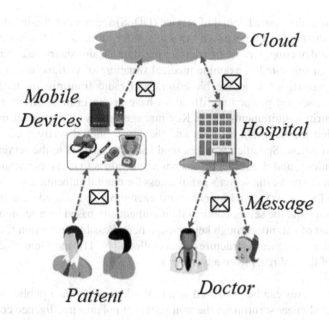

FIGURE 3.1 Overview of a smart healthcare system.

motions that the machine has undergone, such as changes, tilt, shake, cycle and rotate [6].

The mix of cloud computing and IoT for smart healthcare is shown in Figure 3.1, and significantly improves healthcare services, providing a system for continuous monitoring. The patients' health data composed by the sensors are transferred to a medical database. The cloud is used as the data storage, offering flexible storage and processing infrastructure. Thus, medical physicians can do realistic analyses through both kinds (online and offline) of investigations of data. The cloud data centre is common and accessed by healthcare providers, scientists, government organizations, insurance businesses and patients. By facilitating effective cooperation amongst the diverse involved entities, the medical procedures, such as diagnosis and emergency medical response, are advanced, thus significantly refining the efficacy of healthcare. It greatly changes the healthcare facilities of hospitals and health organizations [7, 8].

3.1.3 CHALLENGES IN SMART HEALTHCARE

A range of challenges are faced while trying to implement a sustainable healthcare system. If these challenges are solved, this could benefit the society and economy. IoT helps in the administration of key and non-critical procedures with the ambition of making our lives easier and safer. It leads to an enormously positive impression on our lives. Nevertheless, with these benefits, IoT structures have additionally received undesirable observations from spiteful users and attackers who intend to use flaws inside IoT arrangements for their individual benefit, discussed as security attacks, such as distributed denial of service (DDoS) and man-in-the-middle attacks. Delicate health data can be exposed to various safety attacks and threats at separate stages while detecting, saving or transferring data. Many smart healthcare methods have been suggested to examine medical situations of victims in real time with the speedy growth of wearable biosensors and radio transmission technologies. Nevertheless, several protection difficulties have arisen in these structures due to various security requirements [7–9]. Key management is an important problem in authentication mechanisms, as users and the server should verify each other in a public environment. Specifically, users send some parameters to the server to prove their authenticity, and the server also sends some values to users as a response confirmation and to prove the server's genuineness for mutual authentication. Therefore, it is crucial for the server and users to trust each other in a shared network. In this situation, users and the server confirm their authenticity based on a session key with a short period of validity through key management. Possible protection risks associated with smart healthcare structures are as follows [10, 11], and Figure 3.2 provides an outline of these threats from adversaries.

- *Passive*: This can be portrayed as an intruder spying via a public channel. The challenger scrutinizes the sent packets to obtain intelligence concerning the target (e.g., customers, structure, transmitting objects) instead of trying to damage the system or revise the communicated data (i.e., active attack). Examples of such attacks are side channel attacks, eavesdropping and traffic analysis.
- *Active*: An adversary attempts to alter the transmitted data by intruding in the structure. The challenger would insert phony statistics and potentially distort data in the system. Examples of such attacks are denial of service (DoS), brute force and masquerading.

Chapter structure: In Section 3.2, we give a literature survey of existing authentication mechanisms for medical applications. In Section 3.3, we suggest a lightweight user verification and key-management protocol for medical users to achieve privacy. Section 3.4 presents execution analysis to understand the efficiency of the suggested scheme. We conclude this chapter in Section 3.5.

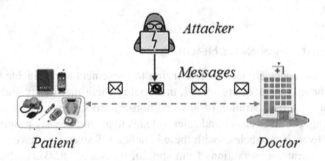

FIGURE 3.2 Real-time attacker scenario for remote medical services.

3.2 LITERATURE SURVEY OF AUTHENTICATION AND KEY-MANAGEMENT PROTOCOL IN A HEALTH INFORMATION SYSTEM

Telecare medicine information systems (TMIS) provide healthcare delivery services via a public network, i.e., the Internet. Patients send their health data using medical devices from their home via this network. Doctors make diagnoses and send results via a public channel. Thus, it becomes crucial to look at the security risks associated with a public network. Hence, sensitive information could be attacked by adversaries. Thus, the need for authenticated and secure communication to deal with various security challenges in this area.

In 2012, Wu et al. [12] offered a secure validation method for TMIS using Advanced Encryption Standard (AES), hash functions and discrete logarithmic problems to improve the security of the mechanism. The usage of these functions adds the precomputing mechanism within the communication process and stores the computed values in advance in a smart card to reduce the computational time during the authentication process. When these values are required, they are extracted from the smart card efficiently, ensuring a high level of security, and it is more practical for TMIS environments to avoid the time-consuming and high-cost computations. He et al. [13] pointed out that the system [12] cannot resist impersonation and insider attacks, and they proposed an advanced authentication scheme using similar cryptographic primitives to overcome the vulnerabilities found in Ref. [12].

In 2012, Wei et al. [14] suggested that both schemes [12, 13] failed to achieve two-factor authentication, which should be achieved by smart card-based authentication schemes. Researchers in Ref. [14] presented an improved authentication technique to enhance efficiency and satisfy the protection constraints of two-factor verification, but it is vulnerable to an offline password-guessing attack when the client's smart card is missing, as described in Zhu [15]. Further, Zhu [15] suggested a method to overcome the discussed weakness by improving the method's strengths against various security threats.

In 2012, Chen et al. [16] presented an economical client verification system for unidentified interaction in TMIS to overcome security flaws of dynamic ID-based schemes. However, Lin [17] illustrated that the design in Ref. [16] fails to comply with client secrecy due to dictionary and password-guessing attacks. Therefore, Lin [17] proposed an unidentified dynamic ID-based scheme based on the RSA algorithm to remove these flaws. Cao and Zhai [18] also found that, in Ref. [16], an intruder can identify a user by a common connection attack or an offline identity-guessing attack. Besides, the scheme in Ref. [16] needs a large amount of computational capacity to verify a permitted client or reject an illicit client on the server-side.

In 2013, Guo et al. [19] presented a new Chebyshev chaotic maps-based password-validated key agreement through smart cards using Chebyshev chaotic maps to create the session key between a client and the server. The study showed that their procedure could give secrecy, resist numerous attacks and fulfil protection needs. The survey in Ref. [20] proved that chaotic map function is more effective than a modular exponential function. Thus, Guo et al.'s system is more appropriate for

TMIS than the schemes based on conventional cryptography, but Hao et al. [21] found that the scheme in Ref. [19] suffers from an inability to offer privacy and the ineffectiveness of the dual-secret keys, leading to a failure of protection of user secrecy. Therefore, they [21] proposed a new chaotic map-based verification system, but it is still vulnerable to a stolen smart card attack, as clarified in Ref. [22].

In 2016, Li et al. [23] presented a safe identity and chaotic maps-based client verification and key arrangement system; nevertheless it is susceptible to impersonation and password-guessing attacks, and it does not offer client secrecy, convenient smart card cancellation or safety to the session key as discussed in Ref. [24]. To deal with these threats, Madhusudhan et al. [24] proposed a robust verification system using chaotic maps, and its computational resources are reasonable while confirming a client. In 2018, Radhakrishnan et al. [25] proposed an RSA-based confirmation method for TMIS to deal with different security threats, but its computation and storage costs are high in the system. Further, Dharminder et al. [26] showed that [25] is vulnerable to linkability problems, as well as insecure to password-guessing and stolen smart card issues. Thus, Dharminder et al. [26] proposed a different protected RSA-based authentication mechanism to advance the user verification system. However, we notice that RSA is not a lightweight cryptographic primitive, and it increases the execution time in Ref. [26] while sending medical data. Besides, the scheme [26] is designed using public key cryptography (i.e., RSA), leading to insecurity against public key attacks. Ultimately, the authentication protocol should be secure and efficient while considering the personal data protection of medical users. Hence, we propose a privacy-preserving lightweight verification and key-management system for medicinal clients.

3.3 THE PROPOSED SCHEME OF AUTHENTICATION AND KEY-MANAGEMENT PROTOCOL

We came up with an economical authentication and key-management protocol for patients using a lightweight cryptographic function, such as one-way hash. In the recommended system, there are primarily two stages: (i) a registration phase and (ii) an authentication phase. The block diagram of the suggested scheme is described in Figure 3.3 to make it easier for readers to understand the workings of the suggested authentication and key-management mechanism.

3.3.1 THE PROPOSED REGISTRATION PHASE

When a patient needs to transmit health data to the server, s/he should be a legitimate user of the system and for this, s/he should firstly enrol himself/herself on the server. In the registration process, a patient selects his/her personal credentials and sends them to the server to complete the registration process. After that, the server checks the availability of the received parameters. If there is no conflict, then the server proceeds further to confirm the registration and sends a smart card by saving registration parameters. In the design of the proposed scheme, we take care of user privacy

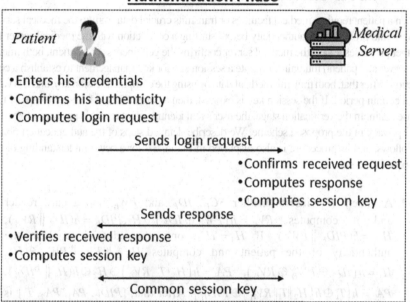

FIGURE 3.3 The block diagram for the proposed mechanism. It consists of a registration phase and an authentication phase.

by using pseudo identities for communication. When a patient needs to share his/her health data with the server in future, these parameters play an important role during the authentication phase to confirm the authenticity of the sender (i.e., patient). The registration process is explained step-by-step as follows.

1. A patient (P_i) decides on an identity (ID_{P_i}), password (PW_{P_i}) and random value (RV_{P_i}) to compute $PID_{P_i} = h(ID_{P_i} \| RV_{P_i})$, $H_1 = h(ID_{P_i} \oplus PW_{P_i} \oplus RV_{P_i})$. After that, P_i sends PID_{P_i} and H_1 to the medical server (MS) securely.
2. MS checks the availability of PID_{P_i} and accordingly computes $H_2 = h(H_1 \| PID_{P_i}) \oplus h\left(RV_{MS} \| RT_{P_i} \| SK_{MS}\right)$ to issue a smart card (SC_{P_i}) to P_i and saves PID_{P_i} and $h\left(RV_{MS} \| RT_{P_i} \| SK_{MS}\right)$ securely in its database. SC_{P_i} contains H_2 and it is given to P_i. Here, SK_{MS} is the secret key of the medical

server, RV_{MS} is a generated random value for P_i and RT_{P_i} is the registration time of P_i at the medical server.
3. After getting SC_{P_i} from the server, P_i calculates $H_3 = h(PW_{P_i} \oplus ID_{P_i}) \oplus RV_{P_i}$, $H_4 = h(PID_{P_i} \| PW_{P_i})$, $H_5 = H_2 \oplus h(RV_{P_i} \| PW_{P_i})$. Further, P_i removes H_2 from SC_{P_i} and saves H_3, H_4 and H_5 in SC_{P_i} to complete the registration phase. Ultimately, SC_{P_i} holds H_3, H_4 and H_5 only.

3.3.2 THE PROPOSED AUTHENTICATION PHASE

When a patient requires medical facilities or transmits crucial data from/to the medical server, s/he should prove his/her authenticity before starting a connection with the medical server for further processes. Once, the medical server confirms the genuineness of a patient, both (medical server and patient) mutually compute a session key for key management to establish a connection. After that, both transmit medical data by using the computed session key, and it is valid for a certain period. If the session key is expired, then a patient should follow all steps of this phase again. In the verification stage, the user's real identity is not revealed anyway, protecting user privacy in the proposed scheme. We describe detailed steps of the authentication phase, as follows, and its procedure is also displayed in Figure 3.4 for a better understanding of the proposed scheme.

1. A patient (P_i) inserts his/her SC_{P_i}, ID_{P_i} and PW_{P_i} into a card reader and it computes $RV_{P_i} = h(PW_{P_i} \oplus ID_{P_i}) \oplus H_3, PID_{P_i} = h(ID_{P_i} \| RV_{P_i})$, $H'_4 = h(PID_{P_i} \| PW_{P_i})$. If $H_4 = H'_4$, only then does it confirm the authenticity of the patient and computes $H_2 = h(RV_{P_i} \| PW_{P_i}) \oplus H_4$, $H_1 = h(ID_{P_i} \oplus PW_{P_i} \oplus RV_{P_i})$, $PA_1 = h(H_2 \| T_1 \| RV_{T_1}) \oplus H_2 \oplus h(H_1 \| PID_{P_i})$, $PA_2 = h(T_1 \oplus h(H_2 \| T_1 \| RV_{T_1}) \oplus PID_{P_i})$. After that, $\{PID_{P_i}, PA_1, PA_2, T_1\}$ is sent to the medical server over an insecure medium.
2. The medical server (MS) checks the time validity based on $T_2 - T_1 \leq \Delta T$. If it is within this period, then MS computes $h(H_2 \| T_1 \| RV_{T_1}) = h(RV_{MS} \| RT_{P_i} \| SK_{MS}) \oplus PA_1$, $PA'_2 = h(T_1 \oplus h(H_2 \| T_1 \| RV_{T_1}) \oplus PID_{P_i})$. If $PA'_2 = PA_2$, then a patient (P_i) is authenticated and MS generates a random value, RV_{T_2}, to compute $PA_3 = h(H_2 \| T_1 \| RV_{T_1}) \oplus RV_{T_2}$, $PA_4 = h(T_2 \oplus RV_{T_2} \oplus PID_{P_i})$. Further, MS sends $\{PA_3, PA_4, T_2\}$ to the patient for mutual confirmation.
3. When the card reader gets a message from MS, it validates the time duration by $T_2 - T_1 \leq \Delta T$. If it is valid, then it calculates $RV_{T_2} = PA_3 \oplus h(H_2 \| T_1 \| RV_{T_1})$, $PA'_4 = h(T_2 \oplus RV_{T_2} \oplus PID_{P_i})$. If $PA'_4 = PA_4$ then it confirms that the patient is connected with a legal medical server.
4. Finally, both compute the session key, $SK_{MSP_i} = h(T_2 \oplus RV_{T_1} \oplus RV_{T_2} \oplus h(H_1 \| PID_{P_i}) \oplus H_2)$ by P_i and $K_{MSP_i} = h(T_2 \oplus h(RV_{MS} \| RT_{P_i} \| SK_{MS}) \oplus RV_{T_1} \oplus RV_{T_2})$ by MS to start data transmission.

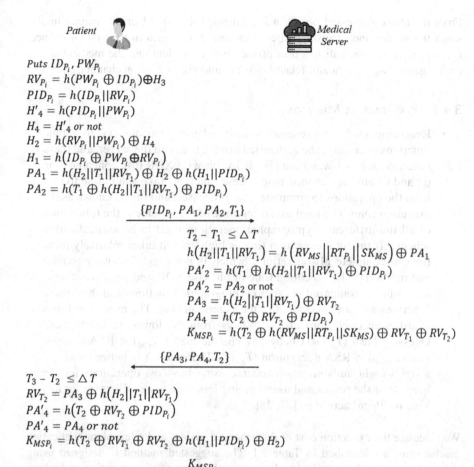

FIGURE 3.4 The proposed authentication scheme procedure.

3.4 EXPERIMENTAL ANALYSIS AND PERFORMANCE MEASUREMENT

We illustrate different performance results of the proposed scheme to understand its efficiency for the authentication. Thus, we describe three performance measures to know the implementation achievement of the proposed scheme and, after that, present the comparison among recent relevant authentication schemes. In the suggested system, a patient (P_i) sends $\{PID_{P_i}, PA_1, PA_2, T_2\}$ to the medical server in which PID_{P_i}, PA_1 and PA_2 are computed using one-way hash. Thus, it is not achievable to recover any given values from PID_{P_i}, PA_1 and PA_2. Here, PID_{P_i} is calculated as $h(ID_{P_i} \| RV_{P_i})$, where ID_{P_i} is the real identity of a patient, and RV_{P_i} is a random nonce. Nobody knows ID_{P_i} and RV_{P_i} other than P_i. Therefore, it is not feasible to guess ID_{P_i} anyhow. Besides, P_i does not share ID_{P_i} with anyone, and thus, an adversary cannot get ID_{P_i}.

From the above-discussed points, it is confirmed that an adversary cannot understand the sender and receiver parties' transferred messages in the system. Hence, the suggested scheme satisfies user privacy when a patient and the medical server exchange messages (of health-related information) via a common channel.

3.4.1 Performance Measures

- **Execution cost**: The scheme is designed using various cryptographic functions to confirm the authenticity of the user and the server, and these functions are one-way hash (H), RSA, bit-wise XOR ($\oplus$), concatenation (||) and Chebyshev chaotic map. These functions take some time to perform the operations to complete their processes, and this is known as the execution time. The total execution time of the scheme is the total count of all the different cryptographic operations used in an authentication scheme. If the total execution time is high, then it takes relatively more time to complete all operations, which is not good for either (sender and receiver). The execution time of bit-wise XOR and concatenation is insignificant compared to other cryptographic functions and thus, these functions are not considered in the execution cost. The execution times of different operations are as follows from the lowest to the highest: One-way hash (T_H) < Chebyshev chaotic map (T_{CCM}) < RSA encryption (T_{RSAE}) < RSA decryption (T_{RSAD}). Therefore, it is better to design a lightweight authentication scheme using low-cost operations for the benefits of the server and users, giving less time to an adversary for any kind of illegal activities [27, 28].

We calculate the execution cost of the proposed system and relevant authentication mechanisms, as described in Table 3.1. The suggested method is designed using only a one-way hash operation, and the execution time of this operation is the lowest among the other mentioned operations. Further, the registration stage is implemented once simply; however the verification procedure is needed every time before connecting to a legal server for medical data transmission. Hence, the proposed scheme gives better results compared to [24–26].

TABLE 3.1
Execution Cost Comparison for Different Authentication Schemes

Scheme	Registration Phase	Authentication Phase
Madhusudhan et al. [24]	$6T_H + 1T_{CCM}$	$15T_H + 3T_{CCM}$
Radhakrishnan et al. [25]	$7T_H + 1T_{RSAE}$	$18T_H + 1T_{RSAE}$
Dharminder et al. [26]	$4T_H$	$10T_H + 1T_{RSAE} + 1T_{RSAD}$
Proposed	$7T_H$	$15T_H$

- **Communication and storage costs**: When both (the server and a patient) are interested in establishing a connection between each other to transmit vital information, they exchange different parameters to confirm each other, and this is called the communication cost. When a patient registers with the server for future data transmissions, various values are saved in the smart card of the patient, which is called the storage cost, and these parameters are used during the authentication phase to verify the user's authenticity. Both costs (storage and communication) are measured in bytes. The numbers of bytes for different parameters are 32 bytes (one-way hash, SHA256), 12 bytes (random value: RV), 8 bytes (timestamp), 32 bytes (Chebyshev chaotic map: CCM) and 384 bytes (RSA) [27, 28].

We calculate these costs by taking the individual costs of separate kinds of parameters as mentioned above. Further, we count the required number of distinct categories of values in each scheme for the communication and storage costs. Table 3.2 describes the required types of parameters in Refs. [24–26], and the suggested mechanism. In Table 3.2, it is noticed that the total communication and storage costs are less compared to [25, 26], whereas the proposed scheme needs 16 bytes more compared to [24] for the communication, but the storage cost in Ref. [25] is 12 bytes more compared to the proposed scheme. Further, the scheme [25] is susceptible to a replay attack, and it has design flaws, because the server verifies the received request without having any base of a patient request. The proposed scheme is designed using a one-way hash function, which requires 32 bytes, and it requires 5 (one-way hash) and 2 (timestamp) for the communication, and 5 (one-way hash) for the storage cost. Therefore, the suggested mechanism needs a smaller number of bytes for storage and communication costs. Figure 3.5 shows the comparison of communication and storage costs for various authentication protocols, and it confirms that the recommended system demands a smaller quantity of bytes for these costs. Thus, the proposed scheme takes less computational power in the implementation.

3.5 CONCLUSION

We have proposed a lightweight authentication and key-management protocol while considering user privacy as a key element in medical applications. The performance

TABLE 3.2
Communication and Storage Costs Evaluation for Various Authentication Mechanisms

Scheme	Communication Cost	Storage Cost
Madhusudhan et al. [24]	4H + 1CCM	4H + 1RV
Radhakrishnan et al. [25]	4H + 1RV + 2TS	2H + 2RSA + 1RV
Dharminder et al. [26]	3H + 1RSA + 2TS	3H + 1RSA + 1RV
Proposed	5H + 2TS	3H

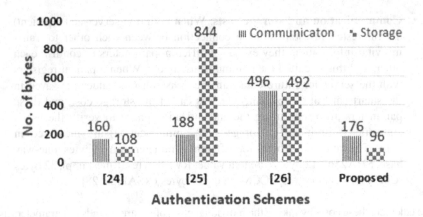

FIGURE 3.5 A comparison of communication and storage costs.

results are verified based on the cost of different performance measures, and the outcomes indicate that the suggested method requires a shorter execution period, less transmission costs and less storage costs compared to recent related authentication mechanisms. Further, the proposed scheme does not disclose the user's real identity during either (registration and authentication) phase to offer secrecy to users. Therefore, the proposed protocol is useful for medical users to confirm their authenticity and exchange crucial data with the medical server without compromising security and privacy while taking relatively fewer computational resources.

REFERENCES

1. Anthopoulos, L. G. (2015). Understanding the smart city domain: A literature review. In *Transforming City Governments for Successful Smart Cities* (pp. 9–21). Cham: Springer.
2. Yuehong, Y. I. N., Zeng, Y., Chen, X., & Fan, Y. (2016). The internet of things in healthcare: An overview. *Journal of Industrial Information Integration*, 1, 3–13.
3. Acampora, G., Cook, D. J., Rashidi, P., & Vasilakos, A. V. (2013). A survey on ambient intelligence in healthcare. *Proceedings of the IEEE*, 101(12), 2470–2494.
4. Mohanty, S. P., Choppali, U., & Kougianos, E. (2016). Everything you wanted to know about smart cities: The internet of things is the backbone. *IEEE Consumer Electronics Magazine*, 5(3), 60–70.
5. Baker, S. B., Xiang, W., & Atkinson, I. (2017). Internet of things for smart healthcare: Technologies, challenges, and opportunities. *IEEE Access*, 5, 26521–26544.
6. Islam, M. M., Razzaque, M. A., Hassan, M. M., Ismail, W. N., & Song, B. (2017). Mobile cloud-based big healthcare data processing in smart cities. *IEEE Access*, 5, 11887–11899.
7. He, D., Ye, R., Chan, S., Guizani, M., & Xu, Y. (2018). Privacy in the Internet of Things for smart healthcare. *IEEE Communications Magazine*, 56(4), 38–44.
8. Ande, R., Adebisi, B., Hammoudeh, M., & Saleem, J. (2019). Internet of things: Evolution and technologies from a security perspective. *Sustainable Cities and Society*, 54, 101728.
9. Gomathi, S. (2014). A cryptography using advanced substitution technique and symmetric key generating algorithm. In IEEE 8th International Conference on Intelligent Systems and Control (ISCO) (pp. 224–228). IEEE.

10. Limbasiya, T., & Shivam, S. (2017). A two-factor key verification system focused on remote user for medical applications. *International Journal of Critical Infrastructures*, 13(2–3), 133–151.
11. Limbasiya, T., & Doshi, N. (2017). An analytical study of biometric based remote user authentication schemes using smart cards. *Computers & Electrical Engineering*, 59, 305–321.
12. Wu, Z. Y., Lee, Y. C., Lai, F., Lee, H. C., & Chung, Y. (2012). A secure authentication scheme for telecare medicine information systems. *Journal of Medical Systems*, 36(3), 1529–1535.
13. Debiao, H., Jianhua, C., & Rui, Z. (2012). A more secure authentication scheme for telecare medicine information systems. *Journal of Medical Systems*, 36(3), 1989–1995.
14. Wei, J., Hu, X., & Liu, W. (2012). An improved authentication scheme for telecare medicine information systems. *Journal of Medical Systems*, 36(6), 3597–3604.
15. Zhu, Z. (2012). An efficient authentication scheme for telecare medicine information systems. *Journal of Medical Systems*, 36(6), 3833–3838.
16. Chen, H. M., Lo, J. W., & Yeh, C. K. (2012). An efficient and secure dynamic id based authentication scheme for telecare medical information systems. *Journal of Medical Systems*, 36(6), 3907–3915.
17. Lin, H. (2013). On the security of a dynamic id-based authentication scheme for telecare medical information systems. *Journal of Medical Systems*, 37(2), 9929.
18. Cao, T., & Zhai, J. (2013). Improved dynamic id-based authentication scheme for telecare medical information systems. *Journal of Medical Systems*, 37(2), 9912.
19. Guo, C., & Chang, C. C. (2013). Chaotic maps-based password-authenticated key agreement using smart cards. *Communications in Nonlinear Science and Numerical Simulation*, 18(6), 1433–1440.
20. Wang, X., & Zhao, J. (2010). An improved key agreement protocol based on chaos. *Communications in Nonlinear Science and Numerical Simulation*, 15(12), 4052–4057.
21. Hao, X., Wang, J., Yang, Q., Yan, X., & Li, P. (2013). A chaotic map-based authentication scheme for telecare medicine information systems. *Journal of Medical Systems*, 37, 9919.
22. Jiang, Q., Ma, J., Lu, X., & Tian, Y. (2014). Robust chaotic map-based authentication and key agreement scheme with strong anonymity for telecare medicine information systems. *Journal of Medical Systems*, 38(2), 12.
23. Li, C. T., Lee, C. C., Weng, C. Y., & Chen, S. J. (2016). A secure dynamic identity and chaotic maps based user authentication and key agreement scheme for e-healthcare systems. *Journal of Medical Systems*, 40(11), 233.
24. Madhusudhan, R., & Nayak, C. S. (2019). A robust authentication scheme for telecare medical information systems. *Multimedia Tools and Applications*, 78(11), 15255–15273.
25. Radhakrishnan, N., & Karuppiah, M. (2019). An efficient and secure remote user mutual authentication scheme using smart cards for Telecare medical information systems. *Informatics in Medicine Unlocked*, 16, 100092.
26. Dharminder, D., Mishra, D., & Li, X. (2020). Construction of RSA-based authentication scheme in authorized access to healthcare services. *Journal of Medical Systems*, 44(1), 6.
27. Limbasiya, T., & Das, D. (2019). ESCBV: Energy-efficient and secure communication using batch verification scheme for vehicle users. *Wireless Networks*, 25(7), 4403–4414.
28. Limbasiya, T., & Sahay, S. K. (2019). Secure and energy-efficient key-agreement protocol for multi-server architecture. In *International Conference on Secure Knowledge Management in Artificial Intelligence Era* (pp. 82–97). Singapore: Springer.

4 Privacy Issues in Medical Image Analysis

Prachi Natu, Shachi Natu and Upasana Agrawal

CONTENTS

4.1 Introduction 51
4.2 Digital Imaging and Communications in Medicine (DICOM) Image Format 53
4.3 Storage and Transmission of Medical Images 55
4.4 Threats to the Privacy of Medical Images 55
4.5 Privacy Protection of Medical Images 56
    4.5.1 Privacy Protection by Encrypting PHI 56
    4.5.2 Privacy Using Encryption and Encoding 56
    4.5.3 Cryptosystem 57
    4.5.4 By De-Identification/Anonymization of Images 58
4.6 Security in DICOM Images 59
4.7 Vulnerabilities in DICOM Images 60
4.8 Conclusion 61
References 61

4.1 INTRODUCTION

Medical images are an integral part of healthcare data and play a vital role in the medical diagnosis of a patient. The development of new medical imaging systems has resulted in huge amounts of medical image data generation. Maintaining the privacy and confidentiality of a patient's healthcare data, whether it is electronic health records (EHR) or medical images, is very much important.

Privacy is a fundamental human right. In the simplest words, privacy is to have control over who knows what about us. As Ruth Gravison says, there are three elements in privacy: secrecy, anonymity and solitude. In the medical field, privacy is legal and ethical too. Patients have the right to decide who can access their health information and to what extent. When it comes to data in healthcare, medical image data have their own significance. Medical image data are acquired for different purposes, such as diagnosis, therapy planning, intraoperative navigation, post-operative monitoring and biomedical research. Privacy is of the utmost importance because patients reveal their personal data to the doctor. The privacy of a patient's healthcare data is necessary to maintain the trust between patient and doctor. A patient's trust in a doctor can help the doctor to collect more accurate data. More accurate data in turn result in an accurate diagnosis and precise conclusion by the doctor. Hence a doctor needs to access all of the patient's data and know all the history related to it.

It will be easy to understand this with the help of a case study reported by Mark Warner [1].

Everyday huge numbers of medical images are available on the Internet and anyone can download them. Nearly half of all the unprotected images which incorporate X-rays, ultrasounds and CT scans belong to patients in the United States. However, despite warnings from security specialists making medical clinics and specialists' workplaces aware of the issue, many have disregarded their alerts and kept on exposing their patients' private wellbeing information. One patient, whose data were uncovered after a visit to an emergency room in Florida a year ago, portrayed her uncovered clinical information as "scary" and "awkward." Another patient with a chronic disease had regular scans at an emergency clinic in California over a period of 30 years. "It appears to deteriorate each day," said Dirk Schrader, who drove the exploration at Germany-based security firm Greenbone Networks, which has been observing the quantity of uncovered servers for as long as a year.

Be that as it may, even in instances of patients with just one or a bundle of medical images, the private information can be utilized to derive an image of an individual's wellbeing, including diseases and wounds. With an end goal to secure the servers, Greenbone reached in excess of a hundred associations a month ago about their uncovered servers.

Rather, he claimed that it was pure negligence that specialist's workplaces neglected to appropriately design and secure their servers. Lucia Savage, a previous senior security official at the US Department of Health and Human Services, said that in the healthcare industry especially, in those organizations that lack the resources, more efforts must be taken in order to improve the security of medical images. Personal information from these data need to be secured from unauthorized access. Penalties can be imposed if the laws are not maintained and followed. One Tennessee-based medical imaging company was fined over $3 million last year for exposing the images of over 300,000 patients.

Deven McGraw, who was the top protection official in the Health and Human Services' implementation arm, the Office of Civil Rights, said if security help was progressively accessible to small organizations, the government could concentrate its requirement endeavours on suppliers that stubbornly disregard their security commitments. McGraw stated that government enforcement is important, as are guidance and support for lower-resourced providers and easy-to-deploy solutions that are built into the technology, as it may be very difficult for an individual agency to enforce it. Schrader mentioned that there is a lot to improve but he and his team would do the best to improve the systems of unprotected data globally.

This brief summary of facts is sufficient to show the severity of not protecting patients' privacy.

The purpose of this chapter is to introduce briefly the techniques to maintain the privacy of medical images. Section 4.2 describes a common medical image storing format: Digital Imaging and Communications in Medicine (DICOM) images, followed by their storage and transmission in Section 4.3. Threats to the privacy of medical images are discussed in Section 4.4. Section 4.5 focuses on privacy protection methods for medical images, which include two major methods: Encryption-based and image anonymization. Cryptography is one of the ways of encrypting personal data in medical images. It is a method of securing the information such that only the intended user can read it without it being stolen or altered by a third party. It uses an encryption key to lock or hide the important data which are the patient's information in this case. On the receiving side, a decryption key is used by the receiver party to unlock this hidden information. Since no other person or entity has this decryption key, the patient's personal information is sent securely without any intervention by an unauthorized user. Anonymization is another way to achieve the privacy of patients' data. In anonymization, annotated personal data written onto the image are removed from the image provided that it does not contain any information about the anatomy of organs or disease specifications. Further, this chapter discusses in detail the security in DICOM images in Section 4.6 and vulnerabilities and securities in DICOM images in Section 4.7.

4.2 DIGITAL IMAGING AND COMMUNICATIONS IN MEDICINE (DICOM) IMAGE FORMAT

Medical images collected via different modalities are stored as DICOM images, which is a worldwide accepted format. It is used for the storage, exchange and display of medical images [2].

DICOM serves many purposes. Physicians can make faster diagnoses using DICOM. DICOM images are sent through a network and assistance in diagnosis can be obtained from experts, located in geographically distant areas. This helps patients get effective treatment.

DICOM images consist of a header and image dataset in a single file. Header files consist of the patient's demographics or protected health information (PHI), image dimensions and acquisition parameters. These data may or may not be visible on screen while viewing the image but can be extracted from the header file. A DICOM viewer is required to view these images with their details.

Figure 4.1 shows sample DICOM images with different modalities for different organs.

The patient's privacy allows the sharing of protected health information (PHI) only with those who need it.

The following is some information called PHI which can violate the privacy of a patient [3]:

1. Name
2. Geographic locators
3. Dates (e.g., birth date, admission and discharge date, date of death and any other kind of date that can reveal the age of the patient)
4. Contact numbers
5. E-mail addresses
6. IP addresses

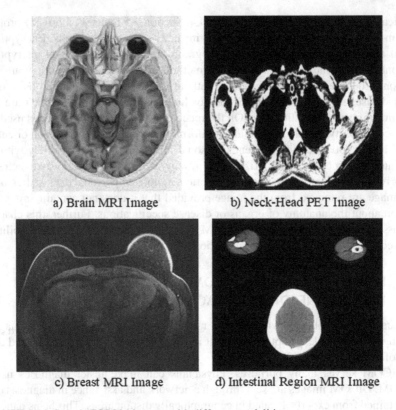

FIGURE 4.1 Sample DICOM images with different modalities.

7. Any kind of licence numbers
8. Biometric identifiers
9. Photo
10. Any unique identifier

But if these medical images are to be used for research purposes or as a learning resource, then the PHI of the patient should not be included in the image, thus ensuring the privacy of the patient.

Ethical and privacy aspects of using medical images are described in the context of the VISCERAL project [4]. This project was aimed at organ segmentation, landmark detection, lesion detection and similar case retrieval. A huge medical image dataset was the primary requirement of the project. These data were collected from three different data providers who play an important role in the anonymization of data. Ethical, legal and privacy aspects need to be handled by the data provider. To anonymize the data, patients' personal information like birth date, name ID, institution name, examination number and study date was removed from the DICOM header. Any text embedded into the image and serial numbers of implants are also removed from images. Whole-body CT scans were defaced by partly blurring the

Privacy Issues in Medical Image Analysis 55

faces. Before actual use of the data, a local/national medical ethics committee (MEC) reviews the data. Once the committee agrees on it, the use of the data is assured for research purposes.

4.3 STORAGE AND TRANSMISSION OF MEDICAL IMAGES

The digitization of medical images has transformed healthcare and medical research. New technologies, smart phones and social media provide instant access to patients and their data by healthcare providers and research collaborators. Advanced storage and transfer capabilities have made it feasible to store medical images along with electronic records, but as the demand for capturing and storing images increases, so does the need for privacy measures. Healthcare professionals are heavily using social media like Facebook, Twitter and Instagram to transmit pathological images. The use of social media opens doors for researchers by allowing them easy access to such images. At the same time, however, it raises the challenges of protecting the privacy of patients' personal information hidden in such medical images. The use of smartphones in order to produce and store medical images on social media also has risks like insecure data storage, tampering with the privacy of patients and the failure of the physician or institution to obtain the patient's consent [5].

A blockchain-based approach has been proposed for retrieving medical images [6]. The inherent characteristics of blockchain technology are decentralization, anonymity and data consistency. These characteristics facilitate the secure sharing of data via cryptographic transactions. Two challenges have been identified and tried to overcome by authors in this paper. The first challenge is to share/retrieve the large-sized medical image through storage-constrained blocks in blockchain, and the second is to protect the privacy of a medical image while retrieving and analysing it. To overcome the first challenge, selected features of the image are used. To overcome the second challenge, a customized transaction structure is designed. Mingyan Lia et al. emphasize the problem of the illegal release of medical images by authorized users in group communication networks and design requirements that must be met to avoid this. A computationally feasible and scalable fingerprint model has been suggested by the authors [7].

This is achieved with the help of watermarking, i.e., the authorized user who leaked the image is traced from the watermark hidden inside the leaked image. Embedding such a watermark introduces restrictions like high image fidelity and robustness to frequency selective operations in medical images.

4.4 THREATS TO THE PRIVACY OF MEDICAL IMAGES

Threats to a patient's privacy from medical images can be of the types shown in Table 4.1 [8].

As shown in Table 4.1, when an image reveals a certain condition or other private information, it is called a direct threat. Re-linkage is a more commonly observed threat wherein the subject along with its metadata can be identified from the image. Existential inference refers to a situation when the existence of an image may suggest

TABLE 4.1
Types of Threats to the Privacy of Medical Images

Type	Description	Example
Direct	Reveals a condition	X-ray reveals fractured wrist
Re-linkage	Metadata reveals identity	Metadata includes gender, age and zip code and tied back to patient
Existential inference	Image known to exist	Subject in imaging study assumed to be a case rather than control
Identification	Inherently identifiable	Facial features identify subject

the presence of a certain condition or private information. Identification refers to a situation where high-resolution images reveal some features of the subject, e.g., high-resolution neuro images reveal the facial features of the subject.

4.5 PRIVACY PROTECTION OF MEDICAL IMAGES

The aim of privacy protection is to restrict the access to the PHI of the patient. It is accessible to the doctors who are involved in diagnosis and treatment but not to other people like researchers or learners. Also, it should remain confidential and integral during transmission. Privacy protection of medical images can be done in two ways depending on the intended recipient.

4.5.1 Privacy Protection by Encrypting PHI

Care should be taken so that during the transmission of medical images, they cannot be accessed (confidentiality) and changed by unauthorized parties (integrity). This situation may arise when geographically dispersed doctors are working on a patient's treatment and hence need to share medical images with each other. In such cases, a patient's PHI is encrypted and embedded in the image, i.e., if the viewer (e.g., the patient's doctor) has the authority to view a patient's personal information, then the information is retained in the image itself in the encrypted form so that it will not be easily visible and can be decrypted only by authorized viewers.

4.5.2 Privacy Using Encryption and Encoding

Ming Yang et al. proposed a technique for the privacy of medical images using encryption and encoding methods. According to the proposed methodology, the patient's data are not visible at the corner of the medical image. This information would be first encoded and then encrypted using an encryption algorithm [9]. The medical image can be seen in one of two structures. In the process, if the viewer doesn't have access to the patient's own data, for instance a medical or researcher (or hacker), the image is seen without any information associated with it. If the authorized person such as the patient or doctor has access to the confidential data, they would then be able to be extracted, decrypted, decoded and then displayed using the encryption/decryption key. The following steps describe the working of this proposed method:

1. Image segmentation: In this step the raw image is divided into sub-segments, regions or parts. This process identifies the region of interest (ROI) and the boundaries that have patient information.
2. Information encryption: The text information in the image is then converted into ASCII format that results in a seven-bit character string. An RSA algorithm is used for the encryption of data.
3. Information embedding: A spatial domain algorithm and transform domain algorithm are used to hide the information of medical images. But a frequency domain algorithm is robust as compared to a transformation-based lossy compression method as it modifies the coefficients in the transform domain, so this can also be used.
4. Information embedding and extraction algorithm: To enable data embedding, a high bitrate transform domain information hiding algorithm is designed and used. For information hiding, low-frequency coefficients are chosen.

Another method used for medical image privacy is a fast probabilistic cryptosystem. This secures medical keyframes that are extracted from wireless capsule endoscopy procedures using a prioritization method.

4.5.3 Cryptosystem

The encrypted images exhibit random behaviour that results from using the cryptosystem. This method not only guarantees a high level of security but also ensures a computational guarantee for the key frames against any attack. Medical data are then processed without any information leakage, which enhances the patient's data privacy. The authors have proposed an encryption cryptosystem for securing medical images based on the Zaslavsky chaotic map which used four iterations of the permutation diffusion process [10]. The steps for using this method are as follows:

1. PRNG based on chaotic maps: The details of encryption keys algorithms are presented in detail in this step, i.e., 2D-Zaslavsky chaotic map, 2D-logistic map, PRGN algorithm.
2. Encryption key: Images are encrypted, adopting permutation diffusion architecture using chaos-based PRNG. The secret keys used are the initial values of 2D-logistic map and ZCM in this algorithm.
3. Decryption key: The key frames are reconstructed at the receiving end without losing their visual appearance.

4.5.4 BY DE-IDENTIFICATION/ANONYMIZATION OF IMAGES

Though the terms de-identification and anonymization are used interchangeably, there is a subtle difference between them. De-identification means obfuscating a patient's identity by hiding medical and personal data as per the Health Insurance Portability and Accountability Act (HIPAA) requirements. Anonymization would prevent a dataset from ever being re-identified, but this is difficult to achieve while retaining useful data [8].

If the viewer of the image (e.g., medical researcher) is not authorized to access the PHI, the information of the patient can be removed from the image, i.e., de-identification can be done.

Since the de-identification system is designed for end-users, it should be effective, accurate and fast. Nettrour et al. have focused on guiding healthcare professionals about how to capture and share the clinical images using smartphones and making them aware of "de-identification." HIPAA has formulated "Privacy Rules" and "Security Rules" for health information [11].

The following information should be removed from a clinical image in order to de-identify that image: The patient's tattoos, birth marks, surgical scars, clothing, body piercings, etc. Apart from this, digital images and smartphones embed some technical metadata in Exchangeable Image File Format (EXIF) into an image when a photo is taken. This includes information like file make, shutter speed, focal length, etc., and should be removed in order to de-identify the image. It is recommended to turn off the smartphone's GPS locating feature to prevent "geotagging." We can also use EXIF removal applications which are commercially available.

Sometimes, PHI information is burned into the image pixel data in some imaging modalities, like ultrasound images. These PHI data should be eliminated from image pixel data, resulting in anonymization of the image. In commonly used DICOM images, the header of the DICOM file contains different tags. Tag 0010 contains the patient's information. One way to remove a patient's information is to export DICOM images to other image formats like JPEG, TIFF, PNG, etc., so that the patient's information can be lost. But there are some major drawbacks of this [12]:

1. During such conversion, fine details in the image are not preserved which results in a loss of diagnostic information.
2. Formats like JPEG produce a compressed version of the image. During compression it generates some artifacts in images.

For accurate diagnosis and interpretation, a greater number of images are taken per patient. These images are annotated with digital text and sometimes reveal the patient's personal information. The removal of these PHI annotations from the image pixels is necessary. Only PHI annotations need to be removed and not any other important text data burned into the image. This is called "anonymization." For example, sometimes, text that is burned into the image may represent an annotation of anatomy or disease relevant for image interpretation. This is important information and should not be removed [13]. Many tools are available for the anonymization

Privacy Issues in Medical Image Analysis

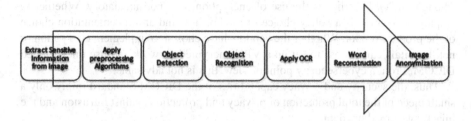

FIGURE 4.2 General flow in the anonymization process.

of text from image pixel data, but removing it using tools requires manual efforts to identify the region, which is time consuming.

Machine learning-based OCR mechanisms can be used to identify sensitive text data in medical image pixel data and anonymize it. It requires a certain sequence of steps to be followed.

Figure 4.2 shows the general flow in the anonymization process.

The first step is to extract sensitive information from the metadata of DICOM images. Image pre-processing activity like denoizing of extracted information is required to improve the visual quality of the image. It is followed by object recognition to identify contours and bounded rectangles in the image. Finally, an OCR system is used to classify the identified objects [14].

4.6 SECURITY IN DICOM IMAGES

DICOM Standard provides options for encrypting and protecting data during transmission in response to the implementation of the Health Insurance Portability and Accountability Act (HIPAA) and not in response to cybersecurity concerns.

Later, DICOM extended the use of Cryptographic Message Syntax (CMS) for encrypting PHI within the DICOM images. Thus, it protects a DICOM object throughout its life, and not just during information interchange. However, encryption of the entire DICOM object is not in the scope of DICOM. It is facilitated by other encryption methods.

Further, several changes have been made to the DICOM Standard to facilitate encryption, including the transfer of encrypted DICOM objects, and reading of encrypted DICOM objects on the receiver's end.

- When sending those objects in an e-mail, DICOM defines how to encrypt the files using CMS encryption methods for e-mail.
- When sending those objects using the traditional DICOM transfer mechanism (the DIMSE protocol), DICOM defines how to use an encrypted TLS connection.
- When sending those objects using the new DICOM transfer mechanism (DICOM web services), DICOM defines how to use an encrypted HTTPS connection.

Though DICOM facilitates the use of encryption, it is not mandatory. Whether to employ encryption is a policy choice of the hospital and an implementation choice of the product vendor. Whether the vendors have chosen to implement encryption or not, hospitals can choose to set up a VPN encrypted network and use unencrypted DICOM. From a cybersecurity point of view, this is not advisable.

Thus, the security and privacy capabilities of the DICOM Standard imply only a small piece of the total protection of privacy and protection against intrusion and the hijacking of medical data.

Hence, hospital and healthcare system authorities are responsible for ensuring the protection of privacy.

4.7 VULNERABILITIES IN DICOM IMAGES

Though DICOM working group 14 (WG-14) handles all aspects of security for DICOM images, the security of institutional networks and archives also influences the security of DICOM images [15]. If the security of these networks and archives is compromised, DICOM images are prone to attacks. Two types of attacks have been observed on DICOM images: Access attacks and injection attacks.

Access attacks were performed by security researchers in 2017 by identifying unprotected DICOM servers. These were attacks by external intruders, we can say. Another way in which DICOM images can be the victim of an attack is by attackers gaining access to a legitimate user's account.

In March 2019, in an injection attack, with the help of two deep neural networks, researchers injected and removed abnormal findings which were not identified by radiologists. Another injection attack was successfully tried by security researchers by hiding malware in the DICOM preamble. In order to track future vulnerabilities, WG-14 focuses on three tasks: First, the management of keys and certificates, the second is the implementation of a creator's digital signature and the third is to systematically wipe out undesired preambles from DICOM files to prevent the execution of embedded malware. Such an encryption-based approach using the RSA encryption algorithm and DCT is proposed [16]. In this approach, the patient's information is encoded in ASCII form and encrypted using the RSA algorithm. The ROI in the image is extracted using a segmentation technique. The encrypted information is embedded in the region outside of the ROI which helps in maintaining image quality and more accurate diagnosis.

Another approach using homomorphic encryption and deep learning has been proposed [17] Sensitive information is encrypted using homomorphic encryption and then deep neural networks are trained on these encrypted data. The result produced by DNN is also in encrypted form, thus securing both input and output.

Silva et al. have proposed the de-identification of PHI from DICOM image metadata and visual anonymization, i.e., the removal of PHI from pixel data using a machine learning model which gives reliable accuracy [18]. First, visual anonymization is performed. If it fails by the automated process, then it is done manually, followed by the de-identification of metadata. The visual anonymization module uses image processing techniques with a convolutional neural network to remove PHI text from the pixel data. A further OCR technique is used to recognize the characters. Wherever a match in the characters is found, it is replaced by a white bar, thus resulting in anonymous data. The anonymization task is carried out at the server, after uploading the image on the server. Once the process is completed, images can be downloaded from the server. As it is executed on the server, fast execution is possible. De-identification of metadata is carried out at the DICOM header itself. Monteiro et al. have proposed a de-identification process for ultrasound images. First, de-identification of the header is done, and then they also have followed a similar sequence of operations, i.e., pre-processing of images, followed by object detection and then character recognition. To reduce misclassification of the OCR system, a method based on the Levenshtein distance between the reconstructed words and the words present in the image is used [14]. Newhauser et al. used filters with different thresholds to identify the region with alphanumeric characters and create a bounding box around them [19]. Low-threshold filters with a threshold value of 1/255 give binary images. A negative image of this result is taken. It isolates non-radiographic information from the original image. High-threshold filters, on the other hand, isolate white pixels in the image. Hence dilation by one pixel is applied to all white pixels, as this type of thresholding removes characters and graticules too from the image. The resulting image is subtracted from the low-threshold filtered image. Further bounding boxes are generated around the identified characters and corresponding regions in the original image are removed by checkerboard pattern. Data identified by the OCR system are matched with PHI data in the DICOM metadata field. In some cases, the embedded annotations are very similar to the patient's data, which may happen due to misspelled characters. In such cases, the OCR system shows poor performance and hence is not reliable [13].

4.8 CONCLUSION

Medical image privacy is very crucial, and it means protecting the PHI of patients. As the DICOM image format is accepted worldwide for the storage and transmission of medical images, removing PHI from DICOM images is the next concern. Converting DICOM images to another image format like .jpg is one solution, but it has its own drawback of loss of image content. Hence other approaches include the encryption of PHI information during storage and transmission and the anonymization of text burned onto medical images. In the latter approach, PHI text is removed using the latest trends of machine learning-based algorithms, whereas annotated text is retained on the images.

REFERENCES

1. Zack Whittaker. (January 10, 2020). Join extra crunch. A billion medical images are exposed online, as doctors ignore warnings. Retrieved from: https://techcrunch.com/2020/01/10/medical-images-exposed-pacs/.

2. Bidgood Jr, W. Dean, Steven C. Horii, Fred W. Prior, and Donald E. Van Syckle. (1997). Understanding and using DICOM, the data interchange standard for biomedical imaging. *Journal of the American Medical Informatics Association*, 4(3), 199–212.
3. Compliance Group. What is Protected Health Information (PHI)? Retrieved from: https://compliancy-group.com/what-is-the-hipaa-safe-harbor-provision/. (Accessed on April 7, 2020).
4. Grünberg, K. et al. (2017). Ethical and privacy aspects of using medical image data. In: Hanbury A., Müller H., Langs G. (eds) *Cloud-Based Benchmarking of Medical Image Analysis*. Springer, Cham. https://doi.org/10.1007/978-3-319-49644-3_3.
5. Bromwich, Matthew, and Rebecca Bromwich. (2016). Privacy risks when using mobile devices in health care. *CMAJ: Canadian Medical Association Journal*, 188(12), 855.
6. Shen, M., Deng, Y., Zhu, L., Du, X., & Guizani, N. (2019). Privacy-preserving image retrieval for medical IoT systems: A blockchain-based approach. *IEEE Network*, 33(5), 27–33.
7. Li, M., Poovendran, R., & Narayanan, S. (2005). Protecting patient privacy against unauthorized release of medical images in a group communication environment. *Computerized Medical Imaging and Graphics*, 29(5), 367–383.
8. Schimke, Nakeisha, Mary Kuehler, and John Hale. (2011). Preserving privacy in structural neuroimages. In IFIP Annual Conference on Data and Applications Security and Privacy (pp. 301–308).Berlin, Heidelberg: Springer.
9. Yang, Ming, Lei Chen, Shengli Yuan, and Wen-Chen Hu. (2011). Secure processing and delivery of medical images for patient information protection. In Proceedings of the International Conference on Security and Management (SAM) (p. 1). The Steering Committee of The World Congress in Computer Science, Computer Engineering and Applied Computing (WorldComp).
10. Hamza, Rafik, Zheng Yan, Khan Muhammad, Paolo Bellavista, and Faiza Titouna. (2020). A privacy-preserving cryptosystem for IoT E-healthcare. *Information Sciences*, 527, 493–510.
11. Nettrour, J. F., Burch, M. B., & Bal, B. S. (2019). Patients, pictures, and privacy: Managing clinical photographs in the smartphone era. *Arthroplasty Today*, 5(1), 57–60.
12. Varma, Dandu Ravi. (2012). Managing DICOM images: Tips and tricks for the radiologist. *The Indian Journal of Radiology & Imaging*, 22(1), 4.
13. Tsui, Gary Kin-wai, and Tao Chan. (2012). Automatic selective removal of embedded patient information from image content of DICOM files. *American Journal of Roentgenology*, 198(4), 769–772.
14. Monteiro, Eriksson, Carlos Costa, and José Luis Oliveira. (2015). A machine learning methodology for medical imaging anonymization. In 37th Annual International Conference of the IEEE Engineering in Medicine and Biology Society (EMBC) (pp. 1381–1384). IEEE.
15. Benoit Desjardins Yisroel Mirsky, Markel Picado Ortiz, Zeev Glozman, Lawrence Tarbox, Robert Horn, Steven C. Horii. (2020). DICOM images have been hacked! Now what? *American Journal of Roentgenology*, 14(4), 1–9.
16. Yang, Ming, Monica Trifas, Lei Chen, Lei Song, D. B. Aires, and Jaleesa Elston. (2010). Secure patient information and privacy in medical imaging. *Journal of Systemics, Cybernetics, and Informatics*, 8(3), 63–66.
17. A. Vizitiu, C. I. Niţă, A. Puiu, C. Suciu and L. M. Itu.(2019). Towards privacy-preserving deep learning based medical imaging applications. In IEEE International Symposium on Medical Measurements and Applications (MeMeA), Istanbul, Turkey (pp. 1–6).

18. Silva, Jorge Miguel, Eduardo Pinho, Eriksson Monteiro, João Figueira Silva, and Carlos Costa. (2018). Controlled searching in reversibly de-identified medical imaging archives. *Journal of Biomedical Informatics*, 77, 81–90.
19. Newhauser, Wayne, Timothy Jones, Stuart Swerdloff, Warren Newhauser, Mark Cilia, Robert Carver, Andy Halloran, and Rui Zhang. (2014). Anonymization of DICOM electronic medical records for radiation therapy. *Computers in Biology and Medicine*, 53, 134–140.

5 Privacy in Internet of Healthcare Things

Mohammad Wazid and Ashok Kumar Das

CONTENTS

5.1 Introduction 65
    5.1.1 Architectures Related to IoHT...66
        5.1.1.1 Introduction..66
    5.1.2 Advantages of IoHT..68
    5.1.3 Chapter Outline 69
5.2 Applications of IoHT...69
    5.2.1 Remote Monitoring of Patients..69
    5.2.2 Hospital Operations Management..69
    5.2.3 Treatment and Detection of Diseases 70
    5.2.4 Remote Surgery 70
    5.2.5 Secure Drug Supply Chain Management 70
5.3 Privacy Issues in IoHT..70
5.4 Threat Model, Security and Privacy Requirements and Various Attacks in IoHT..71
    5.4.1 Threat Model 71
    5.4.2 Security and Privacy Requirements in IoHT...................................72
    5.4.3 Different Types of Attacks in IoHT Environment...........................73
5.5 Analysis of Privacy-Preserving Protocols Related to IoHT Environments....75
    5.5.1 Review of Hamza et al.'s Scheme [50]..75
    5.5.2 Review of Deebak et al.'s Scheme [51] 76
    5.5.3 Review of Pu et al.'s Scheme [63]...82
    5.5.4 Review of Dwivedi et al.'s Scheme [66] 83
    5.5.5 Review of Kim et al.'s Scheme [68]..84
    5.5.6 Comparative Analysis of Existing Privacy-Preserving Protocols 84
5.6 Concluding Remarks 86
References..86

5.1 INTRODUCTION

The Internet of Things (IoT) has opened up numerous possibilities in the healthcare domain. The Internet of Healthcare Things (IoHT) is a specialized version of IoT that consists of uniquely identifiable healthcare devices connected to the Internet. It helps in the localization and gathering of real-time information. Furthermore, it provides remote or automatic management of resources. When connected to the Internet, the medical devices can collect important data that give extra insight into the symptoms and trends. It further enables remote care facilities, and generally provides patients additional control over their lives and treatment. The healthcare industry is now growing rapidly. As the healthcare services are costly than ever, the world's population is ageing and the number of chronic diseases is going to increase day by day. The use of technology cannot stop people from ageing or getting affected by chronic diseases. However, it can at least make healthcare accessible and cheaper on the pocket. Health diagnosis absorbs the biggest share of the hospital bills. The use of technology can move the routines of medical checks from the hospital (i.e., from a hospital-centric approach to the home of the patient). In addition, IoHT helps to establish mutual hope as it permits the medical centres to operate more competently, and the patients to receive ameliorated treatment. With the use of IoHT methods, there are tremendous benefits that can improve the efficiency and quality of treatment, and also patients' health accordingly [1].

5.1.1 ARCHITECTURES RELATED TO IoHT

In this section, we discuss the following possible architectures related to an IoHT communication environment.

5.1.1.1 Introduction
- **Generic architecture of IoHT**: A generic form of the IoHT communication environment is provided in Figure 5.1. It consists of different types of

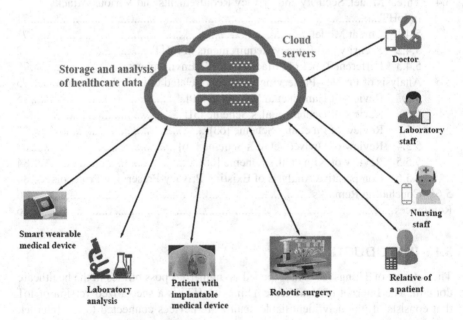

FIGURE 5.1 The generic architecture of IoHT (adapted from [2, 3]).

smart healthcare devices, for example, smart pacemakers (implanted into the body of a patient) and smart wearable medical devices. These devices can monitor and send the data to the cloud servers for further processing, analysis and storage. The scenario also contains different types of users (i.e., doctor, laboratory staff, nursing staff and relative of a patient). The users are interested in accessing the health data (i.e., data of a patient). For such purposes, the users first have to follow the steps of a "user authentication and key agreement protocol" [2, 4–9] to access the data securely through the established session keys with the devices.

- **Fog-based architecture of IoHT**: The generic architecture of an IoHT communication environment discussed in Figure 5.1 has some limitations as it is not delay-efficient. For that purpose, another architecture has been proposed in Figure 5.2. It introduces another layer of servers (i.e., fog server) in between the end devices (i.e., smart healthcare devices) and the cloud servers. Each healthcare device is connected with the fog servers, and it can send the sensed and monitored data to their nearby fog servers. The fog servers are connected with the cloud servers as well as with different types of users (i.e., doctors, nurses and relatives of some patients). The data that are frequently needed by the users are then processed and stored at the fog servers. Therefore, users can access the data from the fog servers after completing the steps of the "user authentication and key agreement

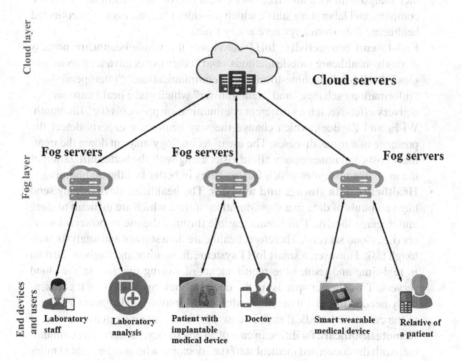

FIGURE 5.2 Fog-based architecture of IoHT (adapted from [3, 10]).

process" through the established session keys. The data which are not frequently required can be stored in the cloud servers. In this architecture, different types of "mutual authentication and key agreement" mechanisms are essential. For example, a mutual authentication and key agreement between fog servers and cloud servers, fog servers and smart healthcare devices, and fog servers and users. In this current era of computing, such architecture is highly recommended as it is flexible and delay efficient [3, 6, 9–11].

5.1.2 Advantages of IoHT

IoHT has several advantages over traditional healthcare practices. Some of them are discussed below [1, 11, 12].

- **Real-time monitoring**: Real-time monitoring through the connected smart healthcare devices can save lives in case of a medical emergency (for example, heart attack, asthma attack and diabetic shock). In real-time monitoring of the health condition, smart healthcare devices are connected to smartphone applications. These devices collect the health data of the patients and use the smartphone applications to transfer collected health data to the concerned medical practitioner (i.e., a cardiac surgeon). The health data of the concerned patient can be stored in the cloud server(s) which can be further shared with an authorized user (i.e., a doctor, the staff of an insurance company and laboratory staff), which provides them access to the collected healthcare data from anywhere at any time.
- **End-to-end connectivity**: IoHT automates the whole healthcare process through "healthcare mobile methods" and "other use of advanced technologies." It allows "machine-to-machine communication," "interoperability," "information exchange" and "data transfer" which make healthcare service delivery effective. It uses different communication protocols (i.e., Bluetooth, Wi-Fi and ZigBee), which change the way healthcare experts detect the presence of various diseases. The use of technology may cut down the treatment costs and unnecessary clinic visits along with the better utilization of the available resources which further helps in better healthcare planning.
- **Healthcare data storage and analysis**: The healthcare devices may send huge amounts of data in a short duration of time which are difficult to store and manage locally. This seems feasible through the use of powerful servers (i.e., cloud servers). Therefore, healthcare data storage and analysis are a tough task. However, a smart IoHT system can monitor and analyse the data in real-time and reduce the requirements of storing the data in the cloud servers. This further speeds up the decision-making process as it is essentially needed in critical health conditions. Moreover, it also provides alerts to the concerned medical staff in case of life-threatening circumstances.
- **Remote healthcare facilities**: In case of an emergency, patients can communicate with the concerned medical staff (i.e., doctors), who may be located miles away, with the help of smartphone applications. With such mobile solutions,

the medical staff instantly can check the patient's health condition to identify his/her illness as quickly as possible. Furthermore, the doctors can prescribe medicines to the patients, which can be delivered to them through the connected medicine delivery partners. This process reduces the number of visits to the hospital and also cuts down the overall healthcare expenses.

5.1.3 CHAPTER OUTLINE

The rest of this chapter is organized as follows. The important applications relevant to an IoHT environment are discussed in Section 5.2. The privacy issues in IoHT are discussed in Section 5.3. The threat model, security and privacy requirements and the associated attacks in IoHT are explained in Section 5.4. A comparative analysis of privacy-preserving security protocols related to the IoHT environment is also provided in Section 5.5. Finally, the chapter is concluded in Section 5.6.

5.2 APPLICATIONS OF IOHT

IoHT can be applied to provide different types of facilities related to the healthcare industry. Some of the potential applications of IoHT are highlighted below [1, 11–15].

5.2.1 REMOTE MONITORING OF PATIENTS

Sometimes patients have to be re-admitted to the hospital after medical treatment due to a lack of monitoring [8]. Emergency medical cases also cause challenges. Remote monitoring of a patient is possible through the involvement of IoT and associated technologies. For example, wearable healthcare devices can monitor the health of the patient throughout the whole day and accordingly notify the concerned doctor as the situation requires. It helps "underprivileged rural people" who do not have access to expert doctors. The proper guidance and on-time treatment of expert doctors can reduce the overall death rate in rural areas. Moreover, it also reduces the expenses of travel as well as hospitalization.

5.2.2 HOSPITAL OPERATIONS MANAGEMENT

Sometimes it becomes very difficult for doctors to inspect multiple patients at the same time. It helps to provide quick responses to the patients from the concerned medical staff(s). This kind of problem can be resolved through the use of IoHT applications. The regular cost of medical equipment can be reduced by monitoring patients' current conditions regularly. IoHT smart devices can be deployed in hospitals to check the expiry dates of equipment. Therefore, hospital authorities can be notified in case of outdated equipment. Moreover, doctors will be able to know the current locations of the required equipment within the required duration of time. IoHT smart devices and applications are then helpful to detect the cleanliness of the hospital and the working staff. Thus, it is clear that IoHT helps in the smooth overall management of hospital operations.

5.2.3 TREATMENT AND DETECTION OF DISEASES

IoHT can be used in the treatment and detection of other diseases, such as diabetes, asthma, hearing impairment, cancer and many more. For the monitoring of diabetes patients, wearable devices or embedded body sensors are used. These devices can continuously monitor the level of blood sugar and alert in case of increased levels of blood sugar. This further reduces the risk of hyperglycaemia. Similarly, IoHT helps to reduce the cases of "asthma attacks." Asthma can be controllable by the use of an inhaler. A patient can realize the symptoms of an asthma attack a half an hour to eight hours before. A smart sensor connected to the inhaler of the patient can alert the patient in case of some triggering factors (for example, air pollution) to prevent the asthma attack. Some techniques to apply IoHT in the detection of "breast cancer" can be also proposed. As we know it is the second most dangerous disease for women after "lung cancer." The methodology behind the detection of breast cancer is the use of "ITbra" which is a kind of wearable device. It is effective as compared to other detection methods. This cloth detects variations in temperature through the seven embedded sensors on breast tissue and notifies healthcare staff of the condition of the patient [13].

5.2.4 REMOTE SURGERY

IoHT applications are useful in performing remote surgery through robots/robotic arms [16]. The robot/robotic arm performs surgical operations inside the body of the patient under the supervision and instructions of the surgeon(s). This procedure helps the surgeon(s) to perform the surgery remotely with more precision and control. This further helps to save many lives, especially in case of war time or natural disaster.

5.2.5 SECURE DRUG SUPPLY CHAIN MANAGEMENT

From the starting point (production of drugs) to the usage of drugs by the patients, the supply chain management can be compromised or misused. Thus, drug supply chain management is another problem of this domain which can be resolved through the deployment of IoHT smart devices [17]. To resolve the issue, "smart tags" can be attached to the drug bags. These devices help in the proper distribution and monitoring of the drugs, especially protecting against the "counterfeiting of the medicines" [18]. The concerned authorities use "radio frequency identification (RFID)" tags to protect the drug bags against counterfeiting. If somebody tries to duplicate or counterfeit a bag, such an incident can be detected easily using the deployed "anti-counterfeiting mechanism." It is further helpful in providing quality medicine to patients.

5.3 PRIVACY ISSUES IN IOHT

IoHT fulfils the health needs of the people. However, public Internet-connected smart healthcare devices are vulnerable to various security and privacy-related attacks. Some of the privacy issues of IoHT are discussed below [19–24].

- **Failure of data protection mechanisms**: Data protection mechanisms use different "encryption algorithms" to protect the stored data as well as transmitted data. However, some of them are vulnerable to various types of attacks, such as "replay," "man-in-the-middle," "impersonation" and other forms of data disclosure attacks. Therefore, the confidentiality (privacy) of data in transit as well as the data at rest is at risk. The sensitive healthcare information of patients may be disclosed to unauthorized third parties, which may further raise privacy concerns.
- **Lack of data transparency**: In an IoHT communication environment, the health data are stored at the servers (i.e., cloud servers). Sometimes, it may cause data transparency issues (for instance, who is the owner of data and where the data are stored). Moreover, there is also a possibility that the data may be exposed during the "data transferring procedure."
  - **Chances of unauthorized usage**: In an IoHT communication environment, since the health-related data are stored at the servers (i.e., cloud servers), it is possible that the service providers re-sell the patients' data to some advertising agencies. Because service providers may get some incentives through the secondary usage of data, it is important to make clear agreements among the customers (patients or relatives of patients) and the service providers that contain important specifications, such as "who can access their data," "when it can be used" and "where and how it can be used."
  - **Failure of legal protection**: Sometimes, "ambiguous data" flow in an instantaneous manner through different regions which creates problems in the enforcement of privacy laws. This may lead to a loss of "legal protection of privacy" if some provider stores the health data in the cloud. Therefore, all legislation for the stored data should be followed.
  - **Lack of skilled staff**: In an IoHT environment, the healthcare data stored over the servers (i.e., cloud servers) are managed and administered by the concerned technical staff. Sometimes, the technical staff is not skilled enough or lacks knowledge. Therefore, there is a requirement to conduct rigorous training for such employees to make them aware of various security attacks and privacy breaches of healthcare data.

5.4 THREAT MODEL, SECURITY AND PRIVACY REQUIREMENTS AND VARIOUS ATTACKS IN IOHT

In this section, we present a "threat model" related with data security and privacy in the IoHT environment. Furthermore, we discuss different security and privacy requirements along with possible attacks in IoHT environments [18, 25].

5.4.1 THREAT MODEL

The widely used "Dolev-Yao (DY) threat model" [26] is also applicable for the security and privacy considerations in an IoHT environment [27, 28]. As per the guidelines of the DY model, any two communicating entities (parties) communicate over an insecure/public channel in which end-point communicating entities (for example, different health data users, smart healthcare monitoring devices and fog/cloud servers) are not trustworthy. An existing adversary may seize, update or delete the messages sent during the communication. Moreover, an adversary can inject fake messages during the communication. Apart from that, they can physically capture some smart healthcare devices and extract the required sensitive information from their memory in an IoHT environment [29, 30] using some sophisticated techniques, such as power analysis attacks [29]. They can manufacture other duplicate malicious nodes for some unauthorized tasks (i.e., routing attacks and blackhole attacks) using the extracted information of captured devices. These manufactured malicious devices can be directly deployed in the network to launch routing attacks [31–33]. During the successful execution of routing attacks, data packets may be lost, dropped, modified or delayed by the attacker nodes. Therefore, the intended recipient may not get the required information on time, which is a very serious issue in an IoHT communication environment. The current *de facto* standard model to design an "authenticated key-exchange scheme" is "Canetti and Krawczyk's adversary model (popularly, known as the CK-adversary model)" [34, 35]. Under the CK-adversary model, it is assumed that an adversary can compromise the "private keys" and "session keys." The security techniques used require an assurance that if somehow the "secret information" is disclosed (for example, long-term private keys or session keys), it should have a minimum effect on the security of other non-compromised nodes of the communicating network [36]. In addition, in a smartphone/smart card-based security protocol, the smartphone/smart card of a legitimate registered user in an IoHT environment may be stolen or lost, which can be further utilized to extract the secret information from its memory by the execution of the steps of "power analysis attacks" as discussed in [29, 30] to mount other potential attacks, such as impersonation and offline guessing attacks.

5.4.2 Security and Privacy Requirements in IoHT

In this section, we provide various security and privacy requirements in an IoHT environment that are listed below [3, 19–24, 37].

- *Confidentiality*: Sometimes, it is also called "privacy." This property provides assurance that the transmitted data should be protected against any form of unauthorized disclosure. In case of confidentiality, the privacy of data in transit and data at rest matters a lot.
- *Integrity*: The integrity property assures "the integrity of the exchanged messages." It means that the content of the received messages should not contain any unauthorized insertion of information or deletion of information. Furthermore, it should not be modified by any unauthorized party during the communication.
- *Authentication*: The authentication property assures the validation of identities of the communicating entities. For instance, the sending and receiving parties first verify their identities mutually, and then they start their communication securely via the established session keys. An IoHT environment

consists of different types of entities, such as devices (for example, smart healthcare devices), fog/cloud servers, gateways and various service providers, which can follow the steps of a "mutual authentication and key establishment process."
- *Non-repudiation*: This property assures that the communicating entity does not refuse the validity of something (i.e., transmitted message). It provides the "proof of the data origin along with its integrity". Therefore, it becomes difficult to deny "who has sent the message" or "from where a message came." Further, it can be classified into two categories:
  - *Non-repudiation of origin*: It confirms the genuineness of the sender (i.e., a message was transmitted by a legitimate party).
  - *Non-repudiation of destination*: It assures the genuineness of the receiver (i.e., a message was received by a legitimate party).
- *Authorization*: This property assures that only the authentic parties (i.e., smart healthcare devices) in an IoHT environment can provide information to other parties (i.e., doctors).
  - *Freshness*: This property also assures the freshness of the exchanged information in order to avoid the re-transmutation of old messages by the existing attacker/hacker.
  - *Availability*: It assures only the affiliated network services should be made reachable to "legitimate parties" even in case of a "denial-of-service (DoS)" attack in an IoHT environment.
  - *Third-party protection*: It assures the protection of various resources (i.e., healthcare data) against the damage done by third parties (i.e., service providers of IoHT) [38].
  - *Forward secrecy*: This property provides assurance of the "forward secrecy" of exchanged messages. It means that if an IoHT device leaves the communication, it must no longer have access to the future messages in the communication environment.
  - *Backward secrecy*: This property provides assurance of the "backward secrecy" of exchanged messages. It means that if an IoHT device joins (recently deployed) a network, it must not have access to the previously exchanged messages.

5.4.3 Different Types of Attacks in IoHT Environment

Various potential attacks are possible in an IoHT environment that can be conducted by passive or active attackers [39]:

- *Eavesdropping*: It is also called a "sniffing or snooping attack." Such an attack occurs when an attacker eavesdrops on the exchanged messages. It also forms the base for other types of attacks (i.e., data disclosure attack).
- *Traffic analysis*: It is another method of message interception in which examination of the intercepted messages is done to find out which kind of communication is going on in the communication environment. By traffic

analysis, an adversary can know which party is communicating with which one and for how long.
- *Replay attack*: This attack occurs when an attacker captures (records) the exchanged messages at one place and later on re-sends them to misdirect the recipient.
- *Man-in-the-middle (MITM) attack*: In a MITM attack, an attacker can capture the exchanged messages, and later on he/she may try to delete or modify the intercepted messages before forwarding them to the recipient.
- *Impersonation attack*: In an impersonation attack, an attacker can successfully compute (identify) the identity of one of the "authorized communicating entities," and later on the adversary may send a modified message or a completely fake message on behalf of the impersonating party to other communicating parties so that the destinations believe that the messages originated from genuine sources.
- *Denial-of-service (DoS) attack*: A DoS attack occurs when an attacker performs some malicious tasks to prevent the legitimate users from accessing the resources of the communication environment (i.e., data resources). There is another variant of DoS attack which is called a "distributed DoS (DDoS)" attack, which can be conducted through multiple attacker machines (i.e., botnets). The examples include various types of flooding attacks (i.e., "Hypertext Transfer Protocol [HTTP] DDoS attack" [40] and "Transmission Control Protocol [TCP] SYN flood attack" [41, 42]) which consume the resources (i.e., bandwidth and memory) of the target (i.e., web servers) very quickly. A SYN flood is considered as a form of DoS attack in which an attacker first transmits "a succession of SYN requests to a target's system in an attempt to consume enough server resources in order to make the system unresponsive to legitimate traffic." The HTTP DDoS attacks happen "when legitimate HTTP requests are initiated in large numbers" [40].
- *Malware attack*: Malware attacks are conducted through the execution of malicious script in a remote system. This helps the attacker to perform unauthorized tasks (for instance, stealing information, encryption of sensitive information and hijacking of the shell of a smart healthcare device). Examples of malware include "trap door," "logic bomb," "viruses," "worms," "adware," "ransomware," "Trojan virus" and "spywares" [37].
- A "trap door" acts as "a secret entry point into a program that permits someone that is aware of the trapdoor to gain access without going through the typical security access mechanisms." A logic bomb is treated as a code that is embedded in some authentic programme which can be set to explode once specific conditions are satisfied. A "Trojan horse" becomes a convenient, or apparently useful, program or command mechanism consisting of hidden code that, when invoked, executes some convenient unwanted or dangerous activity. A virus is considered a code that can contaminate other codes (programmes) by altering them, whereas a worm spreads itself from a system to another system. Ransomware is considered as a form of malware with the ability to encrypt a victim's files containing sensitive and confidential information. The attacker then requests a ransom from the victim

in order to reinstate access to the data based on satisfactory payment [43]. Adware is treated as unwanted software that is developed in order to throw various advertisements up on the victim's screen (most often within a web browser). Adware helps the attacker in generating revenue for the developers maintained by an attacker by "involuntarily displaying online advertisements in the user interface of the software or on a screen that pops up in the user's face during the installation process" [44]. Finally, spyware is treated as "unwanted software that penetrates a victim's computing device, steals the victim's Internet usage data and sensitive information" [45].

- *Database attack*: In an IoHT environment, database-related attacks are quite possible on the database maintained by the healthcare server(s). For example, "Structured Query Language (SQL) injection attacks" and "Cross-Site Scripting (XSS) attacks" may be possible. A SQL injection attack is treated as "an approach that is used by an attacker to inject malicious code into existing SQL statements" [46]. On the other side, an XSS attack is a kind of injection, which helps an attacker to "inject malicious scripts into otherwise benign and trusted websites" [47].
- *Privileged-insider attack*: Although the system is considered as trusted, a privileged insider user may act as an attacker, who has access to the secret credentials of the various entities of the network. The privileged insider user, being the attacker, may misuse the extracted secret information to conduct other unauthorized activities (i.e., offline password guessing attacks, impersonation attacks and session key compromise attacks). This kind of attack sometimes becomes fatal in the system and it requires a strong mechanism to protect against "privileged attacks" [2, 9, 48].
- *Physical stolen of smart healthcare devices*: As mentioned in the "threat model" discussed in Section 5.4.1, the physical stealing of smart healthcare devices is possible by an attacker since the devices cannot be monitored 24/7. Later on, the attacker can easily extract the credentials from these stolen devices by using the "power analysis attacks" as explained in [29, 30]. The extracted credentials can be further utilized to launch other malicious attacks in an IoHT environment (i.e., "illegal session key computation," "impersonation attacks," etc. [2, 48, 49]).

5.5 ANALYSIS OF PRIVACY-PRESERVING PROTOCOLS RELATED TO IOHT ENVIRONMENTS

In this section, we discuss some of the state-of-art privacy-preserving protocols related to IoHT environments. We also provide a comparative analysis among the discussed protocols.

5.5.1 Review of Hamza et al.'s Scheme [50]

Hamza et al. [50] presented a privacy-preserving "chaos-based encryption" scheme for privacy protection of the patients' related data. Their scheme can protect the patient's images against the compromised brokers. A "fast probabilistic cryptosystem" was proposed by them to secure "medical keyframes" which were drawn out from wireless capsule endoscopy procedures. The encrypted images provided in the system had randomness which confirmed the computational efficiency along with security assurance. The "medical data" are processed without leaking the information, and access is only provided to the authorized entities (users). However, their scheme does not support dynamic device addition which is a very important aspect with respect to their scheme. Their proposed scheme has the following components:

- **Pseudorandom number generator (PRNG) model based on chaotic maps**: This component is used to generate the encryption keys for the "medical keyframes." They discussed various methods, such as a "2D-Zaslavsky chaotic map" which is a "nonlinear discrete system with two chaotic orbits," a "2D-logistic map" which is a "discrete dynamic system with a chaotic behavior of the evolution of orbits and attractors" and a "PRNG algorithm" which is designed by employing both chaotic maps ("2D-Zaslavsky chaotic map" and "2D-logistic map").
- **Encryption algorithm**: In this component, the authors described the details of their image encryption method, which adopts "permutation-diffusion architecture" via "chaos-based PRNG."
- **Decryption algorithm**: In this component, the authors elaborated the steps of their decryption algorithm which is used for reconstruction of the keyframes at the receiving end. Because of the utilization of a "randomization process," their proposed system is known as the "lossless cryptosystem." Their provided decryption process can reconstruct the keyframe from an encrypted image without any loss of its visual appearance.

Finally, this discussed scheme can assure the privacy and security of patients.

5.5.2 Review of Deebak et al.'s Scheme [51]

Deebak et al. [51] proposed a "Secure and Anonymous Biometric Based User Authentication Scheme (SAB-UAS)" to assure secure communication in healthcare applications. In their scheme, an adversary cannot impersonate a legitimate user to revoke a smart card in an illegal way. Their conducted simulation study measured the impact of the scheme on various network performance parameters, such as "packet delivery ratio (PDR)," "end-to-end delay (EED)," "throughput transmission rate (TTR)" and "routing overhead (RO)." PDR measures the performance of routing protocols for any communication networks. EED is defined as "the average time taken by the data transmission packets to reach the receiver from the source node." TTR is defined as "the number of bits transmitted per unit of execution time." On the other side, RO is defined as "the total number of routing packets divided by the total number of successfully delivered packets during the mobility interval." In their scheme, the efficient biometric update phase was not provided. Moreover, some of the important phases such as dynamic device addition were missing in their scheme.

The following important cryptographic primitives are utilized in the design of security schemes, which are also used in the scheme of Deebak et al. [51].
- **One-way cryptographic hash function**: It is a function of deterministic type having the form: $h: 0, 1 * 0, 1^l h$ takes any arbitrary length input string $x\ 0, 1\ *$ as a message and produces a fixed-length, say l_h bits, output string $h(x)\ 0, 1^l h$. It has the following important properties:
  - For any input $x\ 0, 1\ *$, it is easy to compute the message digest $h(x)\ 0, 1^l h$. The term "easy" is used to mean that the computation through hash is done in polynomial or less time duration.
  - Any change in an input (even a little change) $x\ 0, 1\ *$, $h(\ )$ causes a drastic change in the result (or an entirely different result). The input value is uncorrelated with its hash value $h(x)$, and is exactly random in nature.
  - *Pre-image resistance*: The "one-way" signifies that it is not computationally possible to get the original message x provided the message digest $h(x)$ of $x\ 0, 1\ *$. This property is also termed as the "one-way property."
  - *Second-preimage resistance*: For a provided input string $x\ 0, 1\ *$, it is not computationally possible to pick another input string $x\ 0, 1\ *$ such that $h(x) = h(x)$. This property is also termed as the "weak-collision resistant property."
  - *Strong-collision resistance*: A collision in a "one-way hash function" is termed as $h(x) = h(x)$ for any two input strings $x, x\ 0, 1\ *$ such that $x = x$. The collision resistance property means that it is also computationally impossible to choose any two input strings $x, x \in \{0, 1\}^*$ such that $x = x$ with $h(x) = h(x)$.

The "one-way hash functions" are extremely useful in "security-sensitive applications," for example, for the generation of a digital signature from original data to ensure their integrity, message authentication code (MAC) and other practical applications including the computation of checksum to ensure no data corruption in the transmission.

- **Burrows–Abadi–Needham (BAN) logic**: An authentication protocol is an essential component for secure communication in the domain of information security. Therefore, it is important to assure the correctness of a designed authentication protocol. Various authentication schemes have been proposed in the literature. However, they are poorly designed and also contain various types of weaknesses. The main motive of the use of an authentication scheme is to assure that an entity is really communicating with the other entity with whom he/she is intending to communicate. Burrows–Abadi–Needham (BAN) logic [52] provides a mechanism to confirm the accuracy of an authentication scheme through some beliefs and or assumptions under the employment of logic or reasoning to analyse the conclusions. In recent years, the proof of "secure mutual

authentication" between communicating entities has been provided in various user authentication protocols through the widely used BAN logic [2, 53].
- **Biometric verification**: In the domain of "information security," it is important to protect sensitive and confidential information from any kind of unauthorized access. Such access is verified by letting the users prove their claimed identity through some authentication technique. Primarily, a user can be authenticated through one of the following methods: (i) "what you know," (ii) "what you have" and (iii) "what you are." The technique "what you know" is one of the most popular authentication techniques which uses information, such as username or user ID and password. The technique "what you have" indicates the use of smart cards or a smartphone. The more secure authentication method is "what you are" which uses the user's personal biometrics information.

Biometrics data contain a user's physical attributes which vary from person to person with a trivial collision rate. The various kinds of physical attributes which can be used as "biometrics for authentication" are iris scans, fingerprints, face recognition, etc. For biometrics-based authentication the following techniques can be used for verification, which are discussed below.

- *Biometric verification using one-way cryptographic hash function*: If we apply the one-way hash function on a user's personal biometric template (for instance, fingerprint), the hash value on the input biometric may completely differ with a slight change in the user's biometrics at the time of biometric verification. As a result, this technique will produce high rates of false alarms. Thus, one-way hash function-based biometric verification is not considered reliable.
- *Biometric verification using biohashing function*: This technique operates on a user's personal biometrics for unique identification to reduce the "false denial of access" without increasing the "false acceptance" [54–57]. Various biohashing-based algorithms have been designed in recent years which make biohashing more useful for applications including in small devices (i.e., sensors and other mobile devices). However, Chang et al. [58] observed an important problem with biometric verification using biohashing function, because it produces a "high rate of false rejection." As a result, the biohashing function may not be considered as a "good candidate for biometric verification."
- *Biometric verification using fuzzy extractor*: To overcome the problems with the "one- way cryptographic hash function" and "biohashing" techniques, a fuzzy extractor technique is preferred in biometric verification procedures which are applied in authentication techniques. The fuzzy extractor method mutates biometric data into random strings to facilitate the cryptographic applications to use biometrics as a secret key for verification purposes. The fuzzy extractor then deduces a uniform random string

from the provided biometric data *BIO* which can tolerate noise up to a certain range. The input *BIO* also results in the same random string in case *BIO* is close to the original *BIO* [53].

A fuzzy extractor (M, m, l, t) consists of a pair of methods: (i) a "probabilistic generation function *Gen*( )" and (ii) a "deterministic reproduction function *Rep*( )", where metric space having a distance function, say *dist*: [0,), m is called the "minimum entropy," l is the "number of bits in the biometric key" and t is the "maximum error tolerance threshold value." The properties of *Gen*( ) and *Rep*( ) are defined as follows:

- *Gen*( ) is a "probabilistic function" that on an input of biometric template *BIO* produces a pair of outputs having a "biometric secret key σ 0, 1^l" and a "public reproduction parameter τ."
- *Rep*( ), a deterministic function, takes the current biometric *BIO* and the "public reproduction parameter τ corresponding to the original *BIO*" as inputs, and regenerates the original "biometric secret key σ" with the exception of the "Hamming distance $dis(BIO, BIO)$ et," where et denotes the "error tolerance threshold value." In other side, $Rep(BIO, \tau) = \sigma$.

As compared to guessing the users' passwords, biometric keys are difficult to guess. In fact, the probability of guessing the biometric secret key $\sigma \in \{0, 1\}^l$ is bounded by-1/2 [59].

Formal security verification using the Automated Validation of Internet Security Protocols (AVISPA) tool: AVISPA is an automated software validation tool which is used for security-sensitive applications and protocols [60]. In recent years, AVISPA has become one of the most powerful software tools for the purpose of formal security verification [2, 48]. It provides different automatic analysis mechanisms with the help of its four back-ends: (i) "On-the-Fly Model-Checker (OFMC)," (ii) "Constraint Logic based Attack Searcher (CL-AtSe)," (iii) "SAT- based Model-Checker (SATMC)" and (iv) "Tree Automata based on Automatic Approximations for the Analysis of Security Protocols (TA4SP)."

The security schemes, which need to be analysed for their security aspect by the AVISPA tool, should be specified and coded in "High Level Protocol Specification Language" (HLPSL). It is a role-based language consisting of different types of roles:

- *Basic roles*: These roles, in general, represent various participating entities in the protocol.
- *Composition roles*: These roles represent various scenarios including the basic roles.

In HLPSL, an intruder always plays one of the basic legitimate roles, represented by i. The HLPSL specification of a protocol is first translated to its "Intermediate Format (IF)" using a translator available in AVISPA, known as the HLPSL2IF translator. The IF is then transformed into its "Output Format (OF)" with the help of one of the four available back-ends. The OF consists of the following important sections [61]:

- SUMMARY: It states "whether the tested protocol is safe, unsafe, or whether the analysis is inconclusive."
- DETAILS: It gives "a detailed explanation of why the tested protocol is concluded as safe, or under what conditions the test application or protocol is exploitable using an attack, or why the analysis is inconclusive."
- PROTOCOL: It defines the "HLPSL specification of the target protocol in IF."
- GOAL: It specifies "the goal of the analysis which is being performed by AVISPA using HLPSL specification."
- BACKEND: It provides "the name of the back-end that is used for the analysis, that is, one of OFMC, CL-AtSe, SATMC and TA4SP."
- Finally, we have "the trace of a possible vulnerability to the target protocol, if any, along with some useful statistics and relevant comments."

We need three verifications for a tested security protocol: (i) "executability checking on non-trivial HLPSL specifications," (ii) "replay attack checking" and (iii) "Dolev-Yao (DY) threat model checking" [26]. The executability check is essential in order to assure that the tested protocol can reach a state where a possible attack can occur during the protocol execution. To check the "replay attack on a tested protocol," it is essential that the back-ends check whether the legitimate agents can execute "the specified protocol by performing a search of a passive intruder." In addition, the back-ends also verify whether any man-in-the-middle attack can be performed by i for the DY model checking. Detailed study on AVISPA and its HLPSL is left to interested readers.

Formal security analysis using random oracle model: The "Real-Or-Random (ROR) model-based formal security analysis" [62] is a famous random oracle model these days, because it provides strong proof on the security of a designed protocol (i.e., user authentication) [6, 8, 48]. It is essential to notice that the "ROR model" uses only the "widely- accepted DY model" as discussed in the "threat model" in Section 5.4. The ROR model is defined as a game between a challenger and an adversary which is modelled by a "probabilistic polynomial-time (PPT)" algorithm. The ROR model includes the following components:

- *Participants.* The instances of the participating entities of the network are defined as random oracles.
- *Accepted state.* A tth instance of a participant, say Π^t, is in an accepted state if, after receiving the last expected protocol message, it goes to the accept state.
- *Partnering.* Any two instances, say Π^{a_1} and Π^{a_2}, are partners to each other, if the following three criteria hold:

  · Π^{a_1} and Π^{a_2} are in "accepted states."

- Π^{a1} and Π^{a2} share the same session identifier, say *sid*. The *sid* is constructed by concatenating all the transmitted and received messages in sequence by a participant.
- Π^{a1} and Π^{a2} are also "mutual partners of each other."

- *Freshness*. The instances are considered to be fresh if the session key established between them is not revealed to the adversary A through a defined reveal query.
- *Adversary*. Since the ROR model uses the widely used "DY model," it can control all the communications entirely. Therefore, adversaries may have chance to not only eavesdrop, but also to update, inject or delete the messages exchanged among the parties (participants).

In addition, the adversary has access to different types of queries, such as "Execute" and "Test." Through the "Execute" query, the adversary can intercept the messages communicated among various entities in the network. The "Test" query helps to appeal to an Π^t to verify the originality of an established session key in an authenticated key agreement scheme, and in turn, Π^t can supply a "random outcome of a flipped unbiased coin" to test whether the computed session key is real or just a random number.

The interested readers can find a detailed description of the ROR model in Ref. [62].

We now start discussing the scheme of Deebak et al. [51]. This scheme contains the following phases:

- **User registration**: In this phase, a wireless gateway access node (*WGAN*) performs the registration of a user upon his/her request. In this process, the user has to provide his/her identity and biometric information. After receiving the information, the *WGAN* further computes some useful information and then stores those credentials in the smart card/mobile device of that user. Furthermore, the smart card is finally issued to the registered user by the *WGAN*.
- **Login and authentication**: In this phase, a registered user first provides his/her identity information along with biometric information to the associated system. The system then verifies the validity of the user by means of checking the inputted identity and biometrics. If the user is a legitimate user, his/her login request is sent to the *WGAN*. The *WGAN* also checks the authenticity of the user's message. If he/she is a valid entity, the *WGAN* further computes a message and sends it to the medical sensor node (*MSN*). Upon its arrival, the associated *MSN* checks the authenticity of the received message. In case of successful authentication, the *MSN* computes another message along with the session key for the user, and then sends that message to the user. After receiving the message, the user checks its authenticity. In case of successful authentication, the user computes and establishes the same session key with the *MSN* for their future secure communication.

- **Smart card revocation**: In case of a lost or stolen smart card of a legitimate registered user, the smart card could also be re-issued. For such purposes, the user first has to prove his/her genuineness to the system. If the user is a genuine user, the *WGAN* computes the useful parameters and stores them in the new smart card. After that the new smart card is issued to the user through some secure medium (for instance, in person).

5.5.3 Review of Pu et al.'s Scheme [63]

Pu et al. [63] proposed two schemes for a "data aggregation mechanism" to preserve the sensitive data of the customers. In their first scheme, each IoT-enabled smart device breaks up the actual data randomly, keeps one part of the data to itself, and then sends the remaining part to the other IoT devices of the network which belong to the same group through a symmetric cryptographic method. Each IoT device does the addition of received pieces. The held piece is used to get the immediate result and this is then sent to the aggregator component. Furthermore, the "homomorphic encryption method" [64] and "Advanced Encryption Standard (AES) encryption method" [65] are applied to achieve secure communication. However, in their second scheme, the slicing method was also used. The noisy data are used to protect the exchanged data of the devices from disclosure attack. Their conducted analysis proves the integrity and confidentiality properties of the IoT device's data. In addition, the dynamic device addition is not supported in their scheme. Their proposed schemes have the following phases:

- **Key generation**: In this phase, a series of keys and other important parameters are distributed. The server first generates a private key, say sk, and its corresponding public key, say pk. A group key is then generated and also broadcasted to all the group members in each group along with other parameters for the update of the group key.
- **Data division and confusion**: In this phase, various devices perform the segmentation of their data and then swap the data pieces in a pairwise manner. A topical residential is assumed which is comprised of an aggregator connected with a large number of devices. The devices collect the data for a particular duration of time. Each device slices the data into a number of pieces randomly. After that the devices exchange their respective pieces with each other to obtain the obfuscated data. After receiving the ciphertext, the device decrypts it to obtain the data slice. Moreover, it was also mentioned that the keys used for device-to-device communication are updated continuously.
- **Reporting and aggregation**: After the exchange of "partial collected data," the actual data need to be blended. For this purpose, all the blended data are encrypted with the public key pk of the server. Furthermore, the devices will compute the hash identity, real time and preceding ciphertext to help the aggregator to check whether the message has been manipulated or not. The devices report the ciphertext, real time and hash value to the aggregator

node for verification purposes. If the verification happens successfully, the aggregator aggregates the ciphertext. Next, the server decrypts it with its private key *sk* and obtains the entire data of that particular region.

5.5.4 Review of Dwivedi et al.'s Scheme [66]

Dwivedi et al. [66] addressed the security and privacy issues in an IoT-based healthcare environment. They proposed a framework based on the blockchain model which is suitable for IoT devices and depends on blockchain's distributed nature. The additional security and privacy properties of their model are based on the advanced cryptographic algorithms. They provided a solution that makes IoT application data and their transactions more secure and anonymous via a blockchain-based computing environment. However, their scheme does not support dynamic device addition or smart card/smart phone revocation phases.

This scheme is based on the following cryptographic primitives:

- **Addition/Rotation/XOR (ARX) encryption algorithm**: ARX is a kind of symmetric key encryption that was used to encrypt the data for blockchain. The algorithm utilizes simple operations like "modular addition," "bitwise rotation" and "exclusive-OR (XOR)" operations, and it provides support for lightweight encryption, particularly in small devices. Some examples of ARX include Speck, ChaCha20, BLAKE and XXTEA.
- **Digital signature**: Digital signature is frequently used for authentication processes. The application of "normal digital signatures" may not be fitted due to deployed resource-restricted IoT devices, as those signature schemes are heavy-weight. Therefore, the use of "lightweight digital signatures" has been suggested. In Dwivedi et al.'s scheme [66], the sender has a pair of private-public keys (sks_{priv}, sks_{pub}), and also the receiver will have another pair of private-public keys (rks_{priv}, rks_{pub}). The sender's private key sks_{priv} is applied to sign the message, whereas the sender's public key sks_{pub} is used for the verification of signed messages at the receiver's end.
- **Digital ring signature**: The "lightweight ring signature technology" is behind the development of the ring signature. It allows a signer to sign the data in an anonymous manner. The signature is then mixed with other groups "named ring" and only the "actual signer" knows which member has signed the message. Using the ring in Dwivedi et al.'s scheme [66], the "signer's anonymity" and "signature correctness" are satisfied.
- **Diffie–Hellman key exchange**: In Dwivedi et al.'s scheme [66], there was a requirement to transfer the public keys in the network. In order to provide a more secure public key exchange, the public keys of the entities are also shared secretly. For the sharing of the public key, say the sender's public key (sks_{pub}), securely in the network, the "Diffie–Hellman key exchange" method has been utilized [67]. It is worth noting that the "Diffie–Hellman key exchange" protocol helps both the sender and receiver to establish a common secret key over an insecure channel. A more secure version of the

"Diffie–Hellman key exchange" protocol, known as the "station-to-station key agreement" protocol, can be further utilized in case the network is vulnerable to a "man-in-the-middle attack" [37].

5.5.5 Review of Kim et al.'s Scheme [68]

Kim et al. [68] proposed a scheme for the privacy-preserving collection of personal health-related data streams, which are characterized as temporal data. The data are collected at fixed intervals through the benefit of "Local Differential Privacy (LDP)." A data contributor is used to provide a privacy budget of the LDP. It reports a small quantity of salient data, which is extracted from the health data stream.

The data collector can reassemble the health data segments based on the noisy salient data received from the data contributor. Through the conducted practical demonstration, it is shown that their proposed scheme can achieve significant accuracy gains over other compared methods. However, "dynamic device addition" and "smart card/smart phone revocation" are not supported in their scheme. A straightforward method might have a high expected error in case of a large sequence length. To overcome this problem, another method has been suggested to collect health data streams. Their proposed system has two components: (i) "data contributor's device-side processing" and (ii) "data collection server-side processing."

Their scheme consists of the following functionalities:

- **Data contributor's device-side processing**: Their technique identifies a small number of salient points from the sequence of the provided "health data stream," unsettles these points under the process of LDP and then reports the noisy salient points to the "data collection server."
- **Data collection server-side processing**: Their scheme has the ability to reconstruct the sequence on the basis of noisy salient points received from the "data contributor" and store it in the database for further use. The proposal behind this method is that it avoids the "high expected error" occurring due to the large sequence length under the selection of the small number of salient points from the health data stream.

5.5.6 Comparative Analysis of Existing Privacy-Preserving Protocols

In this section, we compare various security and functionality features (FR_1–FR_{20}) of the schemes of Hamza et al. [50], Deebak et al. [51], Pu et al. [63], Dwivedi et al. [66] and Kim et al. [68] provided in Table 5.1.

The following features have been considered in the comparative study:

- FR_1: "protection against replay attack"
- FR_2: "protection against man-in-the middle attack"
- FR_3: "mutual authentication"
- FR_4: "session key agreement"
- FR_5: "untraceability property"

TABLE 5.1
Comparison of Functionality and Security Features

Feature	Hamza et al. [50]	Deebak et al. [51]	Pu et al. [63]	Dwivedi et al. [66]	Kim et al. [68]
FR_1					
FR_2					
FR_3	×		×	×	×
FR_4	NA		×	×	×
FR_5	NA		×	×	×
FR_6	NA				
FR_7	NA	×	NA	NA	NA
FR_8	NA	×	NA	NA	NA
FR_9	×	×	×	×	×
FR_{10}	NA	NA	NA	NA	
FR_{11}					
FR_{12}	NA	NA	NA	NA	
FR_{13}	×				
FR_{14}	NA	×	NA	NA	NA
FR_{15}	NA		NA	NA	NA
FR_{16}	×	×	×		×
FR_{17}	NA				
FR_{18}	×		×	×	×
FR_{19}	×		×	×	×
FR_{20}	×	×	×	×	×

Note: ×: "a scheme does not protect against a specific attack or it does not support a particular feature"; ✓ "a scheme protects against a specific attack or it supports a particular feature"; *NA*: "not applicable in a scheme."

- FR_6: "resilience against sensing device physical capture attack"
- FR_7: "support to server independent password update phase"
- FR_8: "support for biometric update phase"
- FR_9: "formal security verification using AVISPA automated software tool"
- FR_{10}: "support to smart card revocation phase"
- FR_{11}: "protection against known session-specific temporary information attack"
- FR_{12}: "user anonymity property"
- FR_{13}: "protection against privileged-insider attack"
- FR_{14}: "protection against off-line password guessing attack"
- FR_{15}: "protection against stolen smart card/mobile device attack"
- FR_{16}: "protection against denial-of-service (DoS) attack"
- FR_{17}: "protection against impersonation attacks"

- FR_{18}: "support to formal security analysis under standard model (e.g., ROR model)"
- FR_{19}: "support to security analysis through BAN logic proof"
- FR_{20}: "support to dynamic sensing device addition phase"

Table 5.1 shows that Hamza et al.'s scheme [50] does not provide the features FR_3, FR_9, FR_{13}, FR_{16} and FR_{18}–FR_{20}. The scheme of Deebak et al. [51] provides the majority of the features except some features FR_7–FR_9, FR_{14}, FR_{16} and FR_{20}. The scheme of Pu et al. [63] does not support the features FR_3–FR_5, FR_9, FR_{16} and FR_{18}–FR_{20}. Similar to Pu et al.'s scheme [63], the scheme of Dwivedi et al. [66] also does not provide the features FR_3–FR_5, FR_9 and FR_{18}–FR_{20}. Finally, similar to Pu et al.'s scheme [63], the scheme of Kim et al. [68] fails to maintain the features FR_3–FR_5, FR_9, FR_{16} and FR_{18}–FR_{20}.

It is then clear that most of the compared schemes do not provide the required security and functionality features, and they are also vulnerable to various types of attacks. Hence, it is essential to come up with more efficient and robust privacy-preserving protocols for the IoHT communication environment that can be deployed for practical applications.

5.6 CONCLUDING REMARKS

IoHT is a smart computing and communication healthcare environment which enables the localization of assets, real-time information exchange and remote/automatic management of resources. It provides assurance of patient safety along with high-quality care within the required duration of time. This chapter deals with the privacy issues related to the emerging IoHT field. It provides the details of various types of architectures of the IoHT environment along with their advantages. Certain important applications related to the IoHT environment are also highlighted in this chapter. Furthermore, the privacy issues and threat model of IoHT are provided. Apart from those, the details of security and privacy issues along with various types of potential attacks in IoHT are also provided. Finally, a number of state-of-art privacy-preserving security protocols related to IoHT have been carefully reviewed, and then a comparative analysis of the discussed privacy-preserving security protocols was given.

REFERENCES

1. P. Nasrullah. Internet of things in healthcare: applications, benefits, and chal- lenges. https://www.peerbits.com/blog/internet-of-things-healthcare-applications-benefits-and-challenges.html. Accessed on March 2020.
2. S. Challa, M. Wazid, A. K. Das, N. Kumar, A. Goutham Reddy, E. Yoon, and K. Yoo. Secure signature-based authenticated key establishment scheme for future IoT applications. *IEEE Access*, 5:3028–3043, 2017.
3. M. Wazid, A. K. Das, J. J. P. C. Rodrigues, S. Shetty, and Y. Park. IoMT malware detection approaches: Analysis and research challenges. *IEEE Access*, 7:182459–182476, 2019.

4. S. Chatterjee, A. K. Das, and J. K. Sing. A novel and efficient user access control scheme for wireless body area sensor networks. *Journal of King Saud University - Computer and Information Sciences*, 26(2):181–201, 2014.
5. A. K. Das, S. Chatterjee, and J. K. Sing. A new biometric-based remote user authentication scheme in hierarchical wireless body area sensor networks. *Ad Hoc & Sensor Wireless Networks*, 28(3–4):221–256, 2015.
6. A. K. Das, M. Wazid, N. Kumar, M. K. Khan, K. R. Choo, and Y. Park. Design of secure and lightweight authentication protocol for wearable devices environment. *IEEE Journal of Biomedical and Health Informatics*, 22(4):1310–1322, 2018.
7. M. H. Ibrahim, S. Kumari, A. K. Das, M. Wazid, and V. Odelu. Secure anonymous mutual authentication for star two-tier wireless body area networks. *Computer Methods and Programs in Biomedicine*, 135:37–50, 2016.
8. J. Srinivas, A. K. Das, N. Kumar, and J. J. P. C. Rodrigues. Cloud centric authentication for wearable healthcare monitoring system. *IEEE Transactions on Dependable and Secure Computing*, 17(5):942–956, 2020. DOI: 10.1109/TDSC.2018.2828306.
9. M. Wazid, A. K. Das, N. Kumar, M. Conti, and A. V. Vasilakos. A novel authentication and key agreement scheme for implantable medical devices deployment. *IEEE Journal of Biomedical and Health Informatics*, 22(4):1299–1309, 2018.
10. M. Wazid, A. K. Das, N. Kumar, and A. V. Vasilakos. Design of secure key management and user authentication scheme for fog computing services. *Future Generation Computer Systems*, 91:475–492, 2019.
11. M. Asif-Ur-Rahman, F. Afsana, M. Mahmud, M. S. Kaiser, M. R. Ahmed, O. Kaiwartya, and A. James-Taylor. Toward a heterogeneous mist, fog, and cloud-based framework for the internet of healthcare things. *IEEE Internet of Things Journal*, 6(3):4049–4062, 2019.
12. P. A. Laplante and N. Laplante. The internet of things in healthcare: Potential applications and challenges. *IT Professional*, 18(3):2–4, 2016.
13. R. Chowdhury. IoT in healthcare: 20 Examples that'll make you feel better. https://www.ubuntupit.com/ iot-in-healthcare-20-examples-thatll-make-you-feel-better/. Accessed on March 2020.
14. H. Habibzadeh, K. Dinesh, O. Rajabi Shishvan, A. Boggio-Dandry, G. Sharma, and T. Soyata. A survey of healthcare internet of things (HIoT): A clinical perspective. *IEEE Internet of Things Journal*, 7(1):53–71, 2020.
15. H. Zhu, C. K. Wu, C. H. KOO, Y. T. Tsang, Y. Liu, H. R. Chi, and K. Tsang. Smart healthcare in the era of internet-of-things. *IEEE Consumer Electronics Magazine*, 8(5):26–30, 2019.
16. M. Wazid, A. K. Das, and J.-H. Lee. User authentication in a tactile internet based remote surgery environment: Security issues, challenges, and future research directions. *Pervasive and Mobile Computing*, 54:71–85, 2019.
17. S. Jangirala, A. K. Das, and A. V. Vasilakos. Designing secure lightweight blockchain-enabled RFID-based authentication protocol for supply chains in 5G mobile edge computing environment. *IEEE Transactions on Industrial Informatics*, 16(11):7081–7093, 2020. DOI: 10.1109/TII.2019.2942389.
18. M. Wazid, A. K. Das, M. K. Khan, A. A. Al-Ghaiheb, N. Kumar, and A. V. Vasilakos. Secure authentication scheme for medicine anti-counterfeiting system in IoT environment. *IEEE Internet of Things Journal*, 4(5):1634–1646, 2017.
19. F. Fernandez and G. C. Pallis. Opportunities and challenges of the internet of things for healthcare: Systems engineering perspective. In 4th International Conference on Wireless Mobile Communication and Healthcare—Transforming Healthcare Through Innovations in Mobile and Wireless Technologies (MOBIHEALTH), pages 263–266, Athens, Greece, 2014.

20. David Goad, Andrew T. Collins, and Uri Gal. Privacy and the Internet of Things–An experiment in discrete choice. *Information & Management*, page 103292, 2020. https://doi.org/10.1016/j.im.2020.103292.
21. Jigna J. Hathaliya and Sudeep Tanwar. An exhaustive survey on security and privacy issues in Healthcare 4.0. *Computer Communications*, 153:311–335, 2020.
22. R. Saha, G. Kumar, M. K. Rai, R. Thomas, and S. Lim. Privacy ensured e-healthcare for fog-enhanced IoT based applications. *IEEE Access*, 7:44536–44543, 2019.
23. Y. Sun, F. P. Lo, and B. Lo. Security and privacy for the internet of medical things enabled healthcare systems: A survey. *IEEE Access*, 7:183339–183355, 2019.
24. Q. Wang, D. Zhou, S. Yang, P. Li, C. Wang, and Q. Guan. Privacy preserving computations over healthcare data. In International Conference on Internet of Things (iThings) and IEEE Green Computing and Communications (GreenCom) and IEEE Cyber, Physical and Social Computing (CPSCom) and IEEE Smart Data (SmartData), pages 635–640, Atlanta, USA, 2019.
25. M. Wazid, P. Bagga, A. K. Das, S. Shetty, J. J. P. C. Rodrigues, and Y. Park. AKM-IoV: Authenticated key management protocol in fog computing-based internet of vehicles de- ployment. *IEEE Internet of Things Journal*, 6(5):8804–8817, 2019.
26. D. Dolev and A. C. Yao. On the security of public key protocols. *IEEE Transactions on Information Theory*, 29(2):198–208, 1983.
27. M. Wazid, A. K. Das, N. Kumar, and J. J. P. C. Rodrigues. Secure three-factor user authentication scheme for renewable-energy-based smart grid environment. *IEEE Transactions on Industrial Informatics*, 13(6):3144–3153, 2017.
28. M. Wazid, A. K. Das, S. Kumari, X. Li, and F. Wu. Provably secure biometric-based user authentication and key agreement scheme in cloud computing. *Security and Communication Networks*, 9(17):4103–4119, 2016.
29. T. S. Messerges, E. A. Dabbish, and R. H. Sloan. Examining smart-card security under the threat of power analysis attacks. *IEEE Transactions on Computers*, 51(5):541–552, 2002.
30. J. Ryoo, D. Han, S. Kim, and S. Lee. Performance enhancement of differential power analysis attacks with signal companding methods. *IEEE Signal Processing Letters*, 15:625–628, 2008.
31. M. Wazid and A. K. Das. An efficient hybrid anomaly detection scheme using K-means clustering for wireless sensor networks. *Wireless Personal Communications*, 90(4):1971–2000, 2016.
32. M. Wazid and A. K. Das. A secure group-based blackhole node detection scheme for hierarchical wireless sensor networks. *Wireless Personal Communications*, 94(3):1165–1191, 2017.
33. M. Wazid, A. K. Das, S. Kumari, and M. K. Khan. Design of sinkhole node detection mechanism for hierarchical wireless sensor networks. *Security and Communication Networks*, 9(17):4596–4614.
34. R. Canetti and H. Krawczyk. Analysis of key-exchange protocols and their use for building secure channels. In International Conference on the Theory and Applications of Cryptographic Techniques– Advances in Cryptology (EUROCRYPT'01), pages 453–474. Springer, Innsbruck (Tyrol), Austria, 2001.
35. R. Canetti and H. Krawczyk. Universally composable notions of key exchange and secure channels. In International Conference on the Theory and Applications of Cryptographic Techniques– Advances in Cryptology (EUROCRYPT'02), pages 337–351, Amsterdam, The Netherlands, 2002.
36. V. Odelu, A. K. Das, M. Wazid, and M. Conti. Provably secure authenticated key agreement scheme for smart grid. *IEEE Transactions on Smart Grid*, 9(3):1900–1910, 2018.

37. W. Stallings. *Cryptography and Network Security: Principles and Practice.* Prentice Hall Press, Upper Saddle River, NJ, USA, 5th edition, 2010.
38. Y. Yan, Y. Qian, H. Sharif, and D. Tipper. A survey on cyber security for smart grid communications. *IEEE Communications Surveys and Tutorials*, 14(4):998–1010, 2012.
39. Ashok Kumar Das and Sherali Zeadally. Data security in the smart grid environment. In A. Tascikaraoglu and O. Erdinc, editors, *Pathways to a Smarter Power System* (1st ed., Chapter, 13, pp. 371–395). Academic Press, Elsevier, 2019. ISBN 9780081025925, Link: https://www.elsevier.com/books/pathways-to-a-smarter-power-system/erdinc/978-0-08-102592-5.
40. G. A. Jaafar, S. M. Abdullah, and S. Ismail. Review of recent detection methods for HTTP DDoS attack. *Journal of Computer Networks and Communications*, 2019:1–10, 2019.
41. W. Eddy. TCP SYN flooding attacks and common mitigations. https://tools.ietf.org/html/rfc4987. Accessed on March 2020.
42. H. Wang, D. Zhang, and K. G. Shin. Change-point monitoring for the detection of DoS attacks. *IEEE Transactions on Dependable and Secure Computing*, 1(4):193–208, 2004.
43. J. Fruhlinger. 2018. Ransomware explained: How it works and how to remove it. https://www.csoonline.com/article/3236183/what-is-ransomware-how-it-works-and- how-to-remove-it.html. Accessed on March 2020.
44. Adware. 2020. https://www.malwarebytes.com/adware/. Accessed on March 2020.
45. What is spyware? And how to remove it. 2020. https://us.norton.com/internetsecurity-how-to-catch-spyware-before-it-snags-you.html. Accessed on March 2020.
46. What is an SQL injection attack? 2020. https://sucuri.net/guides/what-is-sql-injection/. Accessed on March 2020.
47. XSS (Cross Site Scripting). 2020. https://owasp.org/www-community/attacks/xss/. Accessed on March 2020.
48. M. Wazid, A. K. Das, V. Odelu, N. Kumar, and W. Susilo. Secure remote user authenticated key establishment protocol for smart home environment. *IEEE Transactions on Dependable and Secure Computing*, 17(2):391–406, 2020.
49. R. Kumar, X. Zhang, W. Wang, R. U. Khan, J. Kumar, and A. Sharif. A multimodal malware detection technique for android IoT devices using various features. *IEEE Access*, 7:64411–64430, 2019.
50. Rafik Hamza, Zheng Yan, Khan Muhammad, Paolo Bellavista, and Faiza Titouna. A privacy-preserving cryptosystem for IoT E-healthcare. *Information Sciences*, 2019. http://www.sciencedirect.com/science/article/pii/S002002551930088X.
51. A. D. Deebak, F. Al-Turjman, M. Aloqaily, and O. Alfandi. An authentic-based privacy preservation protocol for smart e-healthcare systems in IoT. *IEEE Access*, 7:135632–135649, 2019.
52. M. Burrows, M. Abadi, and R. Needham. A logic of authentication. *ACM Transactions on Computer Systems*, 8(1):18–36, 1990.
53. Anil Kumar Sutrala. Design and Analysis of Three-Factor User Au thentication Schemes for Wireless Sensor Networks. PhD thesis, International Institute of Information Technology, Hyderabad, India, 2018. http://web2py.iiit.ac.in/research centres/publications/view publication/phdthesis/94.
54. R. Belguechi, C. Rosenberger, and S. Ait-Aoudia. Biohashing for securing minutiae template. In 20th International Conference on Pattern Recognition (ICPR'10), pages 1168–1171, Istanbul, Turkey, 2010.
55. Andrew Teoh Beng Jin, David Ngo Chek Ling, and Alwyn Goh. Biohashing: Two factor authentication featuring fingerprint data and tokenised random number. *Pattern Recognition*, 37(11):2245–2255, 2004.

56. A. Lumini and L. Nanni. An improved BioHashing for human authentication. *Pattern Recognition*, 40(3):1057–1065, 2007.
57. Dheerendra Mishra, Ashok Kumar Das, and Sourav Mukhopadhyay. A secure user anonymitypreserving biometric-based multi-server authenticated key agreement scheme using smart cards. *Expert Systems with Applications*, 41(18):8129–8143, 2014.
58. Chin-Chen Chang and Ngoc-Tu Nguyen. An untraceable biometric-based multi-server Authenticated key agreement protocol with revocation. *Wireless Personal Communications*, 90(4):1695–1715, 2016.
59. V. Odelu, A. K. Das, and A. Goswami. A secure biometrics-based multi-server authentication protocol using smart cards. *IEEE Transactions on Information Forensics and Security*, 10(9):1953–1966, 2015.
60. AVISPA (Automated Validation of Internet Security Protocols and Applications). 2019. http://www.avispa-project.org/. Accessed on October 2019.
61. A. von Oheimb. The high-level protocol specification language hlpsl developed in the eu project avispa. In Proceedings of 3rd APPSEM II (Applied Semantics II) Workshop (APPSEM'05), pages 1–17, Frauenchiemsee, Germany, 2005.
62. M. Abdalla, P. A. Fouque, and D. Pointcheval. Password-based authenticated key exchange in the three-party setting. In 8th International Workshop on Theory and Practice in Public Key Cryptography (PKC'05), Lecture Notes in Computer Science, volume 3386, pages 65–84, Les Diablerets, Switzerland, 2005.
63. Yuwen Pu, Jin Luo, Chunqiang Hu, Jiguo Yu, Ruifeng Zhao, Hongyu Huang, and Tao Xiang. Two secure privacy-preserving data aggregation schemes for IoT. *Wireless Communications and Mobile Computing*, 2019:1–11, 2019. https://doi.org/10.1155/2019/3985232.
64. Mark A. Will and Ryan K. L. Ko. Chapter 5—A guide to homomorphic encryption. In Ryan Ko and Kim-Kwang Raymond Choo, editors, *The Cloud Security Ecosystem*, pages 101–127. Syngress, Boston, 2015.
65. AES (Advanced Encryption Standard). FIPS PUB 197, National Institute of Standards and Technology (NIST), U.S. Department of Commerce, November 2001. Accessed on December 2019.
66. Ashutosh Dhar Dwivedi, Gautam Srivastava, Shalini Dhar, and Rajani Singh. A decentralized privacy-preserving healthcare blockchain for IoT. *Sensors*, 19(2):1–17, 2019.
67. W. Diffie and M. E. Hellman. New directions in cryptography. *IEEE Transactions on Information Theory*, 22:644–654, 1976.
68. Jong Wook Kim, Beakcheol Jang, and Hoon Yoo. Privacy-preserving aggregation of personal health data streams. *PLOS ONE*, 13:1–15, 11, 2018.

6 Heath Device Security and Privacy
A Comparative Analysis of Fitbit, Jawbone, Google Glass and Samsung Galaxy Watch

A B M Kamrul Islam Riad, Hossain Shahriar, Chi Zhang and Farhat Lamia Barsha

CONTENTS

- 6.1 Introduction 92
- 6.2 Related Works..93
- 6.3 Analysing Wearable Health Devices 94
  - 6.3.1 Analysis of Fitbit 94
  - 6.3.2 *Analysis of Jawbone* 96
  - 6.3.3 *Analysis of Google Glass* 97
  - 6.3.4 *Analysis of Samsung Galaxy Watch*..99
- 6.4 Comparison and Solution 100
- 6.5 *Data Collection Method and Testing Process* 100
  - 6.5.1 Data Collection 100
  - 6.5.2 Security Test Process 101
- 6.6 Data Securing within Mobile Health Devices...102
- 6.7 Fitness Trackers' Secure Data Communication Model 102
  - 6.7.1 Suggestions to Add Security to Fitness Trackers 102
- 6.8 Future Challenges of Wearable Devices..104
  - 6.8.1 Insecure Network 104
  - 6.8.2 Lightweight Protocols for Devices 104
  - 6.8.3 Data Sharing 104
- 6.9 Conclusion 105
- References..105

6.1 INTRODUCTION

Mobile health devices are most commonly used for health fitness and user health status-recording purposes. These devices have grown significantly in recent years, and these mobile health devices are normally in fashion mobile health device forms such as watches, glasses, wristbands or jewellery items (Mobile Health Device Technology Market Research Report, 2018 [1]). In 2018, nearly 3.7 billion new Bluetooth-enabled devices were shipped worldwide to consumers [2]. Health devices are connected to the cloud server through the Internet, enabling device owners to interact with their user records and exchange personal information such as heart rate, geolocation and daily eating habits. These devices are connected to the Internet, such as Wi-Fi networks, more than ever before and have become part of the Internet of Things (IoT). In theory, connecting devices through the IoT allows users to control or automate digital tasks so that various unexpected user data such as habits, daily activities and location tracking records are delivered to third-party observers (Federal Trade Commission Staff Report on the November, 2013 [3]). Health devices provide less security compared to computing devices because of limited bandwidth and processing power [4].

Therefore, mobile devices bring new challenges in terms of users' security and privacy that increase vulnerability to an array of possible attacks due to the limitation of their space and memory capacity. Mobile health devices require pairing with smartphones to establish the connection with cloud servers for data exchange. The complexity of this communication among various paths generates security vulnerabilities such as personal information leaking and privacy hacking by hackers. Financial loss is possible as some fitness mobile devices allow their users to access their bank accounts for quick payment to a selected financial institute or agency [5].

Researchers raise concerns about the security of wearable devices. HP labs (Internet of Things Security Study, 2015 [6]) found that most of the mobile health devices are vulnerable to user data security breach because of poor security firmware systems in the devices. In many cases, firmware update vulnerability allows attackers to inject malicious codes into devices [7]. At the Hack.lu 2015 security conference in Luxembourg [8], a researcher reported that a PC can be affected through malicious code injection when Fitbit devices plug into the PC through Bluetooth pairing within 10 seconds. The weakness of firmware, the gateway of applications and the service of servers are the main concerns about security and privacy leakage of mobile health fitness devices. The health devices build the connection through smartphone apps as a gateway to connect to web service, the open interface for interoperability. Hackers target the weak point of these interfaces which have become a security threat for these wearable health devices. Therefore, vulnerability to attacks such as SQL injection and Cross-Site Scripting (CSS) is through the connection gateway [9].

In this chapter, we discuss the strengths and features of mobile health devices apart from user data security and privacy attacks that occur due to poor security firmware in mobile health devices. The goal of this analysis is to understand security and privacy on mobile health devices and user data transferring methods with the security testing processes of many mobile health devices including Fitbit, Jawbone,

Google Glass and Samsung Galaxy Watch, based on various related prior works and research.

The chapter is organized as follows. First, we discuss related works. Then, we discuss the security and privacy of four wearable devices, Fitbit, Jawbone, Google Glass and Samsung Galaxy Watch. For each of the devices, we analyse strengths and weaknesses in terms of related security threats stemming from the network and data. We also introduce a testing process to secure the devices. Finally, we conclude the chapter.

6.2 RELATED WORKS

Wearable devices can help users to monitor their health and fitness by tracking data from movements to heart rate and even blood pressure. Meanwhile, continued research actively focuses on the privacy and security of these devices. Many research works have been published with the focus on the user data security and privacy leakage for mobile health devices. In 2014, Britt Cyr published a user data security and privacy properties analysis of Fitbit devices, focusing on the security weaknesses between Fitbit Bluetooth devices and a smartphone application during traffic synchronization [10]. They found that Fitbit collected data without acquiring the device owner's consent and that the MAC addresses of Fitbit devices never changed which enabled correlated attacks [11]. Researcher reports that man-in-the-middle attacks intercepted the Bluetooth Low Energy (BTLE) credential during device pairing over TLS [10–12]. A follow-up study in 2018 by Matthew analysed three devices, Fitbit, Pebble and Jawbone, and found out that all three devices exposed their connection forming packet when pairing, which would enable server attacks because these packets allow an attacker to follow the connection after it is initiated.

In 2016, Ke Wan Ching performed security analysis of wearable health devices, especially Google Glass which is an eyewear device, and they found a lack of authentication due to an unsecure PIN system [7]. In addition, Seyedmostafa and Zarian revealed that Google Glass can take pictures and record videos without the user's consent which breaches the user's privacy [13]. One of the security and privacy concerns is regulated from various research forums, M-health applications that facilitate interactions between mobile health devices and mobile phones to visualize the data record of users. In the General Data Protection Regulation in the EU [14], the European Commission emphasizes data protection, and that tracking and monitoring patients' health information such as activities, locations visited and dieting habits would be made severely vulnerable in future by the use of mobile applications. Similarly, the report in [15] states that users' data security and confidentiality would be challenged to ensure compliance with HIPAA regulations due to mobile health devices' vulnerability and their data being compromised by third parties. Wu identified that even a trustworthy network within the organization, in terms of the enforced process of data encryption and authentication mechanism, is vulnerable because third parties may gain elevated privileges due to secret access keys and certification processes from the users' ends [15]. They suggested that security key agreement and distribution among the nodes in the network could be the strongest possible authentication process in accordance with HIPAA guidelines for privacy and data security [15]. A blog of the vulnerability of fitness trackers [5] pointed out that most wearable fitness trackers need to initiate a built-in security mechanism while connecting to other devices or applications for data collection. The mobile devices' data are stored in a local server without an encryption key. The lack of security mechanism causes the devices to be extremely vulnerable to cybercriminal attacks. In this scenario, the cybercriminal can inject random step computation values into memory and the mobile health devices would generate this count value to the server as a valid encoded frame [5]. A group of researchers (University of Toronto) investigated the Bluetooth privacy, data integrity and transmission security of some fitness trackers. They discovered that all of the mobile health device trackers have numerous user data security and privacy issues [16]. They released the key findings of security and privacy leakage for many of the fitness trackers except Apple Watch. The Jawbone UP application consistently sends out the user's precise geolocation while Bellabeat, Garmin and Withings applications fail to use transit-level security, causing data to be visible in transmission [17].

6.3 ANALYSING WEARABLE HEALTH DEVICES

6.3.1 ANALYSIS OF FITBIT

The Fitbit tracker (https://www.fitbit/whyfitbit) tracks various users' activities including number of steps walked, sleep pattern and quality as well as other personal health measurements such as body temperature, pulse rate, food habits and body weight. Fitbit introduced a series of technology on workout tracking such as PurePulse, SmartTrack and Sleep Tracking—a technology that automatically recognizes users' exercise and records the data through the smartphone app.

- **Strengths of the Fitbit Device**

SmartTracking activities—Fitbit uses a simple accelerometer that is called a smart algorithm. SmartTrack uses a three-axis accelerometer to identify the intensity and patterns of the user's movement and determines the type of activities [2]. To measure heartbeat, photoplethysmography, a low-cost and simple optical technique that can be used to detect blood volume changes, is used for PurePulse. Photoplethysmography is a light-based technology used to measure blood circulation and changes in the volume of the blood in the wrist. With photoplethysmography, Fitbit uses an optical heart rate monitor to detect the pulse by shining a green light through the skin to see blood flow.

- **Data Security of Fitbit Devices**

Data security is one of the major security vulnerabilities found in many mobile health devices. Fitbit continuously adds software patches to improve the users' data security and privacy for its devices [18]. For authenticity security purposes the device protects data through regular firmware updates. However, a lack of authentication is one of the biggest vulnerabilities in Fitbit devices and generally occurs on the trackers' side so the potential cybercriminal can easily collect the user's personal data without their consent.

The University of Edinburgh conducted research on how information could be stolen from Fitbit. It was found that it is possible to intercept messages transmitted between the cloud server and fitness tracker. This allowed researchers to access users' information that would cause unauthorized personal data to be shared with third parties (Tara Seals US/North America News, 2017 [19]).

- **Fitbit System Overview**

The Fitbit devices are designed to rest in a data buffer locally on the device. Data synchronization is performed through smartphone applications for Android, iOS and desktop. Fitbit devices send the user's activity to the Fitbit cloud server over Wi-Fi or Internet connection during data synchronizing. During data synchronization, the Fitbit application forwards the user's activity data to the Fitbit warehouse. User data activities are fetched from Fitbit devices during each synchronization.

In Figure 6.1, synchronization is formed over Bluetooth between the Fitbit device and a smartphone or personal computer. The Bluetooth Low Energy (BTLE) (Fitbit Help) is used for data synchronization between smartphone applications or personal computers over Internet/Wi-Fi Fitbit cloud service revealed in an encrypted session.

- **Analysing Bluetooth Communication**

Mobile health devices have built-in Bluetooth that permits devices such as smartphones, computers and peripherals to transfer data or voice wirelessly over short distances. Bluetooth measures a reasonably protected wireless connection that is encoded, stopping casual snooping or eavesdropping from other devices at short distances [20]. However, there is always a security risk involved, such as malicious attacks through Bluetooth networking by hackers. For instance, "bluesnarfing" is

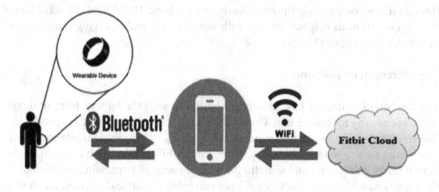

FIGURE 6.1 The Fitbit system components and attack surface.

the unauthorized access to information from a wireless device through a Bluetooth connection, while "bluebugging" allows attacks to take over all functions of mobile phones. A vulnerability in Bluetooth devices including Fitbit allows third parties to gain sensitive information from the devices such as exact locations. The information is leaked as different Bluetooth devices communicate with each other differently to establish a connection. When transmitting information between two devices, one device must first establish a central role in the connection and the other device plays a peripheral role. For example, in a pairing of a Bluetooth Fitbit SmartTrack with an iPhone, the iPhone would play the role of central device and Fitbit SmartTrack would be the peripheral device that indicates an available connection where the signals contain the IP address of a mobile device and a payload containing data about the connection.

- **Fitbit Device Tracking**

The devices originate randomized addresses that automatically configure periodically and attempt to improve privacy instead of maintaining one permanent address [21]. But it was discovered by researchers that the device can be tracked even as its random address originates. Random data are a unique identifier of the device that are supposed to be changed periodically, but in that case this identifier doesn't change in sync with the address. In this case, the research team found that Fitbit devices lack address changes or randomization completely which means they are considered extremely susceptible to tracking even without the use of a sniffer algorithm. The research further addresses that restarting the Fitbit device or draining its battery does not change the access address. It indicates that the data could be tracked in Fitbit devices if the Fitbit's access address never changes.

6.3.2 Analysis of Jawbone

Jawbone is a powerful health activity monitor, food and sleep tracker device worn on the wrist like the Fitbit mobile health device. Jawbone uses an internal accelerometer and algorithm to track users' day-to-day activities and suggests helpful lifestyle tips through the accompanying Up App (Jawbone). Jawbone UP24 fitness tracker had a big upgrade from its original design, with new features and resolving some serious first-generation issues [22, 23].

- **Strength of Jawbone**

The Jawbone UP tracker has a hardware button to save the battery from drainage while not aiming for connection. One of the good security features of Jawbone is the Bluetooth activation switch that requires a user paring PIN code to initiate communication with smartphone applications. While establishing a Bluetooth connection, the device starts publicizing and searching for other peers after pressing the button. In this situation, when paired devices are not reachable to demand devices, the device responds to connection requests from other Bluetooth devices.

- **Data Security of Jawbone Tracker**

As the Bluetooth LE connection described, devices should change the Bluetooth device MAC address randomly in order to improve privacy instead of maintaining one permanent address [24]. But unfortunately, this security feature is found to be absent in the Jawbone tracker device since it uses the same MAC address permanently. This causes potential data security and privacy issues, when the users can be traced easily for their precise location, and user data could be manipulated by the attacker. While using the GattTool command is one of the ways to write and read the potential features of the device, shell script is another way to pretend a Denial of Service (DoS) attack for originating connection requests and reading the characteristics of the devices. In this scenario, if the Jawbone UP tracker is connected to the paired device, it does not accept the further connection request.

- **Jawbone UP Tracker Overview**

Parson's research team [16, 17, 25] found that during the routine use of the device application, Jawbone UP trackers passively share the user's precise current location. It is unclear to the researchers what the reason is for this passive location tracking, and the collection of information is not linked with some given fitness activities. In general, when users open a mobile application, the Jawbone tracker transmits longitude and latitude to its servers; these transmissions are connected with the predefined user events, such as syncing with the device and opening the application. This testing describes that these geographical data have a precision of up to 14 decimal points and it effectively releases the fitness device location within a few millimetres. It is found that users do not know that the location transmission occurs when they restore their timelines. Figure 6.2 shows that the Jawbone UP tracker sends a user's exact location when the user connects with a smartphone application.

Figure 6.2 shows that Jawbone routinely transmits precise geolocation information when users open the apps or sync their mobile health device to their iPhone [25]. The Jawbone UP fitness data transmission between the mobile application and health devices servers is generally secured using HTTPS [25]. However, both Android and iOS applications have vulnerabilities because both applications create false generated fitness data for their individual account. Although HTTPS is a secure communication network between user and server, HTTPS does not cover the security and privacy protection of end users.

6.3.3 Analysis of Google Glass

Google Glass is the earliest mobile health device that boosted the growth of mobile health device technology. The frame of the Google Glass is a pair of glasses into which is built a computer eyewear device. It affords various structures that users feel very comfortable using, but Google Glass is only available for enterprise which means the Google Glass is not available for individuals' usage. However, many concerns about users' data security and privacy issues by many healthcare researchers

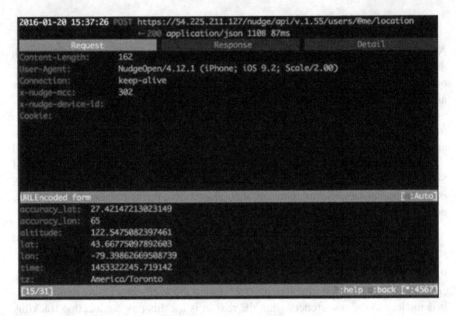

FIGURE 6.2 Jawbone UP application sharing user location.

mean that Google Glass is not free from vulnerability, and client data security and privacy can be threatened.

- **Strength of Google Glass**

Google Glass basically performs through user voice commands [13, 26, 27]. Users can send messages without using their hands, and it has video and camera capabilities that differentiate it from other mobile health fitness devices such as Fitbit and Jawbone. These glasses provide numerous distinct useful applications for health organizations and hospital staff. Video conferences between doctors and medical associates are one of the most unique features of Google Glasses [27, 28]. Google Glass facilitates an ample number of health cases throughout conferences about patient treatment between medical professionals and other co-facilitated health organizations.

- **Data Security of Google Glass**

The connection system of Google Glass is content-based image retrieval (CBIR) which allows health staff to search a patient's medical history for accurate information while consulting with physicians and patients [27, 28]. Apart from these facilities Google Glass has a major concern about patients' data security and privacy. Researchers have found that Google Glass does not have a concrete authentication process to protect the user's data security and privacy due to lack of a secure enough PIN system. The Google Glass privacy threat is significantly different from other fitness trackers that use mobile phones and apps to collect user data. Google Glass supports eye movement tracking that may cause authentication issues [29]. In addition, Syedmostafa and Zarina revealed that [13] Google Glass is able to capture user pictures and has a video-recording capability which may be a violation of users' privacy. Most significantly, there were numerous factual case reports concerning data security and privacy associated with Google Glass when it was first released.

A research team exposed a serious security threat to do with how Google Glass interprets Quick Response (QR) codes while it snaps a photo back; they found that Google Glass can scan a malicious QR code that forces the device to connect to a hostile Wi-Fi access point, so man-in-the-middle attacks can perform session hijacking or sniffing or remotely gain root access to a Glass device and take control without the wearer's knowledge. Moreover, the QR code is not the only way to initiate a security breach; sniffing or session hijacking can be performed by man-in-the middle attacks and such an attack can be implemented without the device recognizing any QR code [29].

- **Google Glass Bluetooth Communication**

Google Glass Bluetooth pairing is comparatively the same as other fitness devices. It is essential to pair Glass to a phone or tablet that has full Bluetooth capabilities via the MyGlass app from the Google Play Store [24, 30]. There is a concern that the Google Glass battery gets drained more quickly while connected through Bluetooth rather than a Wi-Fi connection [31].

6.3.4 ANALYSIS OF SAMSUNG GALAXY WATCH

Another mobile health device which makes people's daily lives easier is the Samsung Galaxy Watch which has a notification feature. By synchronizing all data to the phone, important alerts and notifications are sent directly to the wrist. However, this device is also not free from vulnerabilities. According to an HP study [32], the Samsung Galaxy Watch contains vulnerabilities such as a weak authentication process, lack of encryption and also lack of privacy.

- **Strength of Samsung Galaxy Watch**

The Samsung Galaxy Watch works as a personal trainer by measuring heart rate and can track six activities of a user's exercise by counting the distance and recording the number of steps. It also works as a daily assistant by displaying the next ten hours' schedule. It provides reminders and health data to the user day to day. It is 5 ATM water resistant and has a durability of military standard. Besides this, it can also measure stress levels, calories, sleeping habits and water intake levels.

- **Data Security of Samsung Galaxy Watch**

The Samsung Galaxy Watch has a security lock system and PIN setting. This lock depends on a Bluetooth connection; when the connection is ended the device is automatically locked and has to be unlocked using the PIN. But this security is not strong enough. Brute-force attacks can easily gain access to this device. Romania-based Bitdefender [32] researchers found that a six-digit PIN code and Bluetooth connection between two paired devices can easily be hacked by brute-force attacks which is a risk for users' security and privacy issues. Besides this, because of weak authentication mechanisms, data can be accessed from the computer without unlocking the device. And it also has a lack of encryption which increases vulnerabilities.

- **Samsung Galaxy Watch Bluetooth Communication**

To connect the Samsung Galaxy Watch with a mobile device, the Galaxy mobile health device app needs to be installed on the mobile device. Users can download this app from the Play Store and Samsung Android device users can download this app from the Galaxy Store or Play Store. Since Bluetooth has low energy usage, it has weak security features, so hackers can gain control of the system and data can be stolen [32].

6.4 COMPARISON AND SOLUTION

Analysing the strengths of the selected devices, connection capabilities and data storage structure, such devices have more security and privacy concerns. There is a high chance that user data can be compromised or gained by man-in-the-middle attacks, although there are a lot of improvements that have been made by the device manufacturers. The security vulnerabilities and potential security attacks on the mobile health devices are summarized in Table 6.1.

Table 6.1 shows that the selected mobile health devices are not free from common security vulnerabilities, and the devices that have been chosen for analysis have a lack of authentication. Without implementing proper security authentication, the devices can be accessed by unauthorized activities such as eavesdropping, DoS and brute-force attacks. We find that Jawbone devices can reveal the exact locations that users recently visited. Thus, DoS attacks can be deciphered, and third parties can easily gain access to the device. Similarly, Google Glasses have major privacy issues since Glasses are capable of taking pictures and recording without people's knowledge. Therefore, eavesdropping and spyware attacks can take place.

6.5 *DATA COLLECTION METHOD AND TESTING PROCESS*

6.5.1 DATA COLLECTION

Data collection is a major issue in the healthcare system because it makes it easier to collect patient's information and directly send it to healthcare professionals which allows personalized treatment and improves communication between patients and

TABLE 6.1
Comparison of Security Vulnerability and Attacks for Fitbit, Jawbone, Google Glass and Samsung Galaxy Watch

Mobile Health Devices	Security Vulnerability	Attacks
Fitbit device	Week authentication	Data injection, DOS and battery drain hacks
	Bluetooth Low Energy Technology (BTLE)	Easily tracked
	Privacy: Tracks visited locations	
Jawbone	Lacking privacy features	Denial of service
	Exact location tracked	
Google Glass	Unsecure PIN	Wi-Fi hijacking
	Privacy: Capable of unauthorized picture and video recording	Eavesdropping and spyware
	Suspicious eye movement	Easy recording system by nearby people due to gesture-based authentication scheme
	Unsecure network and hostile environment	
	For Wi-Fi setup, requires QR code	QR photo-bombing malware
Samsung Galaxy Watch	Weak authentication process [7]	Brute-force attack [7]

doctors in figuring out health conditions (The Importance of Data Collection in Healthcare and Its Benefits, 2020 [33]). In this era of advanced technology, the use of mobile health devices in the health sector is increasing. For collecting data through mobile health devices, we can use mobile applications which run on mobile health devices. These mobile applications can build up a connection between patients and doctors and can access information from databases.

6.5.2 Security Test Process

After collecting data, we can test security by the following process.

At first we have to detect the existence of mobile health devices by observing the communication channels of the device, which will also allow us to know the type of the device, software, operating system, etc. Through this we can find whether the device is safe or risky.

Then we have to monitor the device's activity to know about all running processes, memory, etc. After this we have to check whether this running process can be performed without admin privileges or not which will let us know that whether the data are secure or not. Then we have to check if an application of the mobile health device can collect and store sensor data on the device. If it can't then the device is safe; if it can access only normal data then it's not a major issue, but if it can access sensitive data like GPS location then the device is at major risk. After this we can try to manipulate data between the sender and receiver to inject errors or noise into the data. If the device ignores this kind of data, then it's safe, but if it crashes or acts differently, then the device is not safe. At last we have to list all the vulnerabilities so that after improving the device's security we can check again.

6.6 DATA SECURING WITHIN MOBILE HEALTH DEVICES

Data security is a major concern of mobile health devices. Fitness trackers are widely adopted and are easy to use. There are many concerns about the lack of data security in fitness devices and it often escalates to the highly vulnerable risks for users. The following is a summary of the reasons for the lack of data security and privacy in mobile health devices:

Lack of testing: Fitness devices are constantly updating their features due to market competition so there would be possible rushes to release products or new features to the marketplace. As a result, there may be a lack of proper testing and strong security coding oversight [5, 34, 35].

Size of the device: Most of the fitness devices are very tiny and there is very limited space to create security features by adding extra hardware as manufacturers would worry about the device weight and user experience.

Cost down: Due to fierce competition in this market, the fitness devices generally cannot be priced too high, which would be a possible cause for not having sufficient memory space and lack-of-quality coding leading to the failure of the strengthening of device security.

6.7 FITNESS TRACKERS' SECURE DATA COMMUNICATION MODEL

A built-in security mechanism is one of the most important features for the user authentication process because it generates a secure PIN system. A secure PIN system prevents unauthorized access in a device or system because it tends to store data without encryption. Cyber-attacks often take place due to poor security management that causes the devices to be extremely vulnerable. The hacker could control every single aspect of the device through the initial injection called a firmware attack, which allows attackers' access to local data storage. After a successful firmware attack, the devices are open for modification, encrypted key or Bluetooth functionality. As a result, attackers could send or inject random values into memory as a step count to the server as valid encrypted frames [5, 35–37].

6.7.1 Suggestions to Add Security to Fitness Trackers

The following initiatives and practices help cover the minimal security and privacy of fitness trackers:

Firmware needs to be regularly updated or developed for all fitness devices. Gadget LE privacy and changes of MAC address should be required at random periodical times, such as every ten minutes.

While a mobile health device is pairing with a mobile phone, the mobile health device firmware should include a fixed and private Identity Resolving Key (IRK).

In general, mobile health device firmware MAC addresses are permanent, which causes theft of localhost addresses. But if the mobile health device firmware randomly generates new MAC addresses every ten minutes on IRK, hackers would not be able to identify the host address number [17, 25].

HTTPS can be used to minimize the risk of data vulnerability; its main purpose is to maintain data authentication [14]. HTTPS would encrypt data and secure transmitted data. Currently the most common architecture of web services is REST, based on HTTP (The Importance of Data Collection in Healthcare and Its Benefits, 2020 [33]). But the most protection standard method for this model of communication is Transport Layer Security (TLS) or Secure Socket Layer (SSL). HTTPS ensures a safe, encrypted communication channel between the client app and backend server. The implementation of an HTTPS security feature is very simple but has some common pitfalls from the user's perspective. The problem of HTTPS security is mainly an improper implementation that reduces to replacing the protocol name in the URL from http to https. Although HTTP implementation will enable TLS/SSL encryption, it will not ensure a good enough security level. It is very important to implement the HTTPS configuration correctly because HTTPS implementation enables TLS/SSL encryption. The TLS standard is based on X509 certificates and asymmetric encryption (The Importance of Data Collection in Healthcare and Its Benefits, 2020 [33]). X509 certificates in which a public key requires the unique identification that the associated private key is owned by the correct person with which a digital signature or an encryption mechanism is used. In this process, mobile apps verify encryption certificates by just replacing the protocol name, meaning that the attacker can generate their own fake certificates. The certificate allows man-in-the-middle attacks to intercept communications between the user and the cloud server, so HTTPS configuration is vital to avoid such an attack for data transmission.

Cryptography is another form of data encryption that encodes the message or data so that hackers cannot read it but it can be authorized. In cryptography, the Advanced Encryption Standard (AES) algorithm is used. In this process the message block size 128 bits of text is fixed (plain or cipher) where the same key is used on both the encrypt and decrypt sides and the key length is 128, 192 or 256 bits. When a user sends a longer message, the message is divided into 128-bit blocks. One of the advantages of longer keys is that the longer keys make the cipher more difficult to break as well as enforcing longer encryption and decryption.

Using the Public Key Encryption (PKI) method, we can achieve proper authentication of the device to secure data transmission. The device will encrypt data using a public key, and the monitoring application will use the private key to decrypt the data. In case someone manages to get the public key, it's still not possible to retrieve the private key.

Security pinning is another method to ensure secure data transmission where the connection between the device and server will be aborted if any unauthorized identity is present. In this method, the developer implements Certificate Pinning on the server to verify on the client side [33, 38–40]. This verification requires the server certificate and fingerprint to identify the mobile app to establish the connection with the mobile app so the app compares the user fingerprint with a certificate from the remote server. The authentication sends the connection to the server if the user fingerprint is identical. Hence the server connection is rejected immediately if the user fingerprint is not identical, as this means the communication or data will be compromised.

6.8 FUTURE CHALLENGES OF WEARABLE DEVICES

Healthcare system IoT security and privacy systems impact in various ways to enhance data security and privacy. To get a better data security and privacy environment, several challenges require special attention from healthcare device developers.

6.8.1 INSECURE NETWORK

An insecure network is one of the biggest challenges for secure data transfer in wearable health devices because of the convenience and low cost. For data transmission, device and software services rely heavily on wireless networks, such as Wi-Fi, which are the main cause of vulnerabilities to various intrusions including man-in-middle attacks, denial of service attacks, traffic injection, spoofing, unauthorized router access and brute-force attacks. In addition, hotspot wireless service is mostly on free wireless networks in public places and user unconsciously connect to networks which have not been certified and are untrusted.

6.8.2 LIGHTWEIGHT PROTOCOLS FOR DEVICES

In many cases, a wearable device is a low-cost structure which means poor software patches and lightweight protocols are used for built-in security. There is a conflict in health device data security methods because of low-cost software applications based on sensors. At present, if we want to provide high-grade security for the sensor, the device developer must apply high-cost solutions and should follow specific policy and proxy rules to prove secure data transmission service. So developing the different levels of security protocols according to the application scenarios, especially communication network security protocols and authenticated security, is the main task of security protection for wearable health devices in the future.

6.8.3 DATA SHARING

The wearable health device involves sensitive data sharing and data gathering from the healthcare system to monitor the user's activities in many ways, varying widely, which makes it difficult to unify secure data management. So information collaboration and sharing among the diverse data communicating systems of healthcare devices constitute an inevitable unsecure data breach trend of the future. The privatization of user information could be very affected by the security and privacy vulnerabilities of wearable healthcare devices. Employing general data policies to combine different data could provide more comprehensible information and enhance user security and privacy while establishing a hierarchical security model.

6.9 CONCLUSION

The health device faces many challenges such as the massiveness of medical data and sensitivity of patient information. User data on mobile health devices could be compromised through Bluetooth connections to mobile applications that push and pull data from the cloud server. Communication between the server and app is found to be secure, but the MAC address could cause a significant data leak from devices. While all the above-described devices provide a reasonable level of privacy and data security overall, the tangible and secure data REST methods on the server for those health devices would provide more user data security and privacy.

REFERENCES

1. Mobile Health Device Technology Market Research Report (2018). Retrieved from https://www.transparencymarketresearch.com/article/mobile health device-technology-market.htm.
2. Singlesteve. (2019). Your fitbit is definitely broadcasting your location. Retrieved from http://www.bu.edu/articles/2019/fitbit-bluetooth-vulnerability.
3. Federal Trade Commission Staff Report on the November 2013 Workshop Entitled the Internet of Things: Privacy and Security in a Connected World. (2019, March 11). Retrieved from https://www.ftc.gov/reports/federal-trade-commission-staff-report-november-2013-workshop-entitled-internet-things.
4. Al-Muhtadi, J., Mickunas, D., & Campbell, R. (2001). Mobile health device security services. In Proceedings 21st International Conference on Distributed Computing Systems Workshops (pp. 266–271). doi: 10.1109/cdcs.2001.918716.
5. Makarevich, A. (2019, April 23). Vulnerabilities of fitness trackers & how to overcome them. Retrieved from https://r-stylelab.com/company/blog/iot/vulnerability-of-fitness-trackers-risks-they-are-facing-and-tips-to-minimize-them.
6. Internet of Things Security Study: Smartwatches. (2020). Retrieved from https://www.ftc.gov/system/files/documents/public_comments/2015/10/00050-98093.pdf.
7. Ching, K. W., & Singh, M. M. (2016). Mobile health device technology devices security and privacy vulnerability analysis. *International Journal of Network Security & Its Applications*, 8(3), 19–30. doi: 10.5121/ijnsa.2016.830.
8. Storm, D., & Storm, D. (2015). Researcher says Fitbit can be wirelessly hacked to infect PCs, Fitbit says not true. Retrieved from https://www.computerworld.com/article/2997561/researcher-says-fitbit-can-be-wirelessly-hacked-to-infect-pcs-fitbit-says-not-true.html.
9. Konstantinou, C., & Maniatakos, M. (2015). Impact of firmware modification attacks on power systems field devices. In IEEE International Conference on Smart Grid Communications (SmartGridComm). doi: 10.1109/smartgridcomm.2015.7436314.
10. Cyr, B., Horn, W., Miao, D., & Specter, M. A. (2014). Security analysis of wearable fitness devices (fitbit). *Massachusetts Institute of Technology*, 1.

11. Hale, M. L., Lotfy, K., Gamble, R. F., Walter, C., & Lin, J. (2018). Developing a platform to evaluate and assess the security of mobile health device devices. *Digital Communications and Networks*, 5(3), 147–159. doi: 10.1016/j.dcan.2018.10.009.
12. Fitbit Help. (2020). Retrieved from https://help.fitbit.com/customer/portal/articles/987748-how-do-fitbit-trackers-sync-with-android-de.
13. Safavi, Seyedmostafa, & Shukur, Zarina. (2014). Improving google glass security and privacy by changing the physical and software structure. *Life Sciences*, 11, 109–117.
14. Special Eurobarometer 431: Data protection—ecodp. common. ckan. site title. (2020). Retrieved from https://data.europa.eu/euodp/el/data/dataset/S2075_83_1_431_ENG.
15. Wu, M., Luo, J., & Online Journal of Nursing Informatics Contributors. (2020, January 30). Mobile health device technology applications in healthcare: A literature review. Retrieved from https://www.himss.org/resources/mobile health device-technology-applications-healthcare-literature-review.
16. Andrew Hilts et al. Every step you fake. https://openeffect.ca/reports/ Every_Step_You _Fake.pdf.Accessed: 02.07.2020 (not understanding).
17. Hilts, A. (2016, April 5). Every step you fake: Final report released. Retrieved from https://openeffect.ca/every-step-you-fake-final-report-released/.
18. Martin, J. A. (2017). 10 things you need to know about the security risks of mobile health devices. Retrieved from https://www.cio.com/article/3185946/10-things-you-need-to-know-about-the-security-risks-of-mobile health devices.html.
19. Tara Seals US/North America News. (2017, September 18). Fitbit vulnerabilities expose wearer data. Retrieved from https://www.infosecurity-magazine.com/news/fitbit-vulnerabilities-expose/.
20. Pinola, M. (2020, February 2). What Bluetooth Is and How It Works. Retrieved from https://www.lifewire.com/what-is-bluetooth-2377412.
21. Ansley, C. (2019). 2019 Fall Technical Forum. MAC Randomization in Mobile Devices, 12.
22. Jawbone. (2020). Retrieved from https://mobile health devicezone.com/: https://mobile health devicezone.com/companies/jawbone.
23. Rise and fall of the Jawbone UP24: The tracker that changed mobile health device tech. (2019, June 14). Retrieved from https://www.wareable.com/fitness-trackers/remembering-the-jawbone-up24-7320.
24. Woolley Martin, M. (2019, August 26). Bluetooth Technology Protecting Your Privacy. Retrieved from https://www.bluetooth.com/blog/bluetooth-technology-protecting-your-privacy/.
25. Hilts, A. (2016, February 2). Every Step You Fake: A Comparative Analysis of Fitness Tracker Privacy and Security. Retrieved from https://openeffect.ca/fitness-tracker-privacy-and-security/.
26. Advantages & Disadvantages of Google Glasses. (2019, June 4). Retrieved from https://blog.hostonnet.com/advantages-disadvantages-of-google-glasses.
27. Widmer, A., Schaer, R., Markonis, D., & Muller, H. (2014). Facilitating medical information search using Google Glass connected to a content-based medical image retrieval system. In Proceedings of the 36th Annual International Conference of the IEEE Engineering in Medicine and Biology Society. doi: 10.1109/embc.2014.6944625.
28. Schaer, Muller, & Widmer . (2016). Using smart glasses in medical emergency situations, a qualitative pilot study, *2016 IEEE Wireless Health (WH)*, Bethesda, MD, 2016, pp. 1–5, doi: 10.1109/WH.2016.7764556.
29. Privacy Implications of Google Glass. (2013, June 13). Retrieved from https://resources.infosecinstitute.com/privacy-implications-of-google-glass/.
30. Pairing Glass to your Bluetooth phone. (2020). Retrieved from https://support.google.com/glass/answer/3064189?hl=en&ref_topic=3056776.

31. Swider, M. (2017, February 21). Google glass review. Retrieved from https://www.techradar.com/reviews/gadgets/google-glass-1152283/review/7.
32. How to connect Samsung Galaxy Watch to Mobile Device or Bluetooth Headset? Samsung Support Singapore. (2019, October 17). Retrieved from https://www.samsung.com/sg/support/mobile-devices/how-to-connect-samsung-galaxy-watch-to-mobile-device-or-bluetooth-headset/.
33. The Importance of Data Collection in Healthcare and Its Benefits. (2020, April 9). Retrieved from https://www.sam-solutions.com/blog/the-importance-of-data-collection-in-healthcare/39.
34. Emm, D., Nikishin, A., & Gostev, A. (2015). Kaspersky Security Bulletin 2015. Top security stories. Retrieved from https://securelist.com/kaspersky-security-bulletin-2015-top-security-stories/72886/.
35. Vulnerability-of-fitness-trackers-risks-they-are-facing-and-tips-to-minimize-them (September 24, 2018). Retrieved from: https://r-stylelab.com/company/blog/iot/vulnerability-of-fitness-trackers-risks-they-are-facing-and-tips-to-minimize-them.
36. Improving google glass security and privacy by changing. (n.d.). Retrieved from https://www.researchgate.net/publication/265867348_Improving_Google_glass_security_and_privacy_by_changing_the_physical_and_software_structure.
37. Endpoint Protection. (n.d.). Retrieved from https://www.symantec.com/connect/blogs/google-glass-still-vulnerable-wifi-hijacking-despite-qr-photobombing-patch.
38. HP, Study Reveals Smartwatches Vulnerable to Attack. (2020). Retrieved from https://www8.hp.com/us/en/hp-news/press-release.html?id=2037386#.Vi18G7crLIU.
39. Arsene, L. (2015, January 30). Bitdefender Research Exposes Security Risks of Android Mobile health device Devices. Retrieved from http://www.darkreading.com/partnerperspectives/bitdefender/bitdefender-research-exposes-security-risks-of-android-mobile health device-devices/a/d-id/1318005.
40. Markiewicz, M. (2018, May 29). 3 Ways How to Implement Certificate Pinning on Android. Retrieved from N netguru: https://www.netguru.com/codestories/3-ways-how-to-implement-certificate-pinning-on-android.

7 Privacy-Preserving Infrastructure for Health Information Systems

Sheikh Mohammad Idrees, Mariusz Nowostawski, Roshan Jameel and Ashish Kumar Mourya

CONTENTS

7.1 Health Information System (HIS) 109
    7.1.1 Benefits of HIS 110
    7.1.2 Types of HIS 110
    7.1.3 Evolution of HIS 112
7.2 Data Security and Privacy in Health Information Systems 113
    7.2.1 Security and Privacy in the Healthcare Data Life Cycle 114
    7.2.2 Healthcare Data Security Practices 116
    7.2.3 Healthcare Data Privacy Practices 117
7.3 Blockchain and Healthcare 118
    7.3.1 Basic Concepts of Blockchain Technology 119
    7.3.2 Blockchain-Based Infrastructure for Health Information Systems 124
7.4 Discussion 127
References 128

7.1 HEALTH INFORMATION SYSTEM (HIS)

Providing guaranteed quality healthcare services to patients has become a priority for developing countries. The estimation of the morbidity and mortality rates directly affects the healthcare being provided and the research being conducted in the medical industry. With the rise in digitized healthcare data, the demands of security and privacy of stored data and data during exchange are also increasing. The integration of information technology (IT) and the healthcare industry has not only changed the treatment and diagnosis process but has also helped in enhanced data processing and research. Because of the rising expectations of the patients, hospital management, healthcare providers and the stakeholders, the demand for quality in the healthcare systems is rising, resulting in the escalation of implementation costs, lack of resources and several adaptations in medical practices [1]. Healthcare providers are moving towards decision-making processes for the advancement in diagnostics, which require the availability and accessibility of accurate data [2], which is provided by health information systems (HIS) [3]. The motive of designing HIS is to obtain useful information for making decisions and delivering quality services. The quality of the healthcare information systems should be defined by the effectiveness, social acceptance and the cost as per the guidelines provided by WHO [4]. An effective HIS provides integrated patient-centric infrastructure that is cost-effective and delivers measures for promotion in the healthcare industry. The privacy and security of medical data is the most important aspect of HIS as healthcare is totally reliant on data for treatment and research. Privacy denotes that access to the data is restricted to the authorized users only, while security deals with protecting the data from intruders.

7.1.1 Benefits of HIS

A HIS deals with the functional aspect of the healthcare framework that handles the management of the electronic healthcare data. The HIS is responsible for generating useful information that helps in the operational management of hospitals, policy making, efficiency, informed research and decision-making processes [5]. Such systems deal with the collection, storage, management and transmission of healthcare data. It is a fundamental tool for consolidating the planning and managing of healthcare services. The execution of such systems is responsible for providing improved healthcare quality, reduced cost of implementation and operation, error-free administration and organized management. A few of the benefits of HIS are depicted in Figure 7.1.

7.1.2 Types of HIS

The main purpose of HIS is to improve treatment processes by providing the latest information about the patient. This information is sensitive and needs to be accurate and confidential. It is the duty of the HIS to collect, store and analyse this heterogeneous big data of patients in a timely manner and provide access to the authorized users. The HIS could be of several types; a few of the prominent ones are mentioned below. These types of HIS depend on various aspects such as the type of data, level of implementation, government policies, etc., but the main objective is to offer accurate information in a timely, secure and private manner for improving the healthcare industry globally.

- *Electronic health records*: EHRs are the digital records of the patients including health information, lab test results, doctor/hospital visits, diagnosis and treatments. In EHR-based HIS, the facility to collect and store the patient's health data electronically is provided. Moreover, in an open EHR system, the health data are kept in a non-proprietary setup, to avoid the vendor lock-in problem.
- *Strategic systems*: These types of HIS are used in classifying the information. Different provisions are provided for different types of information being handled; usually a pyramid approach is used to differentiate among

Privacy-Preserving Infrastructure

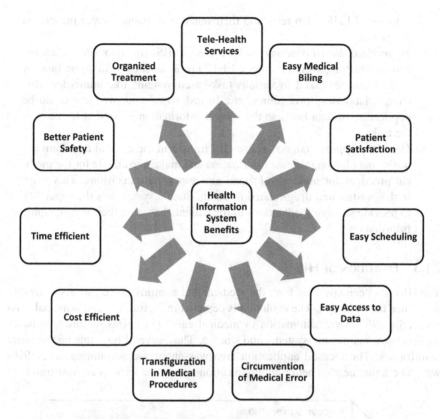

FIGURE 7.1 Benefits of health information systems.

the data. These systems are also known as operational systems. Such HIS are usually developed before the execution, and hence provide the ability to configure the system as per the requirements.

- *Master patient index*: The objective of this type of HIS is to connect the records of the patients from multiple databases. These systems hold the records of the patients listed at a healthcare institute and arrange them into indexed format to avoid the duplication of the data and provide accurate results.
- *Remote patient monitoring*: Such systems provide online medical assistance, by collecting the data from sensor devices and transmitting them for analysis to the healthcare practitioner who is not physically available. Such systems are helpful for monitoring critical diseases like diabetes, heart health, blood pressure, etc. The data collected using the sensing devices can be used by healthcare professionals to monitor health or by researchers to facilitate better systems and decisions.
- *Administrative systems*: Medical systems are reliant on admin data. In such HIS, the patient data are integrated with the medical systems. The patient data are the basic information about the patient, while the medical system

consists of EHRs, lab tests and their outcomes, diagnosis and prescribed drugs, etc.
- *Subject/task-based systems*: Subject-based HIS are associated with the patients/doctors; while task-based HIS are associated with some task. A subject can be linked to various task-based systems like admission, discharge, laboratory procedures, etc. In task-based systems there could be duplication in data because the subject information is needed for each of the tasks.
- *Decision support systems*: These HIS transform the clinical and administrative data into significant information and make it available for the medical practices for making informed and appropriate decisions. This helps in diagnostics and drug-related research. Such a system has the capability to provide suitable medications to the patients based on their demographic information.

7.1.3 EVOLUTION OF HIS

The HIS has been covering both the medical and administrative aspects of healthcare since the 1960s [6]. The evolution is depicted in Figure 7.2. The principal drivers in the 1960s were automation in medical care. The infrastructure was based on expensive mainframe systems and storage. Thus, several hospitals had to share mainframes. The focused application area was automatic accounting. The 1970s was the era that needed better communication among the various administrators of

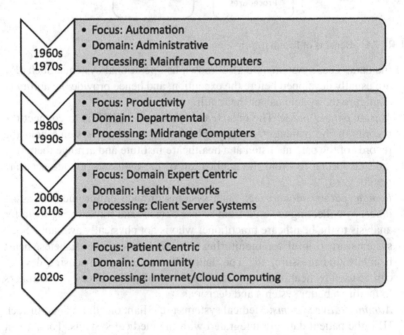

FIGURE 7.2 Evolution of health information systems.

multiple departments. The 1980s saw two big changes in the healthcare sector, first the productivity in terms of resources and reimbursement and second the introduction of midrange computers that encouraged the direct support of doctors, nurses and medical service providers to the systems. The aim was to improve the decision-making procedures and advance the healthcare being provided. In the 1990s, the amalgamation of healthcare and IT was emerging, which pushed the healthcare industry to integrate the hospitals and healthcare providers. The 2000s and 2010s saw the most advancement in the IT industry that has led to the development of integrated systems that have the capability to deal with broader and robust networks. The technology was advanced enough to provide commercially stronger healthcare services and real-time decision support systems. The focus area started to shift from domain expert-centric to patient-centric. The 2020s are going to be an era dedicated to patients. The healthcare systems will be technically advanced to provide real-time patient monitoring. The focus now is shifting towards the storage of the huge amount of healthcare data in a secure manner that is available and accessible all the time. Moreover, healthcare data are confidential, which makes privacy a big concern. Therefore, developing a system that ensures the privacy and security of the stored data as well as data in transit is required. Earlier, the main emphasis of the HIS was on the resource allocation, but in today's world with the Internet, patients demand quality healthcare service in a cost-efficient manner.

7.2 DATA SECURITY AND PRIVACY IN HEALTH INFORMATION SYSTEMS

There has been a paradigm shift in the healthcare industry with digitization. The electronically available healthcare data today are huge, diverse and complex in nature, and hence can be termed as heterogeneous big data. There are various promising opportunities and services that can be provided by these data. Nevertheless, such data are confidential and sensitive, and with the growth of trending technologies like cloud computing, data analytics, clinical mobility, etc., security and privacy are becoming the main concerns [7]. The privacy of the patient is a very sensitive issue, because the patient shares all of their medical history with doctors for better treatment [8]. However, there are certain diseases like HIV, psychotic disorders or any other contagious diseases whose disclosure might become a reason for social discrimination [9]. The healthcare data consist of medical history, path lab records, medication history, diagnosis and treatment details, genetic and sexual information, profession, etc. These data can be used for several purposes apart from the diagnosis, such as public policies deployment, advanced research, insurance claims, pharmacies, pharmaceutical companies, productivity, etc. Figure 7.3 shows how security is linked with all these domains.

Therefore, the HIS must have the ability to keep the personal information of the patients private. It must be capable of not only protecting the sensitive information, but also ensuring that authenticated users do the data collection and sharing in an organized way following the policies and regulations made by the government. Moreover, the data must be safeguarded against unauthorized access and integrity

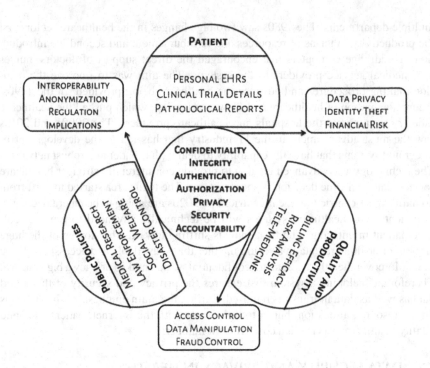

FIGURE 7.3 Data security domains in health information systems.

and availability must be assured. The data should be protected from malicious attacks and data breaches.

7.2.1 SECURITY AND PRIVACY IN THE HEALTHCARE DATA LIFE CYCLE

The healthcare industries deliver efficient and appropriate medical care by storing, managing and transmitting a huge amount of healthcare data. However, the shortcomings are a dearth of technical resources and security of the data. The healthcare data are vulnerable to data disclosure and breaches. Therefore, maintaining the security of the data is very complicated. The security and privacy of the healthcare data need to address both medical as well as administrative data from in-house and external risks. A secure life cycle of the data must be proposed at the beginning of designing the HIS to ensure better decision-making in a cost-effective manner [10]. Figure 7.4 depicts the fundamental components of the life cycle of healthcare data.

- *Data collection*: This is the first phase of the data life cycle. It deals with the collection of medical data of various types from numerous sources in different formats. From a security viewpoint, it is very important to collect the data from trusted data sources and maintain the confidentiality of

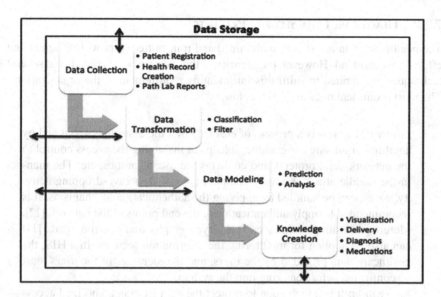

FIGURE 7.4 The data life cycle in healthcare.

the patients. Moreover, some procedures must be implemented to ensure the protection of data from disclosure, duplication, theft, unauthorized access, etc.

- *Data transformation*: After the collection of data, they are filtered on the basis of their structure and classified to find out whether any kind of alteration is needed to analyse them meaningfully. Basically, in this step the noise, missing values, outliers, etc., are removed from the data to improve the quality of the analytics. Moreover, the available data might have sensitive information that needs tremendous precautions to assure its safety [11]. Therefore, access control mechanisms, data partitioning and data anonymizing techniques are defined.
- *Data modelling*: After collecting and transforming the data, they are kept in secure storage and analysis is done to produce useful information. For predictive analysis, several supervised techniques such as clustering, classification, etc., are applied. Furthermore, providing a secure processing environment is also of crucial importance. Since the mining of the data is usually done to extract sensitive data, the mining must be configured in such a way that the data are protected against data breaches.
- *Knowledge creation*: This is the final step in the lifecycle of the data. In this stage, the healthcare professionals use the analysed data to generate some knowledge for better decision-making. The generated knowledge is considered to be extremely sensitive; hence the industries must not make it available publicly. Correspondingly, compliance with security standards and verification processes are the main objectives of this phase.

7.2.2 Healthcare Data Security Practices

The healthcare data are stored, maintained and transmitted to provide efficient and effective medical aid. However, the security of these data is very crucial, and several techniques are applied to fulfil this intimidating requirement of the organizations. The most prominent ones are given below:

- *Authentication*: It is a process of ensuring that the assertions about and by anything or anyone are genuine. It helps in managing the access control to the network/data, protects and confirms the user identities, etc. The man-in-the-middle attack is a very common type of data eavesdropping activity, which can be handled by applying the authentication mechanisms. It is recommended to apply authentication at the end points of the network [12]. Moreover, hashing techniques [13], cryptography and one-time-pads [14] can also be applied for monitoring the information security. In a HIS, the healthcare data provided by the users, and the identities of the users must be confirmed before entering into the system.
- *Encryption*: It is a technique to protect the data from unauthorized access by encoding the information such that only authentic users can decode it. It protects the ownership of the data throughout the lifecycle, i.e., from data generation to cloud-based repository to the end users. It helps in avoiding attacks such as packet sniffing, breaching, theft, etc. Before applying any encryption, it must be ensured that it is easily applicable and can be extended when new health records are being added. There are several encryption techniques available today such as RSA, AES, DES, RC4, etc. [15], and the most suitable one should be selected on the basis of system requirements.
- *Data masking*: It is a technique of replacing the information with some value that is not easily identifiable. It is different from encryption, because in encryption the original data are retrieved as they were, but in masking the mask is used instead of the original data so as to maintain the security and confidentiality of the actual information. This approach maintains the anonymity within the HIS [16]. Some of the masking techniques can protect against identity disclosure, while some could protect against both identity as well as attribute disclosure. Some masking techniques also work by adding noise to maintain anonymity. The masking does not require any other security mechanism to be applied during the transmission as the data are masked already, hence, reducing the overall cost of the system.
- *Access control*: In order to maintain the security of the system, access control mechanisms are applied after the user authentication. The access control policies give privileges to the users based on their rights. It is a mechanism for granting permissions to the users and assuring that a user can only perform activities they have been granted permission for. There are several models for access control; the most widespread for healthcare

data are attribute-based access control (ABAC) and role-based access control (RBAC) [17, 18].
- *Monitoring and auditing*: Monitoring of the system is examining the network to catch intrusions, while auditing is maintaining the chronological record of all the activities performed on the data. These approaches are optional for ensuring the healthcare data system security [19]. Monitoring the entire network and traffic is a complicated process and suggests the implementation of a distributed network.

7.2.3 Healthcare Data Privacy Practices

The privacy of the patient is becoming a concern for healthcare organizations because of the increasing threats and attacks. The HIS should have the capability to verify the users and follow the privacy agreements to ensure the regulations are being maintained. The following are some of the traditional techniques that can be implemented to confirm the patient's privacy:

- *De-identification*: It is a technique of maintaining data confidentiality by not including any information in the content that might reveal any information about the identity of the patient. This could be done in two ways: Either by removing specific identifiers or statistically by the patients after verifying themselves. One such technique is called k-anonymity, in which the k number of identifiers that might help in revealing the patient's identity is removed. But in this scenario, it becomes difficult to retract the original details and might cause data loss. Furthermore, if too many identifiers are removed for data safeguarding, it might lead to information forfeiture and would generate erroneous results.
- *Hybrid execution (HybrEx)*: This model was proposed for handling the privacy and confidentiality of data in cloud environments [20]. In such a framework, the data are deployed on the public cloud if identified as non-sensitive and over a private cloud if classified as sensitive. Furthermore, if at any instance the data are required from both types of clouds, the framework splits itself and run in both environments, hence maintaining the privacy of the stored data by prioritizing the sensitivity of the data over the functionality of the model.
- *Identity-based anonymization*: It is a sanitization technique for filtering the information to protect the data privacy. In this, the identifiers are either removed or encrypted to make the data anonymous. The changes made are irreversible so that the subject of the data cannot be identified directly/indirectly or with the help of any third party. In healthcare data, it means any information like name, address or contact number must be deleted to keep the identity of the patients secured. It is a complex process as it combines data anonymization, for protecting the unintentional disclosure of the data, with data analysis. The identity-based anonymization also helps in detecting the vulnerabilities of the system.

TABLE 7.1
Data Protection Laws in Some Countries

Country Name	Law
India	IT Act and IT (Amendment) Act
United States of America	HIPAA Act
	HITECH Act
	Patient Safety and Quality Improvement Act (PSQIA)
European Union	Data Protection Directive
Canada	Personal Information Protection and Electronic Documents Act
United Kingdom	Data Protection Act (DPA)
Russia	Russian Federal Law on Personal Data
Brazil	Constitution

Besides, in order to effectively safeguard sensitive patient data, different countries have designed laws; a few of them are listed in Table 7.1.

7.3 BLOCKCHAIN AND HEALTHCARE

Blockchain technology is an emerging field of IT that has revolutionized several industries including banking, education, IOT, governance, etc., and is now making its way into the healthcare industry as well [21]. It is transforming the way the health records are being kept and businesses being planned. Blockchain technology provides a distributed and decentralized healthcare ecosystem to assist patients as well as providers. It delivers services for managing health records, health insurance management and medicinal research for social benefits. The blockchain distributed network keeps the data available in real time in encrypted form on a ledger that is decentralized. The basic properties of the blockchain technology that make it best suitable for healthcare domain are given below, and Table 7.2 discusses the application areas of blockchain within the healthcare industry with respect to these properties.

- *Decentralized data management*: The data in a blockchain network are dispersed throughout the network; hence no central authority is responsible for managing them or has any superiority over others.
- *Data security and privacy*: The data within the blockchain are encrypted first, before making their way into the network, therefore maintaining the data privacy. Furthermore, the data are distributed; therefore, they are very difficult to breach or hack.
- *Data provenance*: The data in the blockchain are tracked throughout. From its origin to any modifications, every activity is recorded.
- *Data availability*: Every node of the network holds a copy of the data, thus, making it available to everyone at every time.

TABLE 7.2
Use Cases of Blockchain Technology in Various Healthcare Application Domains

Blockchain Property	EHRs Management	Healthcare Insurance Management	Medical Research
Decentralized data management	Patient-centric model for data management [22].	No fraudulent claims. No intermediaries [23].	More control over data during transmission and analysis [24].
Data security and privacy	The EHRs are encrypted and only authorized users have the key to decrypt [22].	The confidential details are kept protected [25].	Data sharing while preserving the security and confidentiality [26].
Data provenance	Digital signatures are applied to the EHRs to ensure legitimacy [27].	Insurance is processed only after verification [28].	The provenance provides a base for enhanced and authentic research.
Data availability and system robustness	Distributed network makes the data available to everyone, and difficult to breach or attack [22].	The accessibility of data is ensured anytime, anywhere [25].	The availability of the real-time data that improves the social and medicinal research and also helps in handling medical or natural emergencies [26].
Immutable auditing	A track of all the transactions is kept, and the data on the blockchain cannot be transformed or modified by anyone [29].	Fraud can be detected easily because of the auditing [25].	The data blocks in the blockchain keep a record and are time-stamped, therefore can be easily trailed [30].

- *Immutability*: The data in blockchain network can never be altered by anyone. If any modifications are to be made in the data, a new block is generated instead.

7.3.1 Basic Concepts of Blockchain Technology

Blockchain is a distributed decentralized network that was first introduced as a basic supporting technology for the cryptocurrency named Bitcoin. Blockchain is still in its development phase and is being adopted by almost every industry today. Basically, blockchain is a decentralized network that stores the data in a distributed manner and maintains a log of transactions along with the timestamp and assures that the data are tamperproof. Blockchain is a carrier that stores the information in the form of blocks, and these blocks are connected to one another forming a chain. A block consists of a block header and block body. The headers of the blocks are the most important ones, as they keep the details such as version, header of previous block, timestamp, complexity, Merkle root, etc., along with meta-information such as the structure and usage of the block. The version number of the block defines the validation rules of the set of blocks and the complexity of the block. The Merkle root is created for every transaction and assures the immutability of the transactions. The transactions are signed digitally in order to get the hash value. In a Merkle tree, the root values of the hashes are kept in the blockhead. A block consists of a hash value of its own as well as the hash of the previous block that helps in connecting the blocks in order to form a chain.

The size of a blockchain is fixed, as the number total number of blocks in the blockchain is limited. The first block of the blockchain is called the header block. When a block is generated, the information is first stored in local memory in the body of the block. A Merkle tree is created next within the body of the block that contains the information of the transactions. The root value of the Merkle tree is stored in the root, which is located in the header block. Every block has its own hash value. A cryptographic algorithm is applied to the header of the previous block to get the hash value. This is how each block is connected to the previous one. After getting the hash value, the time is saved in the timestamp field. This is how a blockchain is created. The structure of a block within the blockchain is depicted in Figure 7.5.

- **The blockchain infrastructure**: Six layers, namely the application layer, contract layer, incentive layer, consensus layer, network layer and data layer, support the blockchain infrastructure as shown in Figure 7.5. Each of the layers has its own purpose in the overall functioning of the network. The bottommost layer is the data layer, that encapsulates the data from the hardware. The technologies in this layer are timestamping, cryptography, etc. This layer deals with the storage and security of the data and ensures the accomplishment of the transactions. The next layer is the network layer that

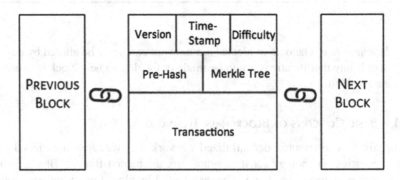

FIGURE 7.5 A block within the blockchain.

deals with the interactions among the nodes within the network in peer-to-peer communication, but in a decentralized manner. The consensus layer is the third layer that consists of consensus algorithms. This is the most important layer within the framework, because in a decentralized network like blockchain, the nodes are not trustworthy, and the consensus assures the accuracy of the data. The next layer is the incentive layer that maintains the verification of the entire network by keeping balance among the nodes. It also assures that the accounts are neither destroyed nor tampered with, in order to uphold uninterrupted operation. The smart contract layer is the fifth layer in the blockchain infrastructure that ensures the execution of the transactions without any third-party intervention. The sixth and last layer is the application layer, which supports the tools and technologies required for the implementation of applications. This layer is being adopted by several industries nowadays to build their business applications.

- **Transactions in blockchain**: There are several types of blockchain frameworks available today, which work differently for distinct applications. Irrespective of the type of system, the working and workflow of the blockchain remain the same. A transaction is the transmission of data from one node to another within the blockchain network. The transaction is a multi-step process as depicted in Figure 7.6 and the necessary steps are as follows:

  Step 1: User A requests a transaction. The private key of the previous transaction along with the digital signature is used while asking for the transaction.

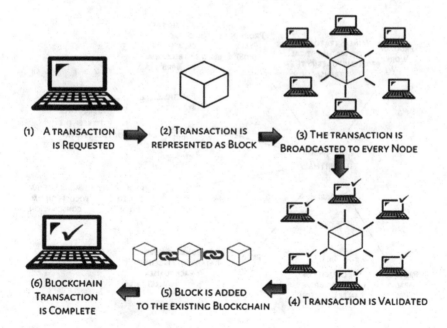

FIGURE 7.6 Typical blockchain transaction.

Step 2: The transaction is represented in the form of a block.
Step 3: This block of the data is represented to each of the nodes within the network.
Step 4: The nodes validate the transaction by solving some complicated mathematical problems.
Step 5: When the problem is solved, the node displays all the time-stamped transactions of the block to the network. Then the block is checked with respect to the timestamp by all the nodes.
Step 6: This is the final step when the transaction is completed after verification. And the non-verified blocks are invalidated.

- **Consensus algorithms in blockchain**: The consensus algorithms are processes that help in decision-making for a group of nodes, in which the individual nodes help in making decision for the betterment of the entire network. The algorithm works on trust, where the nodes would make the decisions for the benefit of the group irrespective of their personal profits. The decisions are made on the basis of voting. Fundamentally, the consensus algorithms not only make the decisions on the basis of majority voting, but also agree for the overall welfare of the network. This ensures equality within the online networking. There are several consensus algorithms available today; some of the most widely accepted ones are depicted in Figure 7.7 followed by their brief introduction. Nevertheless, all these algorithms share common objectives, for example:

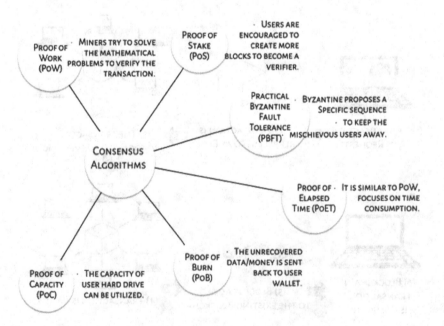

FIGURE 7.7 Blockchain consensus algorithms.

Seeking agreement: A consensus algorithm must gather as much agreement as possible from the nodes of the group.

Collaboration: The group must work in collaboration with each other to work towards the benefit of the group.

Cooperativeness: The members of the group always put the group first, irrespective their own benefits.

Equal weightage: The group working towards the consensus must assure that every member is equally important, i.e., the value of each and every vote is equivalent.

Inclusiveness: All the member nodes in the network are equally involved in the voting; there is no single authoritative or responsible node.

Participation: In order to successfully achieve the consensus mechanism, all the nodes are supposed to participate.

Proof of work (PoW): It is the first ever proposed consensus algorithm and the most widely used in the blockchain technology. This algorithm works on the idea of solving a mathematical problem. This requires a lot of computations, and the node that solves the problem first gets to the mining of the next block. The mathematical problem could be hashing, integer factorization, tour puzzles, etc. It is effective in handling DDoS attacks. However, using this algorithm leads to the network being computationally complex and growing a lot, leading to the sensitivity of the system.

Proof of stake (PoS): This is the consensus algorithm that overcomes the drawbacks faced with the PoW. However, there is a twist in this algorithm. The blocks are validated before getting added into the blockchain. The individuals who have more coins at stake can be considered as miners and can join the mining. Therefore, if an individual wants to be a miner, he/she would need to have more coins; then only would that person be selected to be a part of the network. Furthermore, after becoming a node of the network, a certain amount of coins is deposited to be qualified as a miner. The processing of this algorithm is quite easy; the number of blocks being generated is equal to the number of coins one possesses, i.e., the more coins a node owns, the more blocks it can mine. Moreover, rewards are given in return for generating these blocks.

Practical Byzantine fault tolerance (PBFT): It is an approach to attain consensus even when some of the nodes are not working properly or not working at all. The main focus here is to protect the system against failures. It makes the decisions collectively including both correct and faulty nodes, hence reducing the error impact on the system. It assumes that there might be a few faulty nodes in the network. The nodes are organized in a particular order, and one of the nodes is selected as the primary node while others are kept as backup. All the nodes work together in sync and communicate with each other to verify all the information available on the network in order to get rid of false information.

Proof of elapsed time (PoET): This algorithm is one of the best among all the consensus algorithms. It works on a permissioned blockchain, in which permissions are required to access the network along with voting and mining rights. In order to assure the smooth running of the network, a secure login for the miners into the system is required using identity validation. It provides a fair chance to every node and follows this sequence: Each of the nodes is supposed to wait for a random amount of time and the one who has had its time share would be allowed to create a new block. PoET relies on the CPU named Intel Software Guard Extension that runs random pieces of codes on the network and makes sure the processing is fair.

Proof of burn (PoB): This consensus algorithm is quite remarkable. In this, for keeping the system safe and secure, some of the coins are burnt, i.e., sent to addresses from where they can never be retrieved. Such addresses are called "Eater Addresses," and the coins burnt can never be used for any purpose; a ledger assures this. However, burning causes loss temporarily but provides trust and commitment in return, which is beneficial in the long run. The miners could burn their native currencies or currencies from other chains depending upon the implementation. It is quite similar to PoW, but the difference is, the power to mine goes to the nodes that have burnt the most coins.

Proof of capacity (PoC): The PoC is an upgraded version of PoW, in which instead of investing in hardware or burning coins, the miners are supposed to spend on their own hardware, because the selection of the miners in this algorithm is totally dependent on the space on the hard drive available. The larger the sizes of hard drive the more space available to store the solution values. It has more computational capacity, and hence, can create blocks in less time as compared to PoW. It is a two-step process, plotting and mining. In plotting, a list of possible nonce values is generated using hashing, while in mining, a scoop number is calculated by the user, and has to go to that scoop number of first nonce and calculate the deadline value. This is done repeatedly for each and every nonce on the hard drive and the miner selects the minimum deadline amongst them, where the deadline denotes the elapsed time duration between two blocks.

7.3.2 Blockchain-Based Infrastructure for Health Information Systems

The blockchain technology is defining the healthcare industry in terms of modelling data and deploying governance. This is because of the capabilities and flexibility provided by this technology in sharing medical data. The blockchain technology has become a centre for the developments in multiple application domains within the healthcare industry. The infrastructure can be divided into four layers as shown in Figure 7.8. The lowest layer is the layer where the raw data are. This is the place where data from IoT devices, medical labs, social media, etc., are collected. These data are

Privacy-Preserving Infrastructure 125

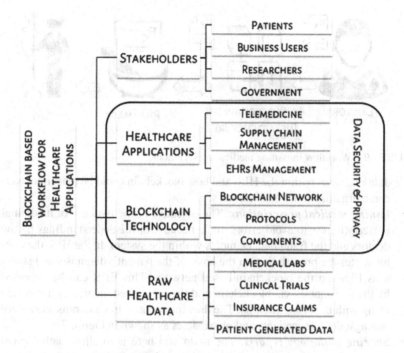

FIGURE 7.8 Workflow of blockchain-based healthcare applications.

heterogeneous and big in nature as the sources are enormous and of various data types. The second layer is the blockchain layer, where the framework for secure healthcare management is created that facilitates the medical data transactions. This layer consists of blockchain-based applications and platforms such as networks, consensus algorithms, peer-to-peer, decentralized, distributed network, etc. The next layer is the application layer, where all these technologies are integrated into a single application. These applications can be categorized as data management, data sharing, R&D, EHRs, handling pharmaceutical supply chains, IoT-enabled telemedicine, etc. The topmost layer of the framework is the stakeholder layer, where the users that are getting benefits from the applications are placed such as businesspersons, patients, researchers, etc. The main interests of this layer are sharing, processing and managing the data effectively without compromising the security and privacy of the data.

- **Data sharing in blockchain-based HIS**: The different application areas within the healthcare domain require different workflows in order to complete specific tasks. The tasks could be as simple as issuing medical prescriptions to as complex as treating the patients with surgery or complicated procedures. All these tasks require the exchange of information, making the chances of breaches very high. Since the healthcare data are very sensitive, blockchain would assure the privacy and security of the data because of its fundamental features. The following are the different scenarios of

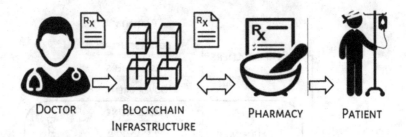

FIGURE 7.9 Workflow in issuing medical prescriptions.

data exchange within the HIS, and how blockchain could be placed to overcome organizational inefficiencies.
- *Issuing medical prescriptions*: The objective of the issuance of medicinal prescriptions is to avoid errors made because of misunderstandings by the doctors and the fraudulent elements within the system. In the HIS, the doctor writes the prescription on the basis of the patient's diagnosis and stores it as EHR on the blockchain-based network. This EHR can be accessed by the pharmacies via blockchain and the prescribed medicines are issued along with the dosage details. The data interactions in such transactions are amongst doctors, patients and pharmacies as shown in Figure 7.9.
- *Sharing pathology reports*: The main aim here is to allow pathological labs, doctors and other stakeholders to share information about the patient's medical lab results as shown in Figure 7.10. When the reports of the patient's tests are available, they are notified, and the records are saved on the blockchain-based network so that appropriate treatment can be provided. Having the lab records on the blockchain eliminates the need to carry them everywhere as these documents can be accessed anytime anywhere; this also reduces the cost of printing, faxing and management.

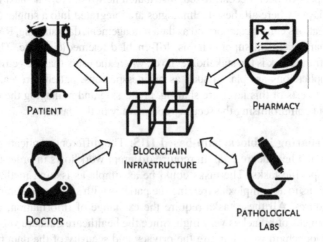

FIGURE 7.10 Workflow in sharing pathological reports.

Privacy-Preserving Infrastructure

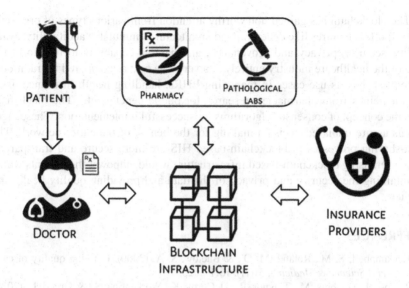

FIGURE 7.11 Workflow in reimbursement of healthcare services.

- *Reimbursement of healthcare services*: The focus here is to accelerate the process of reimbursement and to catch fraudulent claims. Using the blockchain-based network would reduce the probability of errors and misinterpretations. The insurance providers transfer their insurance policies and guidelines over the blockchain network, and other users such as healthcare providers, pharmacies and laboratories work for the verification of the claims made by the patient as can be seen in Figure 7.11. Digital verification using blockchain would save time, manual efforts and costs for the customer, while doctors would start treatment without waiting for confirmation, as everything is transparent. It enables the patients and doctors to customize the treatment and insurance respectively.

7.4 DISCUSSION

Data are the most important asset to the healthcare industry; and the HIS are designed to manage these data efficiently. This provides several benefits like cost and time saving, organized treatment, patient satisfaction, proper circumvention of medicines, etc. There could be several types of HIS depending upon the user requirement. The main focus in implementing the HIS is the security and privacy of the data that must be ensured during the life cycle of the data using various scientific practices. The healthcare data available today are in various formats coming from diverse sources like laboratories, healthcare providers, insurance and pharmaceutical companies, etc. Moreover, there is no standardized way of keeping the records, which might lead to infringement and chaos in the system. Furthermore, the unavailability of safe and secure infrastructure has also obstructed development in research and development processes.

The blockchain has gained noteworthy attention from various types of organizations. It offers features like decentralized architecture, immutable auditability, availability, security, privacy and provenance, and has the capability to transform the face of the healthcare industry entirely at a very low cost as compared to traditional systems. It has its use cases in managing EHRs, handling health insurance, issuing medicines from pharmacies, research for public benefits, etc. The blockchain uses the concept of consensus algorithms for successful implementation. These algorithms assure unbiased decision making for the benefit of the entire network. The data-sharing processes in blockchain-based HIS are more secure and transparent. Moreover, using blockchain-based infrastructure would empower the patients whilst maintaining the security and privacy of the data and providing quality healthcare services.

REFERENCES

1. Campbell, S. M., Roland, M. O., & Buetow, S. A. (2000). Defining quality of care. *Social Science & Medicine*, 51(11), 1611–1625.
2. Yost, J., Dobbins, M., Traynor, R., DeCorby, K., Workentine, S., & Greco, L. (2014). Tools to support evidence-informed public health decision making. *BMC Public Health*, 14(1), 728.
3. Heeks, R. (2006). Health information systems: Failure, success and improvisation. *International Journal of Medical Informatics*, 75(2), 125–137.
4. Tsiknaki, M., Katehakis, D. G., Sfakianakis, S., Kavlentakis, G., & Orphanoudakis, S. C. (2005). An architecture for regional health information networks addressing issues of modularity and interoperability. *Journal of Telecommunications and Information Technology*, 4, 26–39.
5. Collen, M. F. (1999). The evolution of computer communications. *MD Computing: Computers in Medical Practice*, 16(4), 72–72.
6. Houlding, D., & MSc, C. I. S. S. P. (2011). Health information at risk: Successful strategies for healthcare security and privacy. *Healthcare IT Program of Ce Intel Corporation*, White Paper.
7. Applebaum, P. S. (2002). Privacy in psychiatric treatment: Threats and response. *American Journal of Psychiatry*, 159(11), 1809–1818.
8. Idrees, S. M., Alam, M. A., Agarwal, P., & Ansari, L. (2019). Effective predictive analytics and modeling based on historical data. In International Conference on Advances in Computing and Data Sciences (pp. 552–564). Singapore: Springer.
9. Hodge Jr, J. G. (2003). Health information privacy and public health. *The Journal of Law, Medicine & Ethics*, 31(4), 663–671.
10. Zhang, R., & Liu, L. (2010). Security models and requirements for healthcare application clouds. In IEEE 3rd International Conference on cloud Computing (pp. 268–275). IEEE.
11. Shafer, J., Rixner, S., & Cox, A. L. (2010). The hadoop distributed filesystem: Balancing portability and performance. In IEEE International Symposium on Performance Analysis of Systems & Software (ISPASS) (pp. 122–133). IEEE.
12. Yang, C., Lin, W., & Liu, M. (2013). A novel triple encryption scheme for hadoop-based cloud data security. In 4th International Conference on Emerging Intelligent Data and Web Technologies (pp. 437–442). IEEE.
13. Somu, N., Gangaa, A., & Sriram, V. S. (2014). Authentication service in hadoop using one-time pad. *Indian Journal of Science and Technology*, 7(4), 56–62.

14. Fluhrer, S., Mantin, I., & Shamir, A. (2001). Weaknesses in the key scheduling algorithm of RC4. In International Workshop on Selected Areas in Cryptography (pp. 1–24).Berlin, Heidelberg: Springer.
15. Sweeney, L. (2002). Achieving k-anonymity privacy protection using generalization and suppression. *International Journal of Uncertainty, Fuzziness and Knowledge-Based Systems*, 10(05), 571–588.
16. Mourya, A. K., & Idrees, S. M. (2020). Cloud computing-based approach for accessing electronic health record for healthcare sector. In *Microservices in Big Data Analytics* (pp. 179–188).Singapore: Springer.
17. Crosby, M., Pattanayak, P., Verma, S., & Kalyanaraman, V. (2016). Blockchain technology: Beyond bitcoin. *Applied Innovation*, 2(6–10), 71.
18. van der Linden, H., Kalra, D., Hasman, A., & Talmon, J. (2009). Inter-organizational future proof EHR systems: A review of the security and privacy related issues. *International Journal of Medical Informatics*, 78(3), 141–160.
19. Jain, P., Gyanchandani, M., & Khare, N. (2016). Big data privacy: A technological perspective and review. *Journal of Big Data*, 3(1), 25.
20. Linn, L. A., & Koo, M. B. (2016). Blockchain for health data and its potential use in health it and health care related research. In ONC/NIST Use of Blockchain for Healthcare and Research Workshop (pp. 1–10). Gaithersburg, MD, USA: ONC/NIST.
21. Ivan, D. (2016). Moving toward a blockchain-based method for the secure storage of patient records. In ONC/NIST Use of Blockchain for Healthcare and Research Workshop (pp. 1–11). Gaithersburg, MD, USA: ONC/NIST.
22. Culver, K. (2016). Blockchain technologies: A whitepaper discussing how the claims process can be improved. In ONC/NIST Use of Blockchain for Healthcare and Research Workshop. Gaithersburg, MD, USA: ONC/NIST.
23. Kuo, T. T., Kim, H. E., & Ohno-Machado, L. (2017). Blockchain distributed ledger technologies for biomedical and health care applications. *Journal of the American Medical Informatics Association*, 24(6), 1211–1220.
24. Attili, S., Ladwa, S. K., Sharma, U., & Trenkle, A. F. (2016). Blockchain: The chain of trust and its potential to transform healthcare–our point of view. In ONC/NIST Use of Blockchain for Healthcare and Research Workshop. Gaithersburg, MD, USA: ONC/NIST.
25. Blough, D., Ahamad, M., Liu, L., & Chopra, P. (2008). MedVault: Ensuring security and privacy for electronic medical records. In NSF CyberTrust Principal Investigators Meeting. Online at http://www.cs. yale. edu/cybertrust08/posters/posters/158 medvault poster CT08. pdf.
26. Vian, K., Voto, A., & Haynes-Sanstead, K. (2016). A blockchain Profile for Medicaid Applicants and Recipients. ONC/NIST Use of Blockchain for Healthcare and Research Workshop. Gaithersburg, MD:ONC/NIST.
27. Azaria, A., Ekblaw, A., Vieira, T., & Lippman, A. (2016). Medrec: Using blockchain for medical data access and permission management. In 2nd International Conference on Open and Big Data (OBD) (pp. 25–30). IEEE.
28. Yue, X., Wang, H., Jin, D., Li, M., & Jiang, W. (2016). Healthcare data gateways found healthcare intelligence on blockchain with novel privacy risk control. *Journal of medical systems*, 40(10), 218.
29. Mettler, M. (2016, September). Blockchain technology in healthcare: The revolution starts here. In IEEE 18th International Conference on e-Health Networking, Applications and Services (Healthcom) (pp. 1–3). IEEE.
30. Nakamoto, S., & Bitcoin, A. (2008). A peer-to-peer electronic cash system. *Bitcoin*. https://bitcoin.org/bitcoin. pdf.

8 Health Sector at the Crossroads
Divergence vis-à-vis Convergence in the Emergence of New Trends

Arindam Chakrabarty, Uday Sankar Das and Saket Kushwaha

CONTENTS

8.1 Introduction	131
8.1.1 Health Scenario of the World	133
8.1.2 Health Scenario of India	135
8.1.3 Synergy of Treatment in India	137
8.1.4 Advancement of Medical Treatment and Research	137
8.1.4.1 Advancement of Medical Treatment and Research in India	137
8.1.5 Medical Data Regulatory Scene in India	146
8.2 Literature Review	147
8.2.1 Healthcare at the Crossroads	147
8.2.2 Healthcare Strategies in India	149
8.2.3 Health Informatics and Healthcare Data Management	150
8.2.4 Healthcare Data Management and Privacy	151
8.3 Objectives	152
8.4 Research Methodology	152
8.5 Analysis I	152
8.6 Analysis II	152
8.7 Conclusion	157
References	158

8.1 INTRODUCTION

The progression of human society depends on the extent to which it can withstand and adapt to the changing environment and finally develop to achieve a superior quality of life. In the present era, the banyan of knowledge is the backbone of our development story. The knowledge essentially includes the traditional and indigenous as well as high-end technology-led cognitive development processes. But it is still a great irony of mankind that a large section of the population still lacks the basic facilities or resources particularly in the arena of education and health systems, most predominantly in the developing economies of the world. Moreover, it is quite common that a significant proportion of the population still cannot afford to avail these services. The health sector is no longer a single discipline, rather it has linkages with other facets of life and essentially conjugates with a wide range of disciplines. With the advent of the advancement of technology and the introduction of multi-varied domains, the ambit of the health sector has become more diversified and interdisciplinary, which has made the sector more versatile and expanding in nature. Now, high-end electronic circuits, robust computer networks and mental health, etc., are an integral part of a comprehensive healthcare system. The sector has been incorporating various innovations from other core areas of knowledge into the field of medical treatment as a means of concentric applied research. For instance, the IoT has been introduced for the treatment of patients suffering from diabetics, blood pressure, hypertension, etc. The technological revolution has made the medical profession smarter and elevated to a new-generation support system. This divergence mode has made the medical profession stronger and dynamic in nature. The modern technological devices are being used to deal with critical surgical operations. Now, health practitioners are even using controlled as well as self-guided health devices for superior and high-precision operations. This divergent excellence has become the mirror image of the modern healthcare system. The computer-aided medical investigations are the testimony of clinical services. Moreover, it is spectacular and splendid to mention that households are using small health devices for regular domestic uses, like sphygmomanometers, blood glucose monitors and continuous glucose monitors, etc. This has prevented sudden cardiac arrest and other diseases since users can monitor their health indicators domestically regularly, particularly after reaching a certain age. The modern IoT compounded with high configuration sensors can predict a special type of weather change or high concentration of microorganisms that can generate a set of diseases inclusive of both communicable and non-communicable types. Using big data analytics in medical fields, we can do some predictive analytics and can take appropriate preventive measures, so that the loss of life or intensity of medical ailments can be minimized to a large extent.

Big data analytics can enable the "medical care professional" as well as individuals to make up-to-date decisions about their health and form a perspective about future needs and care to be taken. Trends in technological advancements like cyber-physics, blockchain, IoT, cloud computing, service-oriented architecture and business process management, along with industrial integration and interoperability have powered Fourth Industrial Revolution (4IR) to enable possibilities of new comfort and convenience in human life. These advancements of "on-the-go" mobile connectivity have enabled the formulation of new healthcare systems commonly referred to as health telematics and "mobile health." This form of "health telematics" is a new armamentarium for the health industry delivered through ICT-enabled services and helps empower, educate and enforce community health practice and information throughout the targeted population. "Mobile health" is delivered through mobile-enabled services which have helped to bring down the cost of healthcare and overcome the hurdles posed by political boundaries and geographical limitations and reduce the time and distance for the delivery of medical advice to the differently abled, chronically ill and elderly. The cost of medicines and healthcare facilities is increasing day by day with age demographics become more diverse with population growth across the globe. The use of technology along with analytics can help cope with, prevent and cure ailments for the masses in general while ubiquitous computing can make sure that basic medical help is readily available and circumvent otherwise expensive medical care. The rising trends in the use of virtual assistants (like Amazon Alexa, Google Assistant, etc.) along with "human-aware robots" can not only assist but also help the old and elderly feel less lonely and hence help them cope with psychological trauma and loneliness.

Technology, robotics and personal wearable devices can reform the way healthcare is perceived. Wearable technology can track minute-by-minute details of the person and formulate personal data points that can prove crucial to understanding and diagnosing any medical ailments of a person/patient. With the rise of deforestation, new diseases and infections are gaining a foothold in both the third world and developed countries. Examples of diseases like "Ebola," "bird flu," "swine flu" and "coronavirus" could become a pandemic that might bring human civilization to the verge of extinction. Antibiotics have been the boon of the last century; however misuse and overuse have resulted in genetic mutations of bacterial forms that become resistant to the presently prevalent antibiotics. These superbugs are capable of resisting all forms of current medicine. The use of technology to administer, monitor and track health prognosis can help reduce the risk of creating genetically mutated bugs that are drug-resistant. With the rise of technology and higher order of data analytics, it is evident that the increasing complexity of diseases due to the mutational syndrome of microorganisms might be addressed to a large extent. However, the process of collecting, collating and preserving big data is indeed one of the major challenges for achieving health reforms. The dataset should be continuous, comprising various dimensions related to the healthcare system and services, not a discreet or cross-sectional overview.

8.1.1 Health Scenario of the World

Healthy life in modern times is a boon of the medical advancements achieved over the past century paired with the synergy of modern and traditional health practices. Gradually these factors have enhanced the longevity of human life overall.

The Human Development Report of 2019 lists the developed European countries of Norway, Switzerland and Ireland with the highest "life expectancy at birth," i.e. approximately 82 to 83 years. Only Singapore and Hong Kong, China (SAR), make it to the top ten positions from the Asian continent, while India secures the 129th rank with 69 years of average "life expectancy at birth." The report also points out that life expectancy at birth with basic capabilities in low-income groups is 59 years, followed by 66 years in medium-income groups, 72 years in high-income groups and 78 years in very high-income groups. Whereas "life expectancy at age 70" for the low-income group is 9.8 years, for the medium-income group it is 11.2 years, the high-income group 12.6 years and 14.6 years for the very high-income group [1].

Health and happiness are synonymous with each other; countries and regions that performed well in the Human Development Index also have similar results in the World Happiness Ranking. Norway, Switzerland and Ireland, the top 3 performers in Human Development Index 2019, secure the 5th, 3rd and 16th positions. Again the top two performers of the World Happiness Ranking 2020, Finland and Denmark, were ranked 11th and 12th in the Human Development Index 2019 [2].

Disability is part and parcel of the human condition; it is estimated that around 15% of the world population was disabled in congruence with 2010 population estimates. Around 2.2% have significant difficulties in functioning, while 3.8% had extreme difficulty in functioning which is termed as "severe disability." The percentage of disabled children or severely disabled children is estimated to be around 0.7% or around 13 million. The stigmas attached with a disability also mean that people with a disability end up having poor health outcomes. Most existing healthcare systems are not designed keeping in mind the accessibility issues faced by people with disability and need to be redesigned to fix these accessibility issues. Inclusive insurance co-payments will help in reducing out-of-pocket payments. Providing an alternate income source to disabled people helps them to meet health expenses and improve their health condition and chances of survival [3].

One of the most effective ways of evading death due to disease is immunization, and it is with this aim that the Global Immunization Vision and Strategy was launched in the year 2005 as a strategic framework.

An estimate suggests that 2.5 million deaths are averted each year with the help of vaccination. However only 25 licensed vaccines are available, for the diseases anthrax, measles, rubella, cholera, meningococcal diseases, influenza, diphtheria, mumps, tetanus, hepatitis A, hepatitis B, hepatitis E, pertussis, tuberculosis, pneumococcal diseases, typhoid, fever, poliomyelitis, tick-borne encephalitis, haemophilia influenza type b, rabies, varicella and herpes, human papillomavirus (HPV), rotavirus gastroenteritis, yellow fever and Japanese encephalitis virus (JEV). The availability of vaccines has helped reduce death among children under five years from 9.6 million in the year 2000 to 7.6 million in the year 2010 over a decade with the ever-increasing number of childbirths. Besides a persistent gap existing within countries and also between countries, the average coverage for diphtheria-tetanus-pertussis-measles vaccines has improved. The Global Immunization Vision and Strategy targeted 80 to 90% countrywide vaccination coverage at the district and national levels respectively. A total cost of US$50,000 to US$60,000 million is expected to boost immunization efforts over a decade up till 2020 [4].

Word Health Organization estimates the global average number of maternal deaths to be around 295,000 with a lifetime risk of maternal death of 1 in every 190 cases. However, there also has been a decrease in the overall maternal mortality ratio between 2000 and 2017 which stands at 38.4%, and the annual average rate of reduction in the maternal mortality ratio was 2.9% for the same period [5]. Early childhood development has long-term consequences on human life; similarly, health and learning are interrelated for holistic development but are separately planned despite evidence that points out that the foundation of a healthy life-long journey is development in early childhood [6]. Global estimates suggest that around 1.7 million children are living with HIV, with around 5,000 new infections contracted per day by both adults and children. A staggering total of 37.9 million people are living with HIV infection, out of which 36.2 million are adults. The total number of deaths due to HIV stood at 770,000 out of which 100,000 were children in the year 2018. It was also pointed out that there has been an overall 33% reduction in AIDS-related mortality since 2010 [7]. One of the most important mechanisms to curb new HIV infections is a health information system; 62% of countries had some sort of functional health information system in the year 2017, and 90% of countries reported their HIV data through the Global AIDS Monitoring system in 2018. Interestingly 51% of HIV-infected people find out their infection status only when they acquire TB [8].

The environment has a direct impact on human health. Air pollution causes oxidative stress along with inflation in cells, laying the foundation for chronic and long-term cancerous diseases. Chronic obstructive pulmonary disease (COPD) is a common impact of excessive air pollution. Air pollution also affects the health of pregnant women with serious changes in blood pressure impacting fetal heath. Exposure to benzene, a chemical component of gasoline, is associated with causing leukaemia. Apart from regular cardiovascular diseases like asthma, air pollution has been linked to attention-deficit and hyperactivity disorder (ADHD) in children and urban youth populations [9]. The World Health Organization estimates suggest 4.2 million premature deaths across the globe as the result of air pollution. Air pollution results in 29% of lung cancer cases, 17% of acute lower respiratory infections, 24% of strokes, 25% of ischemic heart disease cases and 43% of chronic obstructive pulmonary disease in the global population [10]. Cadmium, mercury and arsenic are the known heavy metals that have been associated with health-related issues in human beings. Cadmium, which is a core component of rechargeable nickel–cadmium batteries, rarely gets recycled and has significant effects on bone and causes fractures. Fish-consuming populations are susceptible to contamination of methyl mercury that results in blood-related issues and causes neurological damage. Prolonged exposure to arsenic in drinking water causes skin cancer and other forms of cancer [11].

Heavy metal pollution has also seeped into food crops produced across the globe with varying degrees of concentration in developing and developed parts of the world. The primary sources of soil contamination are the results of industrial effluents, sewage sludge and fertilizers. Multi-metal toxicity in food crops needs to be checked through environmentally friendly methods; also, studies need to be conducted to investigate the long-term health consequences [12]. Evidence backed by scientific facts suggests that work-related stress can have significant health consequences [13].

8.1.2 Health Scenario of India

Post-independent India was guided by the visionary leadership of the then-prime minister Jawaharlal Nehru who left it to the best of Indian minds to decide the fate of the nation. The outcome of this was the *"Nehru-Mahalanobis strategy"* and the setting up of a planning commission to track the progress of the economy along with a focused approach on the quality of food, nutrition, shelter, education and health [14]. Since 1992, numerous rounds of national health surveys have been conducted in India. Till now four rounds of the National Family Health Survey (NFHS) and District Level Household Survey (DLHS) have conducted and three rounds of the Annual Health Survey (AHS). Some of the shortcomings of these surveys are they are overlapping in nature and are inconsistent [15]. The 71st round of the NSS is the latest national comprehensive health survey, conducted in the year 2014. The focus of this survey was to track the social consumption relating to health. The survey highlighted that 9% and 12% of the rural and urban population needed some sort of hospitalization every 15 days. Around 90% of the population preferred allopathic treatments. The amounts spent for non-hospitalized treatment accounted for Rs. 639 for the urban population and Rs. 509 for the rural population. In rural households, people primarily depended on income or savings (68%), while in urban areas the number stands at 75% for taking care of health expenses [16]. The National Health Policy 2017 was introduced with the objectives of improving health status through policy actions in all sectors, increasing preventative, promotive, curative, palliative and rehabilitative quality services provided by the public health sector. The policy aims at a professional approach, to reduce inequality by reaching the poorest, the marginal populations of gender, poverty, caste, disability and other forms of social exclusion and geographical barriers. Further, it aims at reducing the cost of healthcare. Other key features are the accountability of finances, the decentralization of services and the option to choose between service providers, and dynamism, constantly adapting to new health scenarios and evidence-based learning [17].

The birth rate in 2017 in India was 20.2 while the death rate was 6.3 and the natural growth rate was 13.9. The projected death rate by 2025 is expected to be 7.2; the projected life expectancy in the same period is 72.3 years. The total fertility rate in India stood at 2.3 in the year 2016. As far as health infrastructure is concerned, the total number of hospitals stood at 25,778 with 713,986 beds. The total numbers of PHCs were 25,743, CHCs 5,624 and sub-centres 158,417.

The total number of railway hospitals stood at 122 with 13,355 beds. The total number of ESI hospitals was 155 with 21,931 beds. A total of 288 allopathic, 85 AYUSH, 19 polyclinics, 73 labs and 21 dental clinics are functional in the country in the CGHS scheme. The total number of blood banks was 3,108, and 469 eye banks were functional in the country [18]. The Indian states of Kerala, Andhra Pradesh, Maharashtra, Gujarat, Punjab, Himachal Pradesh, J&K Karnataka, Tamil Nadu, Telangana, Mizoram and the union territory of Chandigarh, Dadra and Nagar Haveli performed significantly well in the health index, followed by West Bengal, Haryana, Chhattisgarh, Jharkhand, Assam, Manipur, Meghalaya, Goa and the union territories of Lakshadweep, Puducherry and Delhi. The rest of the states under aspirants category include Rajasthan, Uttarakhand, Madhya Pradesh, Odisha, Bihar, Uttar Pradesh, Sikkim, Tripura, Arunachal Pradesh, Nagaland and the union territories of Andaman and Nicobar Island and Daman and Diu [19].

The Ministry of Health and Family Welfare has set a priority on the digitization of heath to ensure service delivery and citizen empowerment. This will help create a National Digital Health Ecosystem (NDHE) to leapfrog the evils of traditional health information systems. A National Digital Health blueprint aims at the creation of the seamless exchange of state-of-the-art digital health systems, to create a single source of truth for all heath purposes, the adoption of open standards, the internationalization of patient recording systems, the promotion of SDGs related to the health sector and the promotion of synergy in the federal and state structure, as well as public-private participation, creating portability, promoting clinical decision systems (CDS), the promotion of health analytics, the promotion of quality and ensuring governmental conformity [20].

India has tried to leverage the medical know-how and cost efficiency to promote medical tourism, and the idea is to promote India as a 365-day holistic tourism destination with heath travel as a component. Governmental support is provided under the Marketing Development Assistance (MDA) scheme for Wellness Tourism Service Providers (WTSPs) and Medical Tourism Service Providers (MTSPs) [21].

Experimental work in the sphere of public health was initiated by the government of Delhi in the form of Aam Aadmi Mohallas Clinics (AAMCs). These are neighbourhood clinics set up in 158 locations; they provide around 199 essential medicines free of cost and 212 diagnostic tests free of cost [22].

8.1.3 Synergy of Treatment in India

India has been the home of several formats of medical treatments apart from allopathic treatments. Ayurvedic, Unani, Siddha, naturopathy and homoeopathic treatments are also utilized for achieving healthcare and cures. There are 137 Ayurvedic colleges with a student admission capacity of 4,188 candidates, 11 Unani colleges with a student admission of 127 candidates, 2 Siddha colleges with a student admission capacity of 94 candidates, 3 naturopathy colleges with a capacity of 47 and 50 homoeopathy colleges with a student admission of 1,080 candidates. [18] The Ministry of AYUSH, Government of India, was created to achieve a synergy in the combination of treatment modes where yoga was also included [23] (Figure 8.1, Table 8.1).

8.1.4 Advancement of Medical Treatment and Research

Medical treatment has seen a drastic change since the inception of the concept of the vaccinations, and since then there has been a steady rise in the technologies and healthcare systems. For an indicative list of the timeline of discovery, see Table 8.2.

8.1.4.1 Advancement of Medical Treatment and Research in India

India has witnessed several significant achievements in the field of medical science, after rigorous research and collaboration between the Indian Institute of Science (IISc) and the National Institute of Mental Health and Neurosciences (NIMHANS) led to the discovery of the STIL gene that causes microcephaly disorder, a genetic

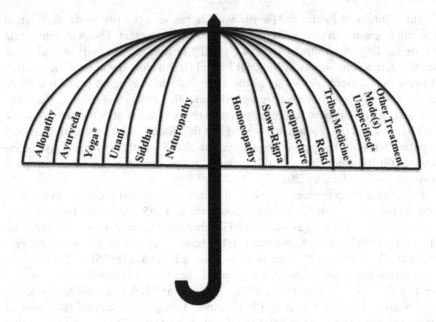

FIGURE 8.1 The nature of treatment protocol/healing practiced in India—umbrella model; adapted and modified from Refs. [23–27].

TABLE 8.1
Various Modes of Treatment in India and Their Governing Bodies

Mode of Treatment Practiced in India	Relevant Controlling/ Monitoring Statuary Council	Apex R&D Monitoring Body	Governing Ministry
Allopathy	Medical Council of India	Indian Council of Medical Research (ICMR)	Ministry of Health and Family Welfare (MoHFW)
Allopathy—dental	Dental Council of India		
Nursing	Indian Nursing Council		
Allopathy—pharma	Pharmacy Council of India		
Ayurveda	Central Council of Indian Medicine		Ministry of AYUSH
Yoga			
Unani			
Siddha			
Naturopathy			
Sowa-Rigpa			
Homoeopathy	Central Council of Homeopathy	Central Council for Research in Homoeopathy	
Acupuncture	Not governed yet		Ministry not assigned
Reiki			
Tribal medicine	Not governed yet		Ministry of Tribal Affairs

condition causing mental retardation. An Indian ophthalmologist achieved a serious feat in the year 2007 by carrying out surgery for a patient suffering from a missing intraocular lens capsule using fibrin glue for the first time. Similarly, surgery was used for the first time to reduce diabetes which makes a significant difference for people suffering from type 2 diabetes. Another important discovery was when the All India Institute of Medical Sciences discovered the link between the HPV virus and cervical cancer and a precise radiation technology was developed to radiate the malignant cells in the uterus and minimize the damage to the healthy cells. St. John's Medical College in Bangalore and the McMaster University of Canada developed a single pill that can cure five different types of heart ailment. As far as medical technology is concerned, there has been a significant advancement.

Portable tuberculosis testing kits by the name of TruNat Rif help detection in a very cost-effective manner. Reversible inhibition of sperm under guidance (RISUG) is a male contraceptive used for solving the problem of accidental conception. Another such development is the personal cooling garment (PCG) by the National Institute of Occupational Health in Ahmedabad that helps reduce the amount of heat for manual labour. The National Institute of Immunohematology developed a nanoparticle-based rapid diagnostic kit, the first of its kind, to identify disease like von Willebrand disease (VWD). The National Institute of Cancer Prevention and Research, Noida, developed the Magnivisualizer, a handheld device that allows the capture of digitized images helpful in the detection of pancreatic cancer [29]. Healthcare services and the delivery landscape have had a steady growth in India despite the lack of an effective public health system as well as the absence of policy focus on public healthcare. The private health sectors have been facing sustainability pressure due to poor financial health. Ayushman Bharat Yojana attempts to provide universal health coverage for people sitting at the bottom of the pyramid. Ayushman Bharat is estimated to reduce revenue by 15–25% on average per occupied bed day. Private hospitals allocate 25% bed capacity for Ayushman Bharat and only 30–35% efficiency and cost-cutting will help maintain the profit margin. The further increase in capacity allocation beyond 25% will reduce the quality of healthcare and subsequently compromise patient safety and care delivery.

Some of the major issues that were seen were related to the billing; for example 66% indicated a mismatch between the estimated and final bill and around 58% were not informed about the additional charges. Despite all of these, the hospital bed occupancy is expected to increase from 70% to 80% by the year 2025 [30].

India spends less than a dollar per person when it comes to public healthcare. This spending, when taking into account the overall spending of the country (1% of GDP), when compared with countries like the USA (17.14% of GDP) and China (5.55% of GDP), seems like an impending disaster waiting for the right circumstances to devastate the already unorganized labour economy, given the size of the population, average education level and geographic spread.

The Indian Council of Medical Research (ICMR) has formulated a five-point agenda or five major pillars to fix the healthcare scenario in India with the following goals: Strengthen research capacity, build data systems to enable research, leverage traditional medicinal knowledge, enable policy translation and strengthen

TABLE 8.2
Indicative List of Discovery and Advancement in Disease Treatment and Cure [28]

Year (Indicative)	Significant Discovery/ Application	Descriptions
1799	Smallpox vaccine	Introduction of smallpox vaccines to the masses in the USA.
1843	Puerperal fever	Cause and prevention identified by Oliver Wendell Holmes.
1846	Anaesthesia	First public demonstration of anaesthesia in surgery by John Collins Warren.
1886	Appendicitis	Reginald Heber Fitz advocates performing appendectomies.
1890–1910	Insect-borne disease mechanism transmission	Theobald Smith identifies the transmission mechanism of insect-borne disease.
1914	Electrocardiograph	Paul Dudley introduces the technology into the USA.
1922	Insulin	Elliott Joslin introduces insulin to the USA.
1923	Heart valve surgery	First successful heart valve surgery is conducted by Eliot Cutler.
1925	Three-flanged nail	Three-flanged nail is devised for bone hip fractures by Marius Smith-Petersen.
1927	Iron lung I Blood test for syphilis	The iron lung is invented by Philip Drinker to help polio-paralysed patients breathe. I Blood test developed by William Hinton to detect syphilis.
1929	Polio patient saved for the first time	First polio patient saved at Boston Children's Hospital using Drinker Respirator (iron lung).
1930–1940	Osteoporosis I rickets I Overactive parathyroid	Fuller Albright identifies disease overactive parathyroid, treatment for rickets and osteoporosis is developed.
1933	Electrolytes and intracellular fluid	James Gamble showed the replacement of intracellular fluid and electrolytes in cases of blood loss.
1938	Corrective heart surgery	First corrective heart surgery is performed by Robert Gross for infants with a congenital heart defect.
1942	Blood banks and emergency response plans I Treatment for burns	New efficiency for treatment in burn cases was first demonstrated at Massachusetts General Hospital. I New blood banks along with emergency plans were formulated.
1945	Pap smear	Detection of cervical cancer was perfected by the use of Pap smear.
1946	Rh disease	First identification of Rh disease at Boston Children's hospital by Louis Diamond.
1947	Artificial kidney I Remission of acute leukaemia for children	Artificial kidney is used first used clinically by Carl Walter, John Merrill and George Thorn. I First successful paediatric remission of acute leukaemia at Boston Children's Hospital.

(*Continued*)

TABLE 8.2 (CONTINUED)
Indicative List of Discovery and Advancement in Disease Treatment and Cure [28]

Year (Indicative)	Significant Discovery/ Application	Descriptions
1948	Stenotic mitral heart valves repair	Repair of stenotic mitral heart valves conducted for the first time.
1949	Development of vaccine culture technique I cortisone I White classification	The first poliovirus grown in culture. I First cortisone treatment in patients with rheumatoid arthritis. I Introduction of White classification for diabetic pregnancies.
1950	Wilms tumour	The first use of remissions in Wilms tumour of the kidney in children.
1951	Brain proteolipids	Abnormalities underlying psychiatric illness understood by the discovery of brain proteolipids.
1952	Kidney transplant	First successful kidney transplant performed on identical twins.
1954	Oral contraceptives	First successful clinical trials of oral contraceptives conducted.
1957	Brain structures	Extracting brain lipids was possible with the improved understanding of brain structures.
1960	Implantable cardiac pacemaker I proton beam therapy I Platelets	Bleeding control mechanism is developed using transfusion of platelets. I First clinical trial of tumour treatment is conducted using proton beam therapy. I Israel develops the first implantable cardiac pacemaker.
1962	Human limb reattachment I heart rhythm restoration	First successful reattachment of a human limb. I First successful use of electric current to restore heart rhythm.
1964	Human blood storage	Innovations make it possible to store human blood for a very long time.
1965	Pan-retinal coagulation	Treatment of pan-retinal coagulation is used to halt the sight-stealing proliferation of blood vessels in people with diabetes.
1968	Telemedicine	Closed-circuit television helped the use of telemedicine.
1969	Intra-aortic balloon catheter	The intra-aortic balloon catheter is developed with the collaboration of cardiac surgeons.
1970	Human oncogene I positron emission tomography scan (PET)	The first demonstration of muting gene RAS that helps prevent many common human tumours. I First non-invasive inspection of the brain and other organs possible through positron emission tomography (PET) scan.
1973	Non-invasive fetal heart monitoring	Accurate non-invasive fetal heart monitoring is developed and used for the first time.

(Continued)

TABLE 8.2 (CONTINUED)
Indicative List of Discovery and Advancement in Disease Treatment and Cure [28]

Year (Indicative)	Significant Discovery/ Application	Descriptions
1974	Photo-chemotherapy	Thomas Fitzpatrick and John Parrish demonstrated the treatment of psoriasis using photo-chemotherapy.
1976	Insulin resistance receptors discovered	Insulin resistance receptors found in obesity, and type 2 diabetes is identified.
1977	Virus particle structure	The structure of an intact virus particle and the mechanisms of viral entry and assembly in the human body are determined.
1978	Prenatal DNA sequencing	New DNA sequencing techniques are developed for the diagnosis of several genetic defects causing thalassemia.
1979	Magnetic resonance imaging (MRI)	Magnetic resonance imaging is pioneered as a diagnostic mechanism for injury or illness.
1980	HIV/AIDS	Several key discoveries made for HIV/AIDS disease.
1981	Artificial skin	premature puberty reversal	Artificial skin created from living skin cells.	Techniques formulated to reverse the premature onset of puberty in girls.
1982	Telomeres are discovered	An important discovery is made by Jack Szostak and Alexander Rich: Telomeres that help in understanding the process of ageing, cancer, etc.
1983	Treatment for congenital birthmark	Huntington's disease	First successful treatment of congenital birthmarks using a pulsed dye laser.	Genetic marker for Huntington's disease is discovered by James Gusella's team.
1984	skin replacement	Oncomouse	Thrombolysis in Myocardial Infarction (TIMI)	Howard Green successfully grows human skin in large quantities in a laboratory.	First genetically engineered mouse model of cancer is created. |New clot-busting drugs improving the survival chances in heart attack is demonstrated in the Thrombolysis in Myocardial Infarction (TIMI) trial.
1986	Kawasaki disease	Alzheimer's disease	Retrovirus identified that causes infectious illness in children below five.	Isolation of chromosomes 21 of people with Alzheimer's disease.
1987	Early onset Alzheimer's gene	Duchenne muscular dystrophy gene	Gene associated with early onset of Alzheimer's is discovered.	Gene associations with Duchenne muscular dystrophy are identified.
1988	Laser tattoo removal	Skin pigment, lesions and tattoos removed using a laser.
1989	Synthetic growth compound developed for tumour blood vessel	A synthetic compound that restricts the growth of blood vessels-associated tumours.

(Continued)

TABLE 8.2 (CONTINUED)
Indicative List of Discovery and Advancement in Disease Treatment and Cure [28]

Year (Indicative)	Significant Discovery/ Application	Descriptions
1990	Proteasome-inhibiting cancer therapy	Investigative foundations laid for the first proteasome-inhibiting cancer therapy.
1992	Diphtheria toxin structure I amyloid-beta	Diphtheria toxin structure is discovered. I Alzheimer's disease-causing protein amyloid-beta is discovered.
1993	Neo-vascular macular degeneration I microRNAs I paralysed vocal cord surgical method I colon cancer gene I VEGF molecule	Photodynamic therapy is pioneered for neo-vascular macular degeneration. I MicroRNAs is discovered. I Surgical method is discovered to restore functions of patients with paralysed vocal cords. I Colon cancer hereditary gene identified. I VEGF molecule causing blindness is discovered.
1994	PR-39 molecule	PR-39 discovered which is a key protein necessary for the mending process.
1995	Triple-organ transplant I blood glucose levels of kidney disease	Triple organs removed from a single donor and transplanted into three different donors. I Blood glucose that limits kidney disease is identified.
1996	Sense cells oxygen I Alzheimer's treatment I immune system advances	Discovery of cells lacking the von Hippel–Laudau (VHL) gene that is incapable of sensing oxygen. I Evidence of a chemical abnormality in the nerve-cell function that later helped identification of treatment for Alzheimer's disease. I Significant insights were developed in the understanding of the human immune system that helped neutralize cells responsible for graft-versus-host-disease.
1997	p73 gene I aspirin	A novel gene, p73, is discovered. I Aspirin targets COX is discovered as a part of inflation response.
1998	Liver transplant in adults	First live-donor transplant is carried out.
1999	Fluorescent molecular probes	Fluorescent molecular probes used to detect tumour enzymes of tumour cells.
2000	Brain abnormalities related to abuse and neglect	Four types of brain abnormalities resulting from childhood abuse and neglect are identified.
2001	Circadian clock	Investigation made into the brain's circadian clock helped understand how it controls the body's regular rhythms.
2002	Rheumatoid arthritis pathway I C-reactive protein	Cartilage deterioration and bone attrition related to rheumatoid arthritis are identified I C-reactive protein's relation to heart disease is discovered.
2003	Multidrug-resistant tuberculosis treatment I preeclampsia source discovered	Multidrug-resistant tuberculosis treatment is evidenced. I Source of preeclampsia causing infant mortality is discovered.

(Continued)

TABLE 8.2 (CONTINUED)
Indicative List of Discovery and Advancement in Disease Treatment and Cure [28]

Year (Indicative)	Significant Discovery/ Application	Descriptions
2004	Blood stem cells I protein transfer	Regulatory molecules disrupting the proliferation of blood stem cells' integrity are discovered. I First transmembrane protein-conducting channel architecture is discovered, clarifying the functioning of proteins.
2005	Prenatal nutrition I herpes vaccine	The relation between prenatal nutrition and permanent damage of the ability to produce insulin is discovered. I Vaccine called dl5-29 is created to fight herpes simplex virus type 2.
2006	Cholesterol mechanism I DNA sequencing techniques	Correlation between fatty food and heart disease risk is identified. I George Church introduces next-generation DNA sequencing technologies.
2007	Cellular switch I rheumatoid arthritis gene I brown-fat cell switch	Magnets were used to turn off and turn on cells to correct cellular functions that diseases interrupt. I Gene discovered that is involved in rheumatoid arthritis. I Bruce Spiegelman discovers molecular switch in mice to turn on beneficial brown-fat cells to counter obesity.
2008	RIPKI inhibitors I metastatic melanoma remission	Therapy necroptosis is discovered for treating amyotrophic lateral sclerosis (ALS) and Alzheimer's disease. I Patient's metastatic melanoma is put into remission using drug targeting.
2009	LIN28 protein I RNA interference I cancer cells' starvation I brown fat	LIN28, a protein abundant in embryonic stem cells, paves the way for new drug development. I A technique called RNA interference (RNAi) is used by Stephen Elledge to determine new drug targets for possible cancer treatment. I New tumour-killing strategies were identified as new discovers were made in apoptosis. I Scientists demonstrated that adults retain energy-burning brown fat paving the way for the treatment of obesity and type 2 diabetes.
2010	Enhancer transcription	A role in driving gene expression is discovered in environmental stimuli as an activator of DNA.
2011	Kidney failure markers I global healthcare budget models	Novel markers identified to accurately predict kidney failure in type 1 and type 2 diabetes. I Medicare and insurance is used to achieve low-cost health care.
2012	Tumour suppressor gene p53 I ancient migration I infectious disease diagnostics	Experiments showed that gene p53 signals DNA repair and cell recovery. I Third human migration wave is discovered through the gene sequencing techniques of DNA sequence. I RNA signature helps identify new treatment for infectious diseases.

(Continued)

TABLE 8.2 (CONTINUED)
Indicative List of Discovery and Advancement in Disease Treatment and Cure [28]

Year (Indicative)	Significant Discovery/ Application	Descriptions
2013	Cardiac hypertrophy reversal	cathepsin k pathways	A substance GDF-11 is found to reverse cardiac hypertrophy.	New therapy for osteoporosis was discovered by the gene cathepsin K prompting bone reabsorption and formation.
2014	Haematopoietic stem cells	pancreatic stem cells	Blood reprogramming to form haematopoietic stem cells opens the possibility for blood transplantation into patients with histocompatibility.	Insulin-producing pancreatic beta cells are produced in vitro.
2015	Bio-artificial replacement limb	PD-1 pathway	pseudo-gene	damaged protein disposal	multiple sclerosis	somatic mutations	deafness gene therapies	Forelimb bio-artificial transplantation is processed for the first time	The first demonstration of pathway blocking immune system cancer cell (PD-1).	Cancerous RNA subclass pseudo-gene is discovered.	Proteins tagged with ubiquitin signals and cellular machine proteasome to pulverize the defective protein are discovered.	Gene discovered that helps patients with multiple sclerosis respond to medication.	Gene therapy is developed to restore hearing.
2016	Sigma-1 receptor structure	Zika vaccine candidate	circadian rhythm-bipolar disorder link	microbiome	Potential therapeutic targets are identified as the molecular structure of the sigma-1 receptor is revealed.	Two variants of vaccines are successful in animals against Zika virus.	Specific neurochemical changes are linked to people with bipolar disorder specifically active in the morning.	Bacterial species are discovered that respond to immuno-inflammation in the human gut.
2017	Blood–brain barrier unlocked	scissor-like enzyme structure deciphered	Understanding of the blood–brain barrier deepens, opening up a new possibility for the treatment of Alzheimer's.	Atomic structure of ADAM10 is deciphered that holds the key to cell-to-cell communication.
2018	The "greying" of T cells	from one cell, a detailed roadmap	The process of ageing is deciphered, pinpointed to a specific pathway efficient in the aged T cells of mice.	A detailed map of the embryonic cells transition into new cell states and types is generated.
2019	New cure for herpes	viral peptides critical to natural HIV control	The CRISPR-Cas9 gene-editing tool is used to disrupt herpes simplex virus in human fibroblast cells hinting at a possibility of permanent viral control.	Critical amino acids in the protein structure of HIV are identified that are critical for the functioning and replication of the virus.

research-oriented programme implantation. One of the paradigm shifts in ICMR's policy pillars is sharing the vast amount of data generated through its intramural and extramural research programme for investigative studies for different stakeholders to accelerate effective research. ICMR plans to achieve this feat by creating efficient data systems, with its policy of access and sharing which will eventually help in the estimation of disease burden, generation of hypotheses, finding evidence for policy formulation, etc. These data repositories will act as a comprehensive data warehouse, comprising individual data sources available to the researchers through an advanced data analytics platform. This database would eventually have extensive epidemiological large-scale datasets from national registers and surveys with the input of big data analytics [31].

The global trend in the marriage of AI and healthcare is also reaching India, which promises to address the patient–doctor ratio and facilitate healthcare in the vast geographic area. Automation is being offered in every aspect of healthcare, including diagnostics, tests, screening, wearable devices, patient management and predictive analytics for disease prevention. Estimates suggest the AI industry will add USD 957 billion which would be around 15% of India's GDP valuation. For instance, the government of Karnataka has mobilized around 2,000 crore rupees supporting AI-based industries. Several tech giants are partnering with private hospital networks in India to develop AI-based applications. The government has already initiated several programmes like the National e-Health Authority entrusted with the responsibility to develop health information exchanges facilitating data interoperability, privacy and security and a certification framework. The Health Data Privacy and Security Act provides the how-to of data ownership, privacy and confidentiality. Health records are one of the most sensitive information data breaches, as such information will force the patients to face social stigma. For example, in 2016 the database of a Mumbai-based diagnostic laboratory was hacked and sensitive patient information was leaked. Accurate datasets/data integrity are essential for algorithmic accuracy for predictive analysis [32].

8.1.5 MEDICAL DATA REGULATORY SCENE IN INDIA

The professional conduct, etiquette and ethics regulations of the Indian Medical Council prescribe the maintenance of patient records for a minimum of three years. A medical record can be requested by the patient, an authorized attendant or legal authorities, and such a record shall be issued within 72 hours. It is compulsory to maintain a register of medical certificates giving full details of certificates issued with patient identification marks; the records may be computerized for quick retrieval [33].

The Ministry of Electronics and Information Technology formulated the National Data Sharing and Accessibility Policy that promotes open government data (OGD) software as a service platform, the aim of which is to make public data transparent and available for research. Interestingly this would also include public health data [34]. The Ministry of Health and Family Welfare in the year 2016 introduced electronic health records to be used by the healthcare providers. The purpose of this was to record a patient's information form birth onwards with every progression of his life and health events. Personal data generated from personal devices can have long-term clinical usage. An electronic health record is an aggregate of various medical records and health information that gets generated by an individual [35]. The Ministry of Communications and Information Technology under the Government of India defines various aspects of biometric and sensitive personal data. It prescribes the collection authority to have a prescribed privacy guideline in congruence with international standard IS/ISO/IEC 27001 for data collection with consent from the information provider. This information cannot be disclosed to any third party unless the consent of the provider is obtained, and even when such consent is obtained it is mandatory that the privacy policy to whom the data are to be transferred matches with the parent organization [36].

8.2 LITERATURE REVIEW

8.2.1 HEALTHCARE AT THE CROSSROADS

Dental health has been sitting at the crossroads contributing to the burden of public health problems. To put things in perspective, an average 17 year old has approximately 11 cavities, malocclusion is a common problem in children of age 12 to 17 years and around 45% of the population over the age of 65 have no teeth [37]. It is evident that old age is defined by the political will, not demography. The United States has seen several phases that had a significant impact on ageing healthcare like the Social Security Act, the Great Society, the federalization of old age assistance, the enactment of comprehensive social services, social security improvements, new federalism and medical cost-containment policies. Involvement of the public sector in long-term healthcare is significant. The need to revamp American healthcare has been felt for a long time [38]. Complete Medicare coverage of Americans of 65 years of age subsequently increased the cost of the burden on taxpayers as the plan to share the expenses between the patient and the federal government was skewed. Out-of-pocket expenses can be reduced and offered Medicare can be broadened for the patient [39]. The United Kingdom responded to a failing health policy with community care. However, community care also slowly drifted towards failure after initial success [40].

Increasing globalization and the mass movement of people from one nation-state to another has facilitated the movement of infectious diseases that pose a threat to the health and economies of the world. For example, the three measles outbreaks in the USA were introduced from different nation-states; similar is the case of influenza that enters nations in different variations.

Vector-borne diseases like malaria, dengue, etc., are usually imported from the Asian continent. The World Health Organization has played an important role in the eradication of infectious diseases globally; however it lacks the facilities and funding for scientific research or collating health information effectively. The three essential goals of healthcare across the world are increasing life expectancy, facilitating universal healthcare and achieving greater equality in healthcare [41].

There is an unparalleled faith of the public in the capability of the pharmaceutical industry, particularly the antibiotics, to resolve all infectious diseases. However, there is a steep decline in the development of antibiotics despite the growing rate of bacterial resistance, resulting in a scarcity in poor regions to treat disease. A fresh approach is needed to tackle these antibiotic crises, as existing antibiotics are insufficient to meet the needs of the population [42].

There has been a lingering question on the validity of intellectual property rights of pharmaceutical patents as they clash with global health concerns. The usual notion is that they help balance out the corporate interests and public healthcare interest [43]. Similarly, in the USA, the clinical research infrastructure is in a state of shambles, fragmented and outdated, which is limiting the improvement of patient care. Complete reengineering needs to take place to effectively deal with future opportunities and the inclusion of both the private and public players [44]. India provides a significant market for the Indian biotech companies that are already sitting at the crossroads addressing global healthcare needs. Support in the form of finance and policy can revive the sector in achieving long-term healthcare commitments. The domestic private sector holds the potential to convert the knowledge of the Indian health biotech sector into real products [45]. China has both the cash and intention to make a balanced investment in healthcare and transform healthcare. However, the problem of investment is that it may not turn out to be productive; rather it might end up in the pockets of the providers as both the government's and providers' primary aim is to care for themselves. There is a knowledge gap amongst the providers which may hinder the process of making an informed choice for the patient. Moreover, international experiences cannot be a copy-paste answer to the problems, as China may not have the prerequisites to make these solutions successful [46]. The President's Emergency Plan for AIDS Relief (PEPFAR) is a historically massive commitment (15 billion dollars in 5 years) by the United States of America to tackle a single endemic disease, AIDS. President Bush further increased the budget to 48 billion dollars in the same period to also focus on malaria and tuberculosis. It has impressive targets to treat 3 million people and prevent 12 million HIV infections, also including orphans and vulnerable children. However, the programme also ended up drawing criticism for underfunding and the politicization of healthcare [47]. There is incremental progress in the reduction of HIV through combined scientific and programmatic efforts; however, there is a need to evaluate the potential of preventive measures [48]. Integrated care, a nascent and an interdisciplinary field of health research, remains to be established as a solid discipline [49]. International health governance (IHG) has transitioned into global health governance (GHG), impacting a whole paradigm including national security, human security, human rights and global public good and the trickle-down effect [50]. The rising healthcare costs and lack of central control have facilitated, through the Patient Protection and Affordable Care Act (PPACA), the driving of innovation in health service delivery. This phenomenon has provided urologists with both the responsibility and opportunity for reshaping healthcare delivery [51]. Private business has become an inseparable part of delivering public healthcare services due to changing health policy. In the UK, the NHS supports this through independent treatment centres [52].

Adolescent reproductive and sexual health (ARSH) has become a priority to help future generations transition into a healthy and happy life. The Indian scenario is contrary to the global trend; it is only recently that the alarming pointers of early marriage, early pregnancy, rising anaemia and ineffective contraception have highlighted the need for government policy on this issue. Official concrete steps are yet not evident in reality [53]. Food insecurity is an ever-changing problem sitting at the crossroads of environmental and health systems. New food insecurity results in both the issues of over- and underconsumption in rich and poor countries which requires a new approach to public health nutrition and food policy [54]. The Millennium Development Goals helped avert millions of death caused by malaria. WHO African Region bears 90% of the burden of new increase, and transmission levels have hardly altered over the last 50 years in some parts of the region. The USA has made a significant contribution towards malaria financing, although this effort still lacks the required total funding as several countries have not fulfilled their prior commitments. Malaria control efforts cannot be relaxed as any leniency may bring back the disease in a significant way [55].

8.2.2 Healthcare Strategies in India

HIV-related stigma is predominant in India, often triggering discrimination towards those receiving or even seeking healthcare services. The knowledge and attitude of the healthcare worker are important for the dissemination of proper services. Although there is a general willingness for the health worker to provide patient care, it can be discriminatory or biased based on the concerns of occupational health or safety which can be overcome by training and development [56].

An attempt was made to understand the state of elderly oral healthcare by understanding the utilization of dental services in the capital region. Prescribed standards of Basic Oral Health Survey criteria were used as suggested by the World Health Organization that showed dental health services were available to a majority of the population. However, a significant number of the elderly population still faces an edentulousness crisis. The provision of oral healthcare is not the only solution, as elderly oral health education is the need of the hour [57].

Injection safety is a concern in India, as alongside the formal sector there is an informal sector that is less trained than its counterpart. There is a common tendency of the informal sector to administer injections with clear consequences for health and safety. Regulations and monitoring need to be implemented for both the formal and informal sector to reduce the safety concerns [58]. Access to healthcare is critical to the health financing mechanism. India spends among the least on healthcare in terms of public spending; hence out-of-pocket expenses are the primary source of healthcare financing. The National Rural Health Mission (NRHM) is evidence of the intuitional will to spend on public healthcare. Appropriate decentralization is a necessity for the social benefit so that healthcare is not left to the vagaries of the market [59].

Healthcare is a rapidly growing service sector in the Indian scenario. The question of sustainability is essential to bridge the gap between customer needs and customer relationship in the context of delivered healthcare services. In the absence of an effective mechanism of customer needs assessment, a combination of QFD and the Kano Model can be utilized by managers to identify customer's health needs [60]. Free health serveries purely financed by tax revenue came up as a suggestion by a panel of Indian doctors. In 2016 the same panel asked to gradually increase the health budget to 3% of GDP so as to put a dent in the out-of-pocket expense incurred by patients. An estimate suggests that approximately 6 million Indian households face the danger of financial catastrophe due to health expenses. A shocking fact is that less than 10% of the 1.5 million medical graduates stay in public health facilities [61].

The rural landscapes of India are heavily dependent on informal biomedical providers often lacking the required medical qualifications, be it in the mountainous terrains of Uttarakhand or the regions of Andhra Pradesh. They prescribe allopathic drugs blended with indigenous medicine which calls for interventions of a different kind. It is obvious that informal healthcare providers are here to play a significant role and are strategically important to improving healthcare [62]. Indian healthcare is growing with investments pouring in from private and public players, particularly the private sector. Quality healthcare has a progressive impact on healthcare service delivery [63]. Health human resource management requires a policy intervention particularly from the government in boosting knowledge circulation to match strides with the current trend. Even the firm-level hybridized approach is necessary to fill the gaps rather than waiting and reacting to a crisis [64].

8.2.3 Health Informatics and Healthcare Data Management

Health informatics has been on the frontiers of healthcare systems ever since the inception of information systems. The application of information technology in public health is referred to as public health informatics which is crucial for achieving significant health improvement [65]. This new domain of information systems presents both renewed opportunities and challenges to make a key transformation in public health services [66]. Health information systems have expanded and there is an attempt to reach the consumers; this branch of medical informatics is popularly known as consumer health informatics. This essentially sits at the crossroads of other disciplines like public health, health promotion, health education library sciences, communication sciences and nursing informatics [67]. This is a period of the unprecedented public will and the ability to access information has resulted in an era of the promulgation of evidence-oriented consumer healthcare [68]. There is a growing number of consumers seeking their health information to make an informed decision; they seek this information from various sources. Consumer health informatics applications face a challenge to meet the consumer needs and support the collaboration between providers and patients [69].

The International Medical Informatics Association recommends a three-dimensional framework (professionals involved in healthcare, specialization in biomedical and health informatics, career progression programme) for improving the knowledge and skill of a healthcare professional [70]. Pervasive health information can be acquired by emerging wearable technologies that may address unfulfilled healthcare needs for the treatment of major diseases, and countering chronic diseases, outbreaks and other challenges that are present in the society [71]. Health informatics analysis has seen rapid growth with the development of underlying communicational techniques like deep learning and artificial intelligence. Deep learning, on the other hand, has helped develop more data-driven solutions, promoting automation and the reduction of human intervention [72].

8.2.4 Healthcare Data Management and Privacy

Healthcare data warehousing is a uniquely daunting task, filled with coding schemas and medical standards that are often incompatible and require careful interpretation and are presented in many formats like published books, spreadsheets, tapes and other data formats. Healthcare data are private and sensitive, shrouded with concerns of privacy and security. However, healthcare data warehousing holds the promise to significantly contribute towards individual as well as community health by providing quantitative insights for decision-making by the healthcare professional [73]. An agent-based DM info-structure (ADMI) may be utilized for targeted support or decision planning services by healthcare professionals analysing hospitalization treatment patterns, ambulatory care and forecasting the patterns of new infectious diseases [74]. Automation has a proven advantage over manual surveillance systems. The intergeneration of analytical technologies for automated infection surveillance systems contributed to the field of data miners and statisticians [75]. Data-mining techniques can be applied to predict the length of an in-patient stay in any hospital. Selection strategy and compression can be very effective at improving and classifying the accuracy of "length of stay" by applying naive Bayesian imputation (NBI) to compensate for the missing datasets [76]. The conflict of sharing healthcare data and the perceived threat to patients' privacy are ever-looming questions. The traditional data anonymization techniques were found to be invalid and stood in conflict with the privacy concerns of data sharing between the Hong Kong Red Cross Blood Transfusion Service and public healthcare facilities. A new anonymization technique, "LKC-privacy," was recommended to overcome the challenges effectively [77]. One single centralized database is difficult to achieve due to the volume and geographic spread of input data. One method to overcome this is a distributed database with different levels of partitions, like vertical or horizontal. Protocols like "zero-knowledge proof" may be a solution to reduce time, communication and the complexity of dealing with the privacy concerns of large datasets [78]. Cloud data storage is necessary for the growing trend of electronic health records (EHR) adopted by healthcare organizations. Cloud-based EHR systems are not immune to privacy concerns which may be overcome by ciphertext policy attribute-based encryption (CP-ABE) [79]. Collective intelligence paired with distributed processing can also overcome the reluctance to share healthcare data for centralized processing [80]. The utilization of a blockchain platform to store and retrieve healthcare data and allow patients to control the privacy paradigm will simplify patient data sharing [81]. Big healthcare data are powered by the theoretical technological exponential growth proposed by

Moore's and Kryder's laws [82]. Healthcare data analytics remains an elusive matter in the lack of a fundamental theory for representation [83]. Big healthcare data have the potential to reduce the cost of healthcare through predictive analysis and improve quality of life in general; techniques like encryption and anonymization will help reduce the privacy concerns [84]. Patient data security and healthcare privacy suffer from a plethora of issues such as infrastructure lag, budget limitations, political will, etc., which leave it vulnerable to potential exploitations from hackers with malicious intent [85].

8.3 OBJECTIVES

1. To overview the phenomenal growth in medical science and healthcare systems across the globe.
2. To explore the emergence of health strategy with references to its synergy, divergence and pre-emptive convergences for a sustainable future of mankind.

8.4 RESEARCH METHODOLOGY

The present study has been developed using secondary information. The researchers have done an exhaustive literature review from available reliable sources, various reports, policy papers, reliable web sources and trusted data sources in the broad domain of healthcare systems. The study highlights the conceptual model based on input, insights from various research papers and available policy documents.

8.5 ANALYSIS I

With the phenomenal growth in science and technology across the world, medical education and research have been gaining massive momentum that contributes to human welfare. The growing penetration of the 4IR ecosystem has enormously empowered almost all the facets of medical treatment to elevate the superior healthcare system globally. An indicative list of augmented technology-driven healthcare excellence and scope of performance has been provided in Table 8.3

8.6 ANALYSIS II

The modern healthcare system is largely embedded in technological development. In a technology life cycle, we have three phases: Introduction (I), growth (G) and maturity (M). The level of technology proceeds from lower to higher, from T1 to T2 to T3, where T3 is the superior technology at a particular point of time, assuming that $T3 > T2 > T1$; however, in any technology life cycle (TLC) there shall be no "decline phase" even though it remains primitive or becomes obsolete. This is simply because technological development is a staircase approach where the obsolete TLC has its foundation of knowledge system that becomes a prerequisite for constructing a higher order of technologies. The world is witnessing rapid development in the field

TABLE 8.3
Indicative List of Advancement in Health Sciences/Technologies

Serial No.	Health Technology/ Sciences Advancement	Application/Usage/Benefits
1	3D bio-printing [86, 87]	Tissues and organs can be printed or manufactured; even 3D-printed limbs can replace amputated organs.
2	Handheld tele-ECG machine [88]	Proven to be game-changer in rural healthcare delivery services for India [89].
3	Direct-to-consumer genetic testing [90]	Helps the individual make informed lifestyle choices based on the genetic information of chronic/hereditary health diseases.
4	Brain–machine interfaces (BMI) [91, 92]	Although in its early phases, this has proven to be a game-changer for therapeutics of paralysed/amputated patients in interfacing with bionic limbs.
5	Mixed reality in healthcare [93]	This technology is enabling the physician/surgeon to carry out an in-depth three-dimensional inspection of affected organs without any incision.
6	Artificial womb technology [94, 95]	The technology is being developed by the Children's Hospital of Philadelphia and will enable and ensure that premature babies can grow in an artificial womb-like environment and thus future health consequences are eliminated.
7	Regenerative medicine [96, 97]	Researchers are studying the limb-generative properties of salamanders to understand and implement them in humans.
8	Immunotherapy [98]	Immunotherapy is a gene-based treatment mechanism that uses gene suppression or activation to respond to diseases like cancer.
9	Medical robots/surgical robots [99, 100]	Robotics is currently used in various healthcare scenarios delivering essential services. Some precision robots are also able to perform surgery, reducing the number of human errors.
10	Wearable nano sensors [101]	Wearable nano sensors are embedded in several devices like wristwatches, bands, etc., which then collect health data like heart rate, blood pressure, glucose level, etc., for analysis and diagnostics.
11	Genome editing [102–105]	The genome-editing technology also known as CRISPR-Cas9 is helping researchers find new r RNA, mRNA-based vaccines and new solutions for a healthier life, even allowing the creation of exceptionally healthy children.
12	Wireless telemedicine [106, 107]	Exceptional growth in wireless technology cloud-enabled storage has enabled the physician to deliver real-time health diagnosis based on patient data, history, etc.
13	Bionic limbs [108]	Bionic limbs are artificial limbs that are electronically controlled with the impulses received from the amputated organ of the patient.
14	Blockchain-based e-health [109–111]	The debate around privacy in healthcare data, electronic health record systems and e-health finally seems to be put to rest with the introduction of a blockchain e-health scenario that is not only secure but highly anonymizes the sharing of data.

(Continued)

TABLE 8.3 (CONTINUED)
Indicative List of Advancement in Health Sciences/Technologies

Serial No.	Health Technology/ Sciences Advancement	Application/Usage/Benefits
15	AI in healthcare [112–114]	AI is changing the way health data are utilized; it now can predict the health outcomes of an individual and predict the necessary precautions to be taken.
16	IoT ecosystem in healthcare [115–117]	IoT in healthcare is changing the health outlook in monitoring vital health measures and delivering precession-based medical care. IoT has become a major game-changer in diabetics care.
17	Internet of Medical Robotic Things (IoMRT) [118]	The Internet of Medical Robotic Things is IoT-based medical robotic devices with a specific focus on solving healthcare issues.
18	Big data analytics in healthcare [119, 120]	A myriad of health data is helping big data analytics predict health outcomes based on predictive, prescriptive or descriptive analysis. Big data are contributing to the creation of a universal health database.
19	Nanotechnology in precision surgery [121–125]	Nanotechnology holds the promise to resolve surgical errors and bring a new level of precision in surgery.

of science and technology, part of which is experimented with and applied in the healthcare system by augmenting sophisticated health devices, surgical instruments or even operative techniques. That makes the healthcare system highly dynamic and bountiful of divergence in the healthcare scenario.

Advancement in the healthcare system is the result of both pull factors (y-axis) and push factors (x-axis) as shown in Figure 8.2. The "pull factor" is predominantly the "striving for excellence" on the frontiers of science and technology with the intervention, commitment to R&D compounded with high investment. The pull factors essentially aspire for the healthcare system to be upgraded with a higher order of robustness and precision mostly in a pre-emptive manner so that the system can yield superior performance in terms of accuracy, speed and reliability. On the contrary, the set of push factors are the growing complexity of diseases, lifestyle disorder and various emerging patterns and criticality of diseases, etc., which force the health researcher and practitioners to come up with reactive measures or solutions; as a result of that the advancement in the healthcare system progresses and proceeds towards excellence. The pattern of healthcare excellence may form a web of divergence which is interactive to each other to focus on achieving superior quality of performance and service delivery mechanisms. An indicative list of elements of the web of divergence in the healthcare system is given below and also mentioned in Figure 8.3:

- Excellence in pharmaceutical innovations (formula/molecules, lifesaving drugs)

Health Sector at the Crossroads 155

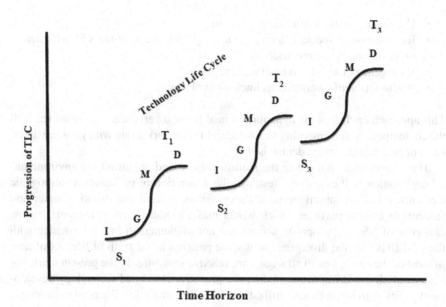

FIGURE 8.2 The technology life cycle curve.

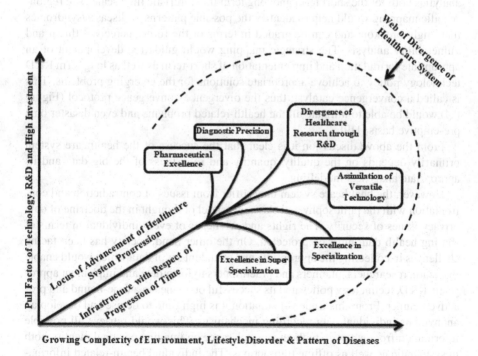

FIGURE 8.3 Web of divergence: Enrichment towards excellence in the healthcare system.

- Excellence in the diagnostic ecosystem
- Introduction of specialization and super specialization systems for a higher order of healthcare precision
- Divergence of advanced healthcare research
- Assimilation of a versatile technological platform

This approach envisages the dynamics of healthcare divergence in consonance with the contemporary and emerging technological framework along with growing diversities of healthcare service demands.

The incremental changes in the nature, volume and magnitude of environmental degradation will essentially result in the generation of pollutants, carcinogenic elements, toxicity contamination of heavy metals in food and drinking water and susceptible carbon particles which would make Mother Earth detrimental to the existence of life if appropriate actions are not implemented in conformance with the UNSDGs. So, the divergence of disease patterns is the truth of life. As of now in most of the cases, health strategies are reactive in nature. In the present alarming state of affairs, it is important to devise a proactive R&D and technology development policy with the optimum utilization of big data analytics. We need to develop a region-specific mapping of environmental indicators and other related factors based on a long-term longitudinal database. This environmental mapping and series of big data would have to be processed in terms of descriptive, predictive and prescriptive analytics both for the short term and long term in a futuristic time scale. The region-specific mapping would help to identify the possible patterns of diseases/syndromes that might breakout and can be graded in terms of the future perceived threat and vulnerability analysis. The strategic mapping would guide the development of an appropriate formulation and implementation of short-term as well as long-term R&D technology policy to achieve appropriate solutions for the emerging problems. This is called a convergence catalyst; thus the divergence-convergence protocol (Figure 8.4) would be able to mitigate all the health-related problems and even disaster on a pre-emptive basis [119].

From the above discussion it is clear that the success of the healthcare system primarily depends on the quality, quantity and robustness of the big data and its appropriate analytical modelling.

However, the healthcare system may suffer from issues of contradiction and confrontation with the philosophy and classical school of thought in the doctrine of data privacy issues of security. The rights and privileges of every individual in terms of sharing health data must be protected. On the other hand, society has been facing challenges in collecting the appropriate and abundant set of data which would enable the heath, researchers, planners and practitioners to formulate and implement appropriate R&D, technology policy and its successful outcomes in a time-bound and pro-active manner. From this trade-off situation it is high time to devise and develop an anonymous individual data-recording mechanism. This would retrieve all possible information from a person without zero tolerance on imaging personal identity both in systematic as well as offline transactions. The individual health-related information will be considered as a numeric entity for designing statistical inferences or

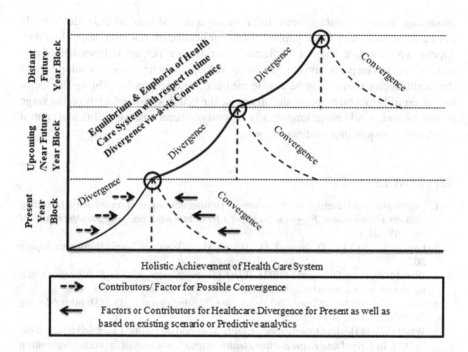

FIGURE 8.4 Divergence-convergence protocol for proactive health strategy.

in big data analytics. Generating a comprehensive health database is inevitable for designing appropriate health strategies, particularly in the reigns of an epidemic, pandemic and endemic and critical diseases [120].

8.7 CONCLUSION

Healthcare is a dynamic process. On one hand, newer forms of diseases emerge as a cascading effect of environmental degradation and changes in lifestyle. The push and pull factors improve scientific knowledge and its application towards progression. However, such divergences would have to be mitigated by adopting appropriate pre-emptive convergence strategies which may be derived from robust big data analytics. Region-specific health mapping based on long-term longitudinal big data analytics has become essential in prioritizing and designing R&D and scientific policies so that accomplishment of health science and its technology ecosystem would be ahead of the present and potential vulnerability of newer forms of diseases. Pandemics like COVID-19 have categorically highlighted that the global preparedness to combat severe acute respiratory syndrome (SARS)-type lung-related illnesses was not up to the mark. There is a need for high-order big data analytics on various dimensions or factors like global warming, growth in pollution, diminishing air quality index, growing influx of antibiotic resistance, antimicrobial resistance due to mutation, lifestyle disorders, etc., which may have correlations with certain disease syndromes or disorders in the body. There lie the challenges of maintaining a standard protocol for protecting individual data privacy. Information collected from an individual should not be personalized or made public. In fact, in healthcare research, individual data appear in a collective sense and reflected as numbers which are independent of personal identity. The pre-emptive approach to R&D and technological development in the health sector would only be able to mitigate the divergences to bring the sector into an equilibrium on a time scale; otherwise the health sector, which is on the verge of a crossroad, would move tangentially beyond our reach and capabilities to control and finally conquer in a continuous cycle.

REFERENCES

1. United Nations Development Programme. Human development report 2019. In *United Nations Development Program*. Retrieved from http://hdr.undp.org/sites/default/files/hdr2019.pdf.
2. Layard, R., Sachs, J. D., Neve, J. De, Huang, H., & Wang, S. *World Happiness Report 2020*.
3. World Report on Disability. (2011). *WHO Library Cataloguing-in-Publication Data*. Retrieved from www.who.int/about/licensing/copyright_form/en/index.html.
4. Global Vaccine Action Plan. (2013). *Vaccine, 31* Supplement 2, B5–B31. https://doi.org/10.1016/j.vaccine.2013.02.015.
5. WHO (World Health Organization). (2019). Maternal mortality: Level and trends 2000 to 2017. In *Sexual and Reproductive Health*. https://www.who.int/reproductivehealth/publications/maternal-mortality-2000-2017/en/.
6. Richmond, J. B., & Health, C. (n.d.). *Connecting the Brain to the Rest of the Body: Early Childhood Development and Lifelong Health Are Deeply Intertwined*.
7. UNAIDS (Joint United Nations Programme on HIV/AIDS). (2019). AIDS data 2019. *Science, 268*(5209), 350–350. https://doi.org/10.1126/science.7716530.
8. WHO (World Health Organization). (2019). WHO-CDS-HIV-19.7-eng. World Health Organization, 1–48, 2016–2021.
9. National Institute of Environmental Health Sciences. 2020. Air Pollution and Your Health. *National Institute of Environmental Health Sciences* 1. November 3, 2020, Retrieved from https://www.niehs.nih.gov/health/topics/agents/air-pollution/index.cfm
10. WHO | Ambient air pollution: Health impacts. (2018). In WHO. https://www.who.int/airpollution/ambient/health-impacts/en/.
11. Järup, L. (2003). Hazards of heavy metal contamination. *British Medical Bulletin*, 68(1), 167–182.
12. Rai, P. K., Lee, S. S., Zhang, M., Tsang, Y. F., & Kim, K. H. (2019). Heavy metals in food crops: Health risks, fate, mechanisms, and management. *Environment International*, 125, 365–385.
13. World Health Organisation. 2007. Occupational Health: Stress at the Workplace. 1–3. November 3, 2020, Retrieved from https://www.who.int/news-room/q-a-detail/ccupational-health-stress-at-the-workplace.
14. Ghosh, C., & Ghosh, A. N. (2019). *An Introduction to Economics*. Singapore: Springer.
15. Dandona, R., Pandey, A., & Dandona, L. (2016). A review of national health surveys in India. *Bulletin of the World Health Organization*, 94(4), 286.
16. National Sample Survey Organization. (2014). Health in India (NSS 71st round). (n.d.). June 25, 2020, Retrieved from http://mospi.nic.in/sites/default/files/publication_reports/nss_rep574.pdf.

17. MoHFW (Ministry of Health & Family Welfare). (2017). National Health Policy 2017. (n.d.). June 25, 2020, Retrieved from https://www.nhp.gov.in/nhpfiles/national_health_policy_2017.pdf.
18. Central Bureau of Health Intelligence, & MHFW, GOI. (2019). National Health Profile (NHP) of India—2019: Ministry of Health and Family Welfare. Retrieved from http://cbhidghs.nic.in/showfile.php?lid=1147.
19. Chhabra, S. (2019). *Healthy States Progressive India: Report on the Ranks of States and Union Territories* (No. 148274, pp. 1–140). The World Bank.
20. Ministry of Health & Family Welfare. GOI (2019). *National Digital Health Blueprint*. https://www.nhp.gov.in/NHPfiles/National_Digital_Health_Blueprint_Report_comments_invited.pdf.
21. Government of India Ministry of Tourism (Niche Tourism Division) Revised Guidelines for the Promotion of Wellness and Medical as Niche Tourism Products. (2015). http://tourism.gov.in/sites/default/files/revised guidelines for wellness %26 medical tourism as on 20.03.2015.pdf.
22. AAP Government Healthcare Facilities Guide: Aam Aadmi Party. (n.d.). June 26, 2020, Retrieved from https://aamaadmiparty.org/aap-government-healthcare-facilities-guide/.
23. Ministry of AYUSH. (n.d.). Ministry of AYUSH. June 27, 2020, Retrieved from https://www.ayush.gov.in/.
24. Elahee, S. F., Mao, H. J., & Shen, X. Y. (2019). Traditional Indian medicine and history of acupuncture in India. *World Journal of Acupuncture-Moxibustion*, 29(1), 69–72.
25. Kloos, S. (2016). The recognition of sowa rigpa in India: How Tibetan medicine became an Indian medical system. *Medicine Anthropology Theory*, 3(2), 19–49.
26. Stein, J. (2012). "Reiki Balances the Chakras": A Japanese Healing Practice in New Age India. In Chao Center for Asian Studies 2011 *Transnational Asia Graduate Student Conference Working Papers*.
27. Vedavathy, S. (2002). Tribal medicine–The real alternative. *Indian Journal of Traditional Knowledge*, I, 25–31.
28. *Timeline of Discovery | Harvard Medical School*. (n.d.). June 27, 2020, Retrieved from https://hms.harvard.edu/about-hms/history-hms/timeline-discovery.
29. New Advancements in Medical Research in India I Medlife Blog: Health and Wellness Tips. (n.d.). June 28, 2020, Retrieved from https://www.medlife.com/blog/new-advancements-medical-research-india/.
30. *Re-engineering Indian healthcare 2.0 Tailoring for inclusion, true care and trust*. (2019).
31. Indian Council of Medical Research. (2017). *ICMR Strategic Plan & Agenda 2030: Transforming Health of Indian People through Responsive Research*. 52. http://www.icmr.nic.in/publications/ICMR_Strategic_plan.pdf.
32. Paul, Y., Hickok, E., Sinha, A., Tiwari, U., Mohandas, S., Ray, S., ... Bidare, P. M. (2018). *Artificial Intelligence in the Healthcare Industry in India*. https://cis-india.org/internet-governance/files/ai-and-healtchare-report.
33. *Indian Medical Council (Professional Conduct, Etiquette and Ethics) Regulations, 2002(Amended upto 8th October 2016)*. (2002). Medical Council of India Pocket-14; Sector 8; Dwarka New Delhi-110077.
34. National e-Governance Division I Government of India, Ministry of Electronics and Information Technology. (n.d.). July 5, 2020, Retrieved from https://meity.gov.in/open-data.
35. EHR (Electronic Health Record) Standards for India 2016 (Standards Set Recommendations v2.0). (n.d.). e-Health Division Department of Health & Family Welfare Ministry of Health & Family Welfare Government of India. https://main.mohfw.gov.in/sites/default/files/17739294021483341357.pdf.

36. (Reasonable security practices and procedures and sensitive personal data or information) Rules, 2011. (2011). Ministry of Communications and Information Technology (Department of Information Technology) Notification. https://meity.gov.in/writereaddata/files/GSR313E_10511%281%29_0.pdf
37. Allukian Jr, M. (1982). Dentistry at the crossroads: The future is uncertain: The challenges are many. *American Journal of Public Health*, 72(7), 653–654.
38. Estes, C. L. (1989). Aging, health, and social policy: Crisis and crossroads. *Journal of Aging & Social Policy*, 1(1–2), 17–32.
39. Thomas, B. (1995). 1965–1995: Medicare at a Crossroads. *JAMA*, 274(3), 276–278.
40. Wistow, G. (1995). Aspirations and realities: Community care at the crossroads. *Health & Social Care in the Community*, 3(4), 227–240.
41. Satcher, D. (1999). Global health at the crossroads: Surgeon General's report on the 50th World Health Assembly. *JAMA*, 281(10), 942–943.
42. Nathan, C. (2004). Antibiotics at the crossroads. *Nature*, 431(7011), 899–902.
43. Amado, R., & Gewertz, N. M. (2004). Intellectual property and the pharmaceutical industry: A moral crossroads between health and property. *Journal of Business Ethics*, 55(3), 295–308.
44. Crowley Jr, W. F., Sherwood, L., Salber, P., Scheinberg, D., Slavkin, H., Tilson, H., ... Genel, M. (2004). Clinical research in the United States at a crossroads: Proposal for a novel public-private partnership to establish a national clinical research enterprise. *JAMA*, 291(9), 1120–1126.
45. Frew, S. E., Rezaie, R., Sammut, S. M., Ray, M., Daar, A. S., & Singer, P. A. (2007). India's health biotech sector at a crossroads. *Nature Biotechnology*, 25(4), 403–417.
46. Yip, W., & Hsiao, W. C. (2008). The Chinese health system at a crossroads. *Health Affairs*, 27(2), 460–468.
47. Gostin, L. O. (2008). President's emergency plan for AIDS relief: Health development at the crossroads. *JAMA*, 300(17), 2046–2048.
48. Vermund, S. H., Allen, K. L., & Karim, Q. A. (2009). HIV-prevention science at a crossroads: Advances in reducing sexual risk. *Current Opinion in HIV and AIDS*, 4(4), 266.
49. Stein, K. V., & Rieder, A. (2009). Integrated care at the crossroads: Defining the way forward. *International Journal of Integrated Care*, 9(2).
50. Ng, N. Y., & Ruger, J. P. (2011). Global health governance at a crossroads. *Global Health Governance: The Scholarly Journal for the New Health Security Paradigm*, 3(2), 1.
51. Shelton, J. B., & Saigal, C. S. (2011). The crossroads of evidence-based medicine and health policy: Implications for urology. *World Journal of Urology*, 29(3), 283–289.
52. Waring, J., & Bishop, S. (2011). Healthcare identities at the crossroads of service modernisation: the transfer of NHS clinicians to the independent sector? *Sociology of Health & Illness*, 33(5), 661–676.
53. Gupta, M., Ramani, K. V., & Soors, W. (2012). Adolescent health in India: Still at crossroads. *Advances in Applied Sociology*, 2(04), 320.
54. Ashe, L. M., & Sonnino, R. (2013). At the crossroads: New paradigms of food security, public health nutrition and school food. *Public Health Nutrition*, 16(6), 1020–1027.
55. Alonso, P., & Noor, A. M. (2017). The global fight against malaria is at crossroads. *The Lancet*, 390(10112), 2532–2534.
56. Kermode, M., Holmes, W., Langkham, B., Thomas, M. S., & Gifford, S. (2005). HIV-related knowledge, attitudes & risk perception amongst nurses, doctors & other healthcare workers in rural India. *Indian Journal of Medical Research*, 122(3), 258.

57. Goel, P., Singh, K., Kaur, A., & Verma, M. (2006). Oral healthcare for elderly: Identifying the needs and feasible strategies for service provision. *Indian Journal of Dental Research*, 17(1), 11.
58. Kermode, M., & Muani, V. (2006). Injection practices in the formal & informal healthcare sectors in rural north India. *Indian Journal of Medical Research*, 124(5), 513.
59. Duggal, R. (2007). Healthcare in India: Changing the financing strategy. *Social Policy & Administration*, 41(4), 386–394.
60. Gupta, P., & Srivastava, R. K. (2011). Customer satisfaction for designing attractive qualities of healthcare service in India using Kano model and quality function deployment. *MIT International Journal of Mechanical Engineering*, 1(2), 101–107.
61. Mudur, G. (2011). India plans to move towards free universal healthcare coverage.
62. Gautham, M., Shyamprasad, K. M., Singh, R., Zachariah, A., Singh, R., & Bloom, G. (2014). Informal rural healthcare providers in North and South India. *Health Policy and Planning*, 29 Supplement 1(suppl_1), i20–i29.
63. Srinivasan, V., & Chandwani, R. (2014). HRM innovations in rapid growth contexts: The healthcare sector in India. *The International Journal of Human Resource Management*, 25(10), 1505–1525.
64. Agarwal, V. (2017). Implementing quality healthcare strategies for improving service delivery at private hospitals in India. *Journal of Health Management*, 19(1), 159–169.
65. Friede, A., Blum, H. L., & McDonald, M. (1995). Public health informatics: How information-age technology can strengthen public health. *Annual Review of Public Health*, 16(1), 239–252.
66. Yasnoff, W. A., O Carroll, P. W., Koo, D., Linkins, R. W., & Kilbourne, E. M. (2000). Public health informatics: Improving and transforming public health in the information age. *Journal of Public Health Management and Practice*, 6(6), 67–75.
67. Eysenbach, G. (2000). Consumer health informatics. *BMJ*, 320(7251), 1713–1716.
68. Eysenbach, G., & Jadad, A. R. (2001). Evidence-based patient choice and consumer health informatics in the Internet age. *Journal of medical Internet research*, 3(2), e19.
69. Lewis, D., Chang, B. L., & Friedman, C. P. (2005). Consumer health informatics. In *Consumer Health Informatics* (pp. 1–7). New York, NY: Springer.
70. Mantas, J., Ammenwerth, E., Demiris, G., Hasman, A., Haux, R., Hersh, W., ... Wright, G. (2010). Recommendations of the International Medical Informatics Association (IMIA) on education in biomedical and health informatics. *Methods of Information in Medicine*, 49(02), 105–120.
71. Zheng, Y. L., Ding, X. R., Poon, C. C. Y., Lo, B. P. L., Zhang, H., Zhou, X. L., ... Zhang, Y. T. (2014). Unobtrusive sensing and wearable devices for health informatics. *IEEE Transactions on Biomedical Engineering*, 61(5), 1538–1554.
72. Ravì, D., Wong, C., Deligianni, F., Berthelot, M., Andreu-Perez, J., Lo, B., & Yang, G. Z. (2016). Deep learning for health informatics. *IEEE Journal of Biomedical and Health Informatics*, 21(1), 4–21.
73. Berndt, D. J., Fisher, J. W., Hevner, A. R., & Studnicki, J. (2001). Healthcare data warehousing and quality assurance. *Computer*, 34(12), 56–65.
74. Zaidi, S. Z. H., Abidi, S. S. R., & Manickam, S. (2002). Distributed data mining from heterogeneous healthcare data repositories: Towards an intelligent agent-based framework. In Proceedings of 15th IEEE Symposium on Computer-Based Medical Systems (CBMS 2002) (pp. 339–342). IEEE.
75. Obenshain, M. K. (2004). Application of data mining techniques to healthcare data. *Infection Control & Hospital Epidemiology*, 25(8), 690–695.
76. Liu, P., Lei, L., Yin, J., Zhang, W., Naijun, W., & El-Darzi, E. (2006). Healthcare data mining: Prediction inpatient length of stay. In 3rd International IEEE Conference Intelligent Systems (pp. 832–837). IEEE.

77. Mohammed, N., Fung, B. C., Hung, P. C., & Lee, C. K. (2009). Anonymizing healthcare data: A case study on the blood transfusion service. In Proceedings of the 15th ACM SIGKDD International Conference on Knowledge Discovery and Data Mining (pp. 1285–1294).
78. Elmisery, A. M., & Fu, H. (2010). Privacy preserving distributed learning clustering of healthcare data using cryptography protocols. In IEEE 34th Annual Computer Software and Applications Conference Workshops (pp. 140–145). IEEE.
79. Alshehri, S., Radziszowski, S. P., & Raj, R. K. (2012). Secure access for healthcare data in the cloud using ciphertext-policy attribute-based encryption. In IEEE 28th International Conference on Data Engineering Workshops (pp. 143–146). IEEE.
80. Patil, H. K., & Seshadri, R. (2014). Big data security and privacy issues in healthcare. In IEEE International Congress on Big Data (pp. 762–765). IEEE.
81. Yue, X., Wang, H., Jin, D., Li, M., & Jiang, W. (2016). Healthcare data gateways: Found healthcare intelligence on blockchain with novel privacy risk control. *Journal of Medical Systems*, 40(10), 218.
82. Dinov, Ivo D. (2016). Volume and value of big healthcare data. *Journal of Medical Statistics and Informatics*, 4(1), 3.
83. Dinov, I. D. (2016). Methodological challenges and analytic opportunities for modeling and interpreting big healthcare data. *Gigascience*, 5(1), s13742-016.
84. Abouelmehdi, K., Beni-Hessane, A., & Khaloufi, H. (2018). Big healthcare data: preserving security and privacy. *Journal of Big Data*, 5(1), 1.
85. Kagalwalla, N., Garg, T., Churi, P., & Pawar, A. (2019). A survey on implementing privacy in healthcare: An Indian perspective. *International Journal of Advanced Trends in Computer Science and Engineering*, 8(3), 963–682.
86. Ventola, C. L. (2014). Medical applications for 3D printing: Current and projected uses. *Pharmacy and Therapeutics*, 39(10), 704.
87. Singh, D., & Thomas, D. (2019). Advances in medical polymer technology towards the panacea of complex 3D tissue and organ manufacture. *The American Journal of Surgery*, 217(4), 807–808.
88. Sinha, V., Jain, R. K., Mandalik, S. A., Joshi, G., Das, D., Pithawa, C. K., & Haldavnekar, H. (n.d.). Handheld 12-channel Tele-ECG Machine. Retrieved from http://www.hwassociation.org/conf/HWC-2015/papers/03ID_HWC2015.pdf
89. Singh, M., Agarwal, A., Sinha, V., Manoj Kumar, R., Jaiswal, N., Jindal, I., ... Kumar, M. (2014). Application of handheld tele-ECG for health care delivery in rural India. *International Journal of Telemedicine and Applications*, 2014, 981806.
90. Direct-to-Consumer Genetic Testing Kits—Harvard Health Publications. (n.d.). July 21, 2020, Retrieved from https://www.health.harvard.edu/newsletter_article/direct-to-consumer-genetic-testing-kits.
91. Shih, J. J., Krusienski, D. J., & Wolpaw, J. R. (2012, March). Brain-computer interfaces in medicine. In *Mayo Clinic Proceedings*, 87(3), 268–279.
92. Musk, E. (2019). An integrated brain-machine interface platform with thousands of channels. *Journal of Medical Internet Research*, 21(10), e16194.
93. John, B., & Wickramasinghe, N. (2020). A review of mixed reality in health care. In *Delivering Superior Health and Wellness Management with IoT and Analytics* (pp. 375–382). Cham: Springer.
94. Romanis, E. C. (2018). Artificial womb technology and the frontiers of human reproduction: Conceptual differences and potential implications. *Journal of Medical Ethics*, 44(11), 751–755.
95. *Recreating the Womb: New Hope for Premature Babies | Children's Hospital of Philadelphia*. (n.d.). July 21, 2020, Retrieved from https://www.chop.edu/video/recreating-womb-new-hope-premature-babies#.

96. Song, F., Li, B., & Stocum, D. L. (2010). Amphibians as research models for regenerative medicine. *Organogenesis*, 6(3), 141–150.
97. Mao, A. S., & Mooney, D. J. (2015). Regenerative medicine: Current therapies and future directions. *Proceedings of the National Academy of Sciences*, 112(47), 14452–14459.
98. Till, S. J., Francis, J. N., Nouri-Aria, K., & Durham, S. R. (2004). Mechanisms of immunotherapy. *Journal of Allergy and Clinical Immunology*, 113(6), 1025–1034.
99. Lanfranco, A. R., Castellanos, A. E., Desai, J. P., & Meyers, W. C. (2004). Robotic surgery: A current perspective. *Annals of Surgery*, 239(1), 14.
100. Kucuk, S. (2020). Introductory chapter: Medical robots in surgery and rehabilitation. In *Medical Robotics-New Achievements*. Londond: IntechOpen.
101. Yao, S., Swetha, P., & Zhu, Y. (2018). Nanomaterial-enabled wearable sensors for healthcare. *Advanced Healthcare Materials*, 7(1), 1700889.
102. Genetic Home Reference. (2020). What are genome editing and CRISPR-Cas9?: Genetics Home Reference—NIH. In U.S. National Library of Medicine. https://ghr.nlm.nih.gov/primer/genomicresearch/genomeediting.
103. Hsu, P. D., Lander, E. S., & Zhang, F. (2014). Development and applications of CRISPR-Cas9 for genome engineering. *Cell*, 157(6), 1262–1278). https://doi.org/10.1016/j.cell.2014.05.010.
104. Gupta, R. M., & Musunuru, K. (2014). Expanding the genetic editing tool kit: ZFNs, TALENs, and CRISPR-Cas9. *Journal of Clinical Investigation*, 124(10), 4154–4161. https://doi.org/10.1172/JCI72992.
105. Lander, E. S. (2016). The Heroes of CRISPR. *Cell*, 164(1–2), 18–28). https://doi.org/10.1016/j.cell.2015.12.041.
106. Wootton, R. (2001). Telemedicine. *BMJ*, 323(7312), 557–560.
107. Pattichis, C. S., Kyriacou, E., Voskarides, S., Pattichis, M. S., Istepanian, R., & Schizas, C. N. (2002). Wireless telemedicine systems: An overview. *IEEE Antennas and Propagation Magazine*, 44(2), 143–153.
108. Bumbaširević, M., Lesic, A., Palibrk, T., Milovanovic, D., Zoka, M., Kravić-Stevović, T., & Raspopovic, S. (2020). The current state of bionic limbs from the surgeon's viewpoint. *EFORT Open Reviews*, 5(2), 65–72.
109. Rifi, N., Rachkidi, E., Agoulmine, N., & Taher, N. C. (2017). Towards using blockchain technology for eHealth data access management. In 4th International Conference on Advances in Biomedical Engineering (ICABME) (pp. 1–4). IEEE.
110. Zhang, A., & Lin, X. (2018). Towards secure and privacy-preserving data sharing in e-health systems via consortium blockchain. *Journal of Medical Systems*, 42(8), 140.
111. Casado-Vara, R., & Corchado, J. (2019). Distributed e-health wide-world accounting ledger via blockchain. *Journal of Intelligent & Fuzzy Systems*, 36(3), 2381–2386.
112. Davenport, T., & Kalakota, R. (2019). The potential for artificial intelligence in healthcare. *Future Healthcare Journal*, 6(2), 94.
113. Jiang, F., Jiang, Y., Zhi, H., Dong, Y., Li, H., Ma, S., ... Wang, Y. (2017). Artificial intelligence in healthcare: Past, present and future. *Stroke and Vascular Neurology*, 2(4), 230–243.
114. Yu, K. H., Beam, A. L., & Kohane, I. S. (2018). Artificial intelligence in healthcare. *Nature Biomedical Engineering*, 2(10), 719–731.
115. Adhikary T., Jana A.D., Chakrabarty A., & Jana S.K. (2020) The internet of things (IoT) augmentation in healthcare: An application analytics. In: Gunjan V., Garcia Diaz V., Cardona M., Solanki V., & Sunitha K. (eds.), ICICCT 2019 – System Reliability, Quality Control, Safety, Maintenance and Management. Singapore: Springer.
116. Biswas R., Pal S., Cuong N.H.H., Chakrabarty A. (2020) A novel IoT-based approach towards diabetes prediction using big data. In: Solanki V., Hoang M., Lu Z., & Pattnaik P. (eds.), *Intelligent Computing in Engineering. Advances in Intelligent Systems and Computing* (vol 1125). Singapore: Springer.

117. Biswas R., Pal S., Sarkar B., Chakrabarty A. (2020) Health-care paradigm and classification in IoT ecosystem using big data analytics: An analytical survey. In: Solanki V., Hoang M., Lu Z., & Pattnaik P. (Eds.), *Intelligent Computing in Engineering. Advances in Intelligent Systems and Computing* (vol 1125). Singapore: Springer.
118. Guntur, Sitaramanjaneya Reddy, Gorrepati, Rajani Reddy, & Dirisala, Vijaya R. (2019). Robotics in healthcare: An internet of medical robotic things (IoMRT) perspective. In *Machine Learning in Bio-Signal Analysis and Diagnostic Imaging* (pp. 293–318). Elsevier.
119. Chakrabarty, A., & Das, U. S. (2020). Big data analytics in excelling health care: Achievement and challenges in India. In P. Tanwar, V. Jain, C.-M. Liu, & V. Goyal (Eds.), *Big Data Analytics and Intelligence: A Perspective for Health Care* (pp. 55–74). Emerald Publishing Limited. doi:10.1108/978-1-83909-099-820201008
120. Chakrabarty, A., & Das, U. S. (2020). Universal health database in India: Emergence, feasibility and multiplier effects. In A. Mishra, G. Suseendran, & T.-N. Phung (Eds.), *Soft Computing Applications and Techniques in Healthcare* (pp. 215–234). CRC Press.
121. Wang, C., Fan, W., Zhang, Z., Wen, Y., Xiong, L., & Chen, X. (2019). Advanced nanotechnology leading the way to multimodal imaging-guided precision surgical therapy. *Advanced Materials*, 31(49), 1904329.
122. Chen, X. J., Zhang, X. Q., Liu, Q., Zhang, J., & Zhou, G. (2018). Nanotechnology: A promising method for oral cancer detection and diagnosis. *Journal of Nanobiotechnology*, 16(1), 52.
123. Grobmyer, S. R., Morse, D. L., Fletcher, B., Gutwein, L. G., Sharma, P., Krishna, V., ... & Brown, S. C. (2011). The promise of nanotechnology for solving clinical problems in breast cancer. *Journal of Surgical Oncology*, 103(4), 317–325.
124. Schulz, M. D., Khullar, O., Frangioni, J. V., Grinstaff, M. W., & Colson, Y. L. (2010). Nanotechnology in thoracic surgery. *The Annals of Thoracic Surgery*, 89(6), S2188–S2190.
125. Weng, Y., Liu, J., Jin, S., Guo, W., Liang, X., & Hu, Z. (2017). Nanotechnology-based strategies for treatment of ocular disease. *Acta Pharmaceutica Sinica B*, 7(3), 281–291.

9 ITreatU
An Effective Privacy and Security Solution for Healthcare Data Using the R3 Corda Platform of Blockchain Technology

Priyank Hajela, Ambika Pawar and Shraddha Phansalkar

CONTENTS

9.1 Introduction 165
    9.1.1 Components of Blockchain Technology 166
9.2 Related Work 166
9.3 Research Gaps 168
9.4 Research Problem 168
    9.4.1 Choice of Blockchain Platform 168
9.5 Proposed Solution 169
    9.5.1 The Architecture of the System 171
    9.5.2 ITreatU Corda Flow 173
    9.5.3 Algorithm 173
9.6 Performance Analysis 174
9.7 Conclusion and Future Scope 174
References 177

9.1 INTRODUCTION

Blockchain technology is a decentralized ledger that holds encrypted blocks that contain permanent or immutable data records that certain participants are allowed to view and exchange, with assured consistency throughout its usage from the time it is created, without human interference. Over the years, as the importance of data has grown, so has their vulnerability and misuse, and the healthcare sector is no exception. Hackers can leak patients' data [1], and other cyber-attackers can use the data to conduct medical fraud and other financial gains, and hence the healthcare sector must protect the personal information of its patients. Blockchain technology would enable the various systems to communicate with each other and have a fully integrated patient profile without the need for any specific verification from an intermediary. Records must be maintained in an independently verifiable, time-stamped and permanent ledger, ensuring that they could never be modified fraudulently by either entity.

R3 Corda [2] is an effective blockchain platform that has been used to tackle the issues of data privacy through some of the state-of-the-art CorDapps such as ZKP3, Medical Claim Management System and RevBlox, a CordDapp that assesses and scores claims using a combination of machine learning and rule-based formatting prior to actual submission to either the clearinghouse or payer. Other such examples where blockchain has been employed in the healthcare sector are pharmaceutical supply chains, claims management and health records exchange.

9.1.1 COMPONENTS OF BLOCKCHAIN TECHNOLOGY

Blockchain technology is a decentralized and peer-to-peer (P2P) ledger system with three main components [3, 4]:

- Distributed network: The shared P2P system has nodes composed of network members, where each user holds the same copy of the blockchain and is allowed to verify and approve cryptographic transactions in the network.
- Shared ledger: The participants of the network report ongoing digital transactions in a distributed and shared ledger. The algorithms are run by the members/participants to validate the proposed transaction, and when a major number of the participants approve the transaction, they append it to the shared ledger. The transactions are immutable and tamper-proof.
- Digital transaction: Any information or digital property that could be stored in blockchain counts as a digital transaction. Every transaction is organized into a "block," and each block includes a cryptographic hash for inserting transactions in a chronological sequence. Any structured or multimedia document can now be safely stored on the blockchain with hash.

9.2 RELATED WORK

In this section, we discuss some of the state-of-art privacy-preserving proof of concepts and applications related to the healthcare industry. We also provide a comparative analysis of the discussed solutions with other solutions using different technologies. Figure 9.1 provides a brief overview of the related work done in the field of the healthcare industry.

Abdullah Al Omar et al. introduced Medibchain [5], a data-storage platform, which stores healthcare data as a blockchain in the cloud, and the data are encrypted by using cryptographic functions. The patient is accountable for his data and has the overall control of them. Experimental performance assessment reveals that the application is working well in a decentralized environment. Patra et al. used

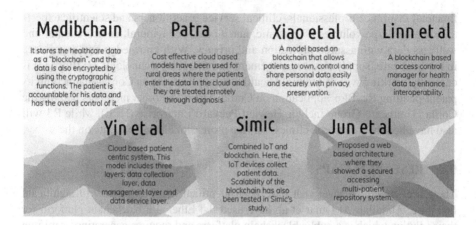

FIGURE 9.1 Related work in the healthcare industry. The figure consists of the work of seven researchers.

cost-effective cloud-based models in rural areas where the patients enter the data in the cloud and they are treated remotely through diagnosis [6]. Rolim et al. suggested collecting the medical data using sensors and sending them directly to the system. The Exchange Service [7] gathers data from sensors and submits them to relevant cloud-hosted computing facilities. Yin et al. implemented a patient-centric system in the cloud. This model consists of three modules: The data-storage module, the data-processing module and the data-operating module [8]. This paper introduced a digital health framework powered by the cloud and big data. Xiao et al. suggested a blockchain-based architecture [9] that enables patients to possess, monitor and exchange personal data conveniently and safely while protecting their privacy. Simic combined IoT and blockchain [10]. Here, IoT devices collect patient data. IoT devices and monitoring systems can collect huge amounts of data and automatically update patient electronic health records. IoT combined with blockchain reduces the expense of sharing patient information between organizations, decreases regulatory costs and makes auditing simpler. The literature shows that Simic's solution is scalable as well. Ekblaw et al. suggested a project named "MedRec" [11] that used blockchain to identify protection options for electronic health records. Patient-initiated sharing of data between medical jurisdictions is rendered possible by permission control on the blockchain. In order to uphold the necessity for secrecy on a granular basis, MedRec calls for unique authorizations. Jun et al. proposed a web-based architectural design that demonstrates secure access to a multi-patient repository system [12]. The research proposal is valuable for developing a patient-centric system for the sharing of health information over the Internet, which is especially essential for collaborative healthcare activities between medical professionals and institutions, and for preserving long-term health records. Linn et al. defined the Health Data Access Management System [13] focused on blockchain technology to improve interoperability. Linn et al. use the public blockchain for this study, because the usage of the new safety blockchain has the ability to connect millions of people, financial insurance professionals, clinical service practitioners and scientific experts to exchange large volumes of genomic, nutritional, behavioural, environmental and wellness data with assured protection and privacy. With knowledge and experience in medical care, supply chain management and financial technology, HSBlox [14] is currently working with R3 to build healthcare applications on Corda—launching its patent-pending RevBlox application on Corda. The many other members helping the Corda Healthcare Group include Hewlett Packard Enterprise (HPE), while R3 will also have healthcare payers, clinics, service professionals and patients on the web.

9.3 RESEARCH GAPS

There are some challenges that have been identified from the review of significant literature. Abdullah Al Omar et al. have used the Ethereum blockchain platform for their solution which is a public blockchain platform and requires generating or mining hashes which involves a high computational cost as well as vulnerability in terms of the hash key. The hash, once shared, becomes always available and cannot be changed. The patient is responsible for keeping track of his hash. Also, Abdullah Al Omar et al. have not been successful in investigating the interoperability of various institutions (e.g., research facilities, clinics, physicians, patients) in the healthcare sector, so they need to tackle the problem of managing key theft/loss processes or key delivery strategies.

The reviewed literature of Patra et al. shows that the operational benefits of their solution are cost-effectiveness, ease of implementation and the availability of data for study from anywhere in the world, but the researchers have not addressed the problem of data security and quality of service which is an area of concern in cloud computing. The literature also does not show significant work that focuses on patient-centric data privacy, where the patient can selectively give access and revoke access to his data. In the forthcoming sections, we have proposed a solution and discuss how these issues can be resolved.

9.4 RESEARCH PROBLEM

The goal of the chapter is to study the research gaps in the field of healthcare privacy using blockchain and develop an interoperable and secure solution using blockchain technology. This chapter will help the research community, as other researchers who are working on the same topic can read the chapter and use it to do further research or to solve some research problems. The first task in the process was to identify a good blockchain platform that meets the requirements of the problem statement. Once the blockchain platform was recognized, in the next phase, we designed the architecture and flow of the project. The forthcoming sections will discuss the same.

9.4.1 Choice of Blockchain Platform

The possible choices for our use case were Ethereum, Hyperledger Fabric and R3 Corda. After performing a detailed evaluation of the three blockchain platforms and comparing the features and limitations of each, we decided to go ahead with R3

FIGURE 9.2 Blockchain platforms—Ethereum, Hyperledger Fabric and R3 Corda. The figure is a brief overview of the three blockchain platforms

Corda for our research project. Figure 9.2 shows a brief overview of the three blockchain platforms. As seen in Table 9.1, R3 Corda has features that make it the ideal choice for our proposed solution.

We chose the Corda platform for our project due to some of the features of R3 Corda identified in the study as follows:

- Corda prohibits the unwanted exchange of data on the blockchain, as just users who have specific requirements have connections to the network. Many other distributed ledger technology (DLT) platforms like Hyperledger Fabric use global broadcast and gossip protocols to propagate data in the network, whereas Corda uses point-to-point messages, and propagates the messages on a need-to-know basis only (lazy propagation).
- The Corda platform allows data exchange on the network with no need for a central controller. The consensus is achieved at the micro-level transacting, rather than the system as a whole.
- Corda achieves uniqueness consensus through notary clusters. A notary cluster is a network service attesting that, for a given transaction, other transactions are not already signed that consume any of the proposed transaction's input states.
- Corda provides support for various consensus mechanisms based on the requirements in terms of privacy, scalability, legal-system compatibility, algorithmic agility and the structure of notary clusters. For example, it may choose to run a high-speed, high-trust algorithm such as RAFT, a low-speed, low-trust algorithm such as BFT or any other consensus algorithm.
- The nodes in the Corda platform discover each other via a network map service. One can imagine this service as a phone book, which publishes a peer nodes list that includes metadata about the node and the services it offers. Figure 9.3 shows some of the features of the R3 Corda platform.

9.5 PROPOSED SOLUTION

The proposed blockchain project in the healthcare scenario will be called I Treat You (ITU), which refers to a treatment (business) transaction between bilateral parties,

TABLE 9.1
Comparison between Ethereum, Hyperledger and Corda Blockchain Platforms

Parameters	Ethereum	Hyperledger	Corda
Type (Public/Private)	Public	Private/permissioned	Private
Consensus algorithm	Proof of work	PBFT	Notaries
Smart contract lang.	Solidity	Golang	Kotlin, Java, Scala
Smart contract enable	Turing complete	Yes (Chaincode)	Yes
Performance	16 transactions per second	1,500 transactions per second	1,500 transactions per second
Block time	16 secs	5 secs	No blocks
DDoS resistant	Yes	No	No
Quantum resistant	No	No	Yes
Storage capacity for data	1 Mb	1 Mb	Based on RAM (2–64 GB)
Disadvantages	1. Requires high computational power to mine a block 2. Throughput is low 3. Issue of scalability	1. There is a proposal that consensus algorithms in the hyper ledger fabric are not very secure	None
Interoperability	Cosmos/Polkadot	Hyperledger Quilt	Corda foundation
Applications	Cryptocurrency/business	Lifecycle assets/supply chain technologies/travel report retention/bond asset network/finance	Loans/finance/insurance/healthcare record-keeping applications

that is, the doctor and patient in Corda. The implementation of the Corda platform will be as in Figure 9.4.

Let us consider a simple case study to understand how the proposed solution helps us to attain privacy between two parties—the doctor and patient in the system. First, in the Corda network, if two participants, say, Alice and Bob, transact with each other, then owing to Corda's property of being a private blockchain platform, it allows only these two parties to agree or reach a consensus on the state of the ledger. Hence, the data remain private between the parties involved in the transaction. Also, once the transaction is notarized, it is stored in the vaults of Alice and Bob only. No other participant is aware of the transaction between Alice and Bob. Likewise, if Alice and Charlie transact, then only Alice

R3 Corda Platform of Blockchain Technology

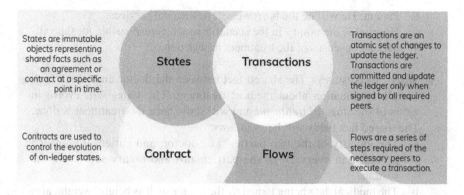

FIGURE 9.3 Overview of the R3 Corda concepts. The figure consists of four circular-shaped images.

and Charlie will be involved in reaching a consensus and no other participant can view the data between the involved parties.

9.5.1 THE ARCHITECTURE OF THE SYSTEM

1. There will be three types of participants involved in the system, namely, *doctor*, *patient* and hospital.
   a. Doctor: The issuer of the transaction. He will be the lender of the medical services.

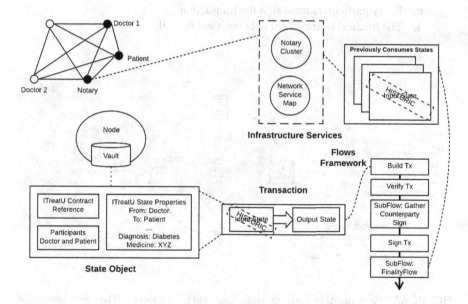

FIGURE 9.4 Architecture overview of the doctor–patient transaction (ITU).

b. Patient: He will be the borrower of the medical services.
c. Hospital is the notary in the scenario which is responsible for the validation consensus of the treatment transaction.

2. Shared facts (states): The shared fact between the doctor and patient will contain information about medical treatment. The states will evolve in terms of the *stage of treatment* and will settle once the treatment is done. The shared fact fields will be as follows:
    a. The identity of the two parties, i.e., doctor, and patient. Figure 9.5 provides an overview of the participants and notary service in the system.
    b. The medical data being issued by the doctor such as height, weight, age, blood group and the gender of the patient.
    c. The diagnosis and the medicines being issued by the doctor.

3. Validation rules or constraints of the transaction:
    a. The doctor and patient are the registered parties in the ecosystem, and the doctor and the patient cannot be the same entity.
    b. The transaction between the doctor and the patient will be private and no other doctor can see their transaction.
    c. An ITU in the bilateral ledger must be unique for every new visit and the doctor–patient interaction in the past must be traceable. Thus, a treatment history is created.
    d. There must only be one output state created, that is, after every interaction only one new ITU state must be created.
    e. Every participant must sign the transaction.
    f. The medical or treatment data must not be null.

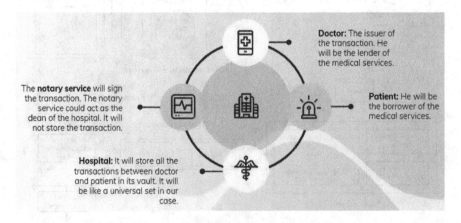

FIGURE 9.5 Participants of the transaction, vault and notary service. The figure consists of four elements, namely the doctor, patient, hospital and notary service.

R3 Corda Platform of Blockchain Technology

4. The notary service (hospital) will sign the transaction. The notary service could act as the dean of the hospital. R3 Corda supports *"need-to-know"* data sharing. Thus, the notary only carries validation and uniqueness consensus. It cannot store business transactions.

However, our implementation allows the notary to be the third participant as a hospital entity and thus empowered to store all the transactions. This implementation also allows the hospitals to have a central repository of the treatment records for future reference and helps to build trust in the practical implementation. Moreover, building data analytics algorithms is possible with this repository. The notary access can be easily revoked, thus making the transactions completely private for the patients.

9.5.2 ITreatU Corda Flow

1. The doctor node will propose the transaction, check for updates and sign it. The ledger is sent to the patient with one signature for verification.
2. The patient will verify and check the ledger for valid updates to the shared fact in the transaction, approve, sign and send it back to the doctor. Now, the ledger has two signatures, one from the doctor and one from the patient. To finalize the transaction and update the records, the ledger is sent to the notary pool.
3. The hospital notary will sign the transaction, and once it is committed it will be shared with the hospital (third participant). Figure 9.6 shows a schematic of the ITreatU flow.

9.5.3 Algorithm

We will go through the algorithm for ITreatU Corda Flow to understand the working of the blockchain network to simulate the transaction between the doctor and the patient. The main flow is split into initiator and acceptor flow. The initiator flow consists of four steps, namely, generating a transaction, verifying the transaction, signing transactions and gathering signatures. And the acceptor flow has the check_ transaction method that contains logic for verification from the counterparty.

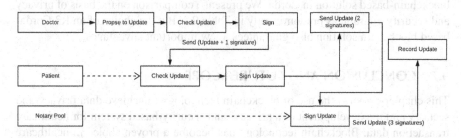

FIGURE 9.6 Node run flow to update the ledger. The figure consists of 11 rectangular boxes in a progressive manner from left to right.

- **Algorithm for signing the transaction**

Below are the algorithm steps for the initiation and signing of a transaction:

1. The initiator constructor initializes the ledger values with the medical data such as height, weight, age, blood group, the gender of the patient, diagnosis and medicine offered by the doctor.
2. We create issue_command using the command class. Commands in Corda provide information about the intention of a transaction.
3. Build the transaction by creating the transaction_builder object. Initialize the object of the transaction builder with the state object (which contains ledger data), and the issue command object created earlier, i.e., transaction_builder(itreatyou_state, issue_command).
4. We call the verify method of the contract class. Contracts are used to control the evolution of on-ledger states. Corda mandates that each state must reference a contract. The contract is meant for verification of the transactions to check if the transaction is valid with constraints like:
   a. There should be no inputs consumed when issuing an ITU, tx.getInputs().isEmpty()
   b. Only one output state is created, tx.getOutputs().size() == 1
   c. The doctor and the patient are not the same entity, out.getDoctor() != out.getPatient()
   d. Every participant signs the transaction
   e. The medical data are not null and are non-negative.
5. The first party signs the transaction, i.e., the doctor in our case.
6. The second party signs the counterparty, i.e., the patient in our case.
7. Finally, we get the signature of the notary, i.e., the hospital, using FinalityFlow and store the transaction in the vault. The hospital notary assures the authenticated doctor and patient contracting the contract.

9.6 PERFORMANCE ANALYSIS

Once we have accomplished a solution in the blockchain using the R3 Corda platform, we will now compare the different non-blockchain-based solutions with our blockchain-based solution in Corda. We present a comparison on the basis of privacy and security guarantees predominantly in Table 9.2. But the choice of an R3 Corda-based blockchain solution also guarantees a few important advantages.

9.7 CONCLUSION AND FUTURE SCOPE

This chapter explores the use of blockchain technology to achieve data privacy and security and the development of a privacy- and security-based system for healthcare transaction data. Blockchain technology has become a proven choice in healthcare solutions because of its guarantees of tamper-proof, secured and access-based control to healthcare data. The research work is an attempt to leverage these guarantees

TABLE 9.2
Performance Analysis of the Proposed Solution with Other Healthcare Privacy Solutions

Parameters	Non-blockchain-Based Application	Performance of the Non-Blockchain-Based Technology	Performance of R3 Corda Solution
Levels of data privacy and security	A smart mobile medical care system for patient–doctor interaction	Yongjun et al. have developed a self-management mobile application for chronic patients [15]. The application is intelligent, user-friendly and provides easy access to medical data but relies on identity and access management rules as per the OAuth and OpenID standards. It is not very secure as it only authenticates the users and does not **encrypt the data**. Any doctor who has the credentials can see any other patient's data. *Patient-centric privacy* not assured.	The use of permission-based blockchain such as Corda enables a private interaction between the doctor and the patient and ensures that the data are secure and accessible only to the participants of the transaction. ***Patient-centric privacy*** with the constraints in the smart contract and ***need-to-know*** data sharing.
Storage and computational efficiency	Health-CPS: Cyber-physical network supported by cloud and big data	Yin et al. implemented a patient-centric system in the cloud [8]. The medical data are stored in the distributed file storage which enhances the storage performance in terms of I/O. The adapter encrypts the pre-processed data while in transmission and decrypts before storage.	R3 Corda does not need data encryption as it is a **distributed ledger platform** where the ledger is only **bilateral**. The data security at the storage level is never an issue, unlike public blockchains. **Bilateral storage enforces trust as a service**.
Scalability	Automation of healthcare information collection using sensors	Rolim suggested collecting the medical data using sensors and sending them directly to the system [7]. The sensor nodes on the patient's bed are fitted with tools to capture, encrypt and relay data via wireless communication technology. The non-blockchain applications are **not scalable** because the data are centrally stored and the central node is a bottleneck. In other blockchain-based solutions, **every node stores all data**, and again **consensus** protocols make it unscalable.	Corda is a **linearly scalable** blockchain platform which considerably improves performance as the data are shared **only with the members of the network** that are concerned with the transaction.

(Continued)

TABLE 9.2 (CONTINUED)
Performance Analysis of the Proposed Solution with Other Healthcare Privacy Solutions

Parameters	Non-blockchain-Based Application	Performance of the Non-Blockchain-Based Technology	Performance of R3 Corda Solution
Throughput	Cloud-based rural healthcare information system	Patra et al. used cost-effective cloud-based models [6] in rural areas where the patients enter the data in the cloud and they are treated remotely through diagnosis. Patra et al. have however not addressed the problem of data security and quality of service which is a challenging area of research in cloud computing.	By virtue of its architecture, Corda ensures the security of data. Cordapps guarantee a high throughput with asynchronous **Corda Flows** and sub-flows that can be **checkpointed** in the **persistent storage**. This ensures a high quality of service.
Decentralized architecture	Stable web-based access from several patient databases	Jun et al. proposed a web-based architectural design that demonstrates secure access to a multi-patient repository system [10]. The application can safely access public health data stored in various hospitals. The disadvantage of the solution is that it relies on a **central access control** system; hence it is not scalable and requires high computational power.	Corda is a **decentralized blockchain platform** which increases the speed and flexibility as well as the independence of the system.

with a better healthcare privacy and security solution, with the adoption of the R3 blockchain platform. The platform has established applications in the finance domain, but its unprecedented levels of trust are exploited in this work to guarantee patient-centric data privacy. In this chapter, we have shown that the doctor–patient treatment interaction can be made private using a permission-based and bilateral ledger-based blockchain platform like Corda. The patient and doctor can now have treatment transactions stored as a trusted contract between them and the notary for validation only. The role of the notary in this application will be precisely defined in our future work. The future application is interoperable across different hospitals that use different blockchain platforms to store patient data.

REFERENCES

1. Mansfield-Devine, S. (2017). Leaks and ransoms–the key threats to healthcare organizations. *Network Security*, 2017(6), 14–19.
2. Mohanty, D. (2019). Corda architecture. In *R3 Corda for Architects and Developers* (pp. 49–60). Berkeley, CA: Apress.
3. Siano, P., De Marco, G., Rolán, A., & Loia, V. (2019). A survey and evaluation of the potentials of distributed ledger technology for peer-to-peer transactive energy exchanges in local energy markets. *IEEE Systems Journal*, 13(3), 3454–3466.
4. Zhang, K., & Jacobsen, H. A. (2018). Towards dependable, scalable, and pervasive distributed ledgers with blockchains. In IEEE 38th International Conference on Distributed Computing Systems (ICDCS) (pp. 1337–1346).
5. Al Omar, A., Rahman, M. S., Basu, A., & Kiyomoto, S. (2017). Medibchain: A blockchain-based privacy-preserving platform for healthcare data. In International Conference on Security, Privacy, and Anonymity in Computation, Communication, and Storage (pp. 534–543). Cham: Springer.
6. Patra, M. R., Das, R. K., & Padhy, R. P. (2012). CRHIS: Cloud-based rural healthcare information system. In Proceedings of the 6th International Conference on Theory and Practice of Electronic Governance (pp. 402–405).
7. Rolim, C. O., Koch, F. L., Westphall, C. B., Werner, J., Fracalossi, A., & Salvador, G. S. (2010). A cloud computing solution for patient's data collection in health care institutions. In 2nd International Conference on e-Health, Telemedicine, and Social Medicine (pp. 95–99). IEEE.
8. Zhang, Y., Qiu, M., Tsai, C. W., Hassan, M. M., & Alamri, A. (2015). Health-CPS: Healthcare cyber-physical system assisted by cloud and big data. *IEEE Systems Journal*, 11(1), 88–95.
9. Yue, X., Wang, H., Jin, D., Li, M., & Jiang, W. (2016). Healthcare data gateways: Found healthcare intelligence on the blockchain with novel privacy risk control. *Journal of Medical Systems*, 40(10), 218.
10. Simić, M., Sladić, G., & Milosavljević, B. (2017). A case study of IoT and blockchain-powered healthcare. In The 8th PSU-UNS International Conference on Engineering and Technology (ICET-2017).
11. Azaria, A., Ekblaw, A., Vieira, T., & Lippman, A. (2016). Medrec: Using blockchain for medical data access and permission management. In 2nd International Conference on Open and Big Data (OBD) (pp. 25–30). IEEE.
12. Choe, J., & Yoo, S. K. (2008). Web-based secure access from multiple patient repositories. *International Journal of Medical Informatics*, 77(4), 242–248.

13. Linn, L. A., & Koo, M. B. (2016). Blockchain for health data and its potential use in health IT and healthcare-related research. In ONC/NIST Use of Blockchain for Healthcare and Research Workshop (pp. 1–10). Gaithersburg, MD, USA: ONC/NIST.
14. Katuwal, G. J., Pandey, S., Hennessey, M., & Lamichhane, B. (2018). Applications of blockchain in healthcare: Current landscape & challenges. arXiv:1812.02776.
15. Jon, Y., Kim, D., Lee, D., Kim, B., & Lee, I. (2017). Smart mobile healthcare system development for patient-doctor interaction and self-management* Yongjun Jon," Dongkyun Kim, "Dongin Lee," Bonghwan Kim," Insoo Lee and" Kyunghan Chun" School of Computer Science and Engineering. *Journal of Engineering and Applied Sciences*, 12(19), 4856–4861.

10 Personalized Medicine and a Data Revolution
Hope and Peril

Subhajit Basu and Adekemi Omotubora

CONTENTS

10.1 Introduction	179
10.2 Personalized Medicine: The Development	180
10.3 Is Personalized Medicine the New "Eugenics"?	182
10.4 The Power of Data in Medicine	184
10.5 Privacy and Personalized Medicine	186
10.6 Conclusion	191
Notes	192
References	193

10.1 INTRODUCTION

Our technology-enabled healthcare system is becoming increasingly information intensive. Healthcare is being transformed into a system that is expertly tailored to the needs of individual patients. Over the past two decades, genomic sequencing and other technologies have generated an unprecedented amount of data about the human genome, informing our understanding of human health and enabling rapid advances in the development of medicines [1]. A large volume of data is collected regularly, and once we manage to analyse large datasets of genetic and health information, we may uncover previously unknown connections between patient characteristics, symptoms and medical conditions. It is the integration and analysis of this information that forms the core of personalized medicine.

Personalized medicine unlocks the value of patient data to consider individual differences in a person's genes, environment and lifestyle [2]. This will allow researchers to take the guesswork out of healthcare, as "increased utilisation of molecular stratification of patients, for example assessing for mutations that give rise to resistance to certain treatments, will provide medical professionals with clear evidence upon which to base treatment strategies for individual patients" [3]. In most typical situations, clinicians are pushed to follow a non-optimal trial-and-error approach in prescribing treatment options for the average patient. However, most of us are not average, so if the medication does not work after a while, the patient might be switched to another medication. This approach often leads to adverse drug responses and, in worst-case scenarios, serious health problems [34].

Any data-focused intervention comes at a price. Personalized medicine may well enhance healthcare, but its future will depend upon how we address relevant legal and ethical issues arising from both challenges and limitations concerning data. This chapter examines the challenges posed by such technological breakthroughs, including the complexity of data, and in particular the role to be given to consent that would provide transparency and foster patients' trust in the development of personalized medicine. This chapter sets out a framework to ensure the appropriate balance between emerging scientific discoveries with commercial gains and the rights of individuals within a system designed for the express purpose of exchanging critical personal information.

10.2 PERSONALIZED MEDICINE: THE DEVELOPMENT

The age of "one size fits all" in healthcare is slowly becoming obsolete. Healthcare, as we know it, is primarily reactive—the medical community is trying to shift from reactive care to proactive and preventive technology-oriented care [5], in Foucauldian terms, shifting the role of healthcare beyond the management of sickness to the management and optimization of health [6]. Cancer, neurodegenerative diseases and rare genetic conditions take an enormous toll on individuals, families and societies [7]. However, one disease may have many different forms, or "subtypes," resulting from the complex interaction of our biological make-up and the diverse pathological and physiological processes in our bodies. These will not only vary between patients who have the same disease but also within an individual patient as they get older and their body changes [2]. Personalized medicine is one of the most promising approaches to tackling diseases that have thus far eluded effective treatments or cures [8, 9].

We envision a world where diseases can be prevented before they strike and cured decisively by harnessing the vast datasets of biomedical information now available to us [10]. Health systems, including those of the US, Germany, France, Canada, Australia, China and India, are formulating policy and research programmes to support the adoption of more personalized approaches to healthcare [2, 11] These policies are based on the convergence of the scientific and technological tools of systems medicine, the digital revolution and patients' involvement in their health decisions [12]. In one way or another, physics, chemistry, biochemistry, biology, mathematics and social sciences are becoming involved in medical problem-solving [13].

It is well known that genomics can improve the treatment of disease, because of learning from the Human Genome Project and subsequent scientific work.

> Molecular data analysis based on genetic data acquired from large numbers of people can provide not only a massive volume of health-related information, but also a diversity in the kinds of information we can derive, from responsiveness to drugs, to likelihood of contracting a particular disease, and ways to prevent or reduce the risk of certain diseases later on in life.
>
> [1]

Genomics, as it is argued, enables the tailoring of treatments to the genomic basis of each individual's disease-pharmacogenomics [14]. Personalized medicine recognizes that complex diseases should no longer be considered as a single entity [15]; instead "it seeks to focus on 'causes of cases' and to target more specifically the biological pathways to disease in individuals" [16]. In 2015, the European Commission defined personalized medicine as:

> A medical model using the characterisation of individuals' phenotypes and genotypes (e.g. molecular profiling, medical imaging, lifestyle data) for tailoring the right therapeutic strategy for the right person at the right time, and/or to determine the predisposition to disease and/or to deliver timely and targeted prevention. Personalised medicine relates to the broader concept of patient-centred care, which considers that, in general, healthcare systems need to better respond to patient needs.
>
> [17]

There is, however, debate around the meaning and scope of the concept [18] and what precisely the concept should include [19]. The National Research Council (NRC) has expressed concern that "personalized medicine" may be misconstrued to mean that completely individualized treatments are available for every unique patient, which is not the case [17]. In its 2011 report "Towards Precision Medicine," the NRC states:

> Precision medicine refers to the tailoring of medical treatment to the individual characteristics of each patient. It does not mean the creation of drugs or medical devices that are unique to a patient, but rather the ability to classify individuals into subpopulations that differ in their susceptibility to a particular disease … or in their response to a specific treatment. Although the term "personalised medicine" is also used to convey this meaning, that term is sometimes misinterpreted as implying that unique treatments can be designed for each individual. It should be emphasized that in "precision medicine," the word "precision" is being used in a colloquial sense, to mean both "accurate" and "precise."
>
> [17]

According to the PHG Foundation's report on personalized medicine technology, while genomics is a critical element of personalized medicine, it is not the only element. Different technology areas will potentially have a significant impact either on patient outcomes or on health system implementation [20]. These technologies can broadly be grouped into one of the following four categories:

- Technologies for greater molecular characterization of individuals or disease, e.g., genomics, metabolomics, proteomics
- Technologies for personalized therapeutic interventions, e.g., stem cell therapy, genome editing/therapy, robotics
- Technologies for personalized disease and health monitoring, e.g., consumer mHealth apps, digitally enabled wearables, sensors
- Underpinning and enabling technologies to transform the performance or capabilities of other technologies, e.g., artificial intelligence and machine learning, microfluidics, nanomedicine [20]

"Personalised medicine fundamentally relies on the successful digitisation of patient records, other healthcare data sets, and increasingly 'citizen-generated' health-related data" [20]. However, as was explained earlier, policy in this area is continually evolving [20]. In the UK, the NHS aims to "exploit the information revolution" with specific goals for the health system to go paperless by implementing fully interoperable electronic health records (EHR) and for citizens to be able to access and share their medical and care records [20]. In response to these targets, the National Information Board[1] in the UK [20] published a framework for action and strategic priorities for delivering digital ambitions [21]. In the past few years, there has been real progress, from large-scale EHR and health analytics platforms such as Kaiser Permanente's HealthConnect to the use of deep learning and AI technologies such as IBM Watson [22] and DeepMind [23].[2] A "new generation of more agile point-of-care focused clinical decision support tools, are becoming available" [24].

Individualizing patient treatment is a core objective of the medical field. This objective has been elusive owing to the complex set of factors contributing to both disease and health; many factors, from genes to proteins, remain unknown in their role in human physiology [25]. The traditional approach has been to discover a novel biomarker, clinically validate it and then use it to segment patients into corresponding therapy response groups; design a clinical trial and approval process and put a new drug on the market[3] [25]. This approach has been hard for several reasons first it takes a minimum of 10–15 years to put a drug on the market, and it costs a significant amount of money. Second, smaller responder populations may improve the efficiency and success rate of approvals, but this will mean a reduction of the economic potential of the drug once on the market. Third, having more specific patient cohorts can vastly increase the cost and complexity of patient recruitment. [24] With much more digital data available and the computing power to crunch the numbers, it has now become possible to uncover new relationships between genes, drugs and populations [25].

Personalized medicine will also disrupt current drug manufacturing protocols. Without a regulatory framework and guidance on how best to design a successful clinical trial for personalized therapy [26], personalized medicine developers risk presenting suboptimal evidence about stratification options. Companies are reluctant to make this investment without an equal increase in the certainty of regulatory approval [26]. Incidentally how personalized medicine will affect the manufacturing and distribution of medicines remains unclear, but, in our view, the pharmaceutical industry will undoubtedly need to adapt to fulfil individualized production needs [27].

10.3 IS PERSONALIZED MEDICINE THE NEW "EUGENICS"?

We argue that cost, regulations and ethical issues are some of the main challenges that urgently need to be addressed before progress can be made in this area [28, 29]. There are several viewpoints on the explosion of genetic medicine. Eugenics, a practice of preventing genetic diseases before they happen, calls back to the ideology of Nazi Germany. This connects to a further concern, that genomic testing can cultivate a practice of discrimination, particularly in employment and insurance. This concern is genuine as there are divergent interests among stakeholders in personalized medicine; the patients' desires may differ from the goals of clinicians or pharmaceutical [30] companies.

Insurance companies and even employers in the future could ask for predictive genetic tests for asymptomatic individuals to predict the risk of disease [30]. This kind of testing is different from diagnostic genetic testing used to confirm or rule out a known or suspected genetic disorder in an asymptomatic individual. This would be "genetic discrimination" because even small genomic differences can have significant economic implications [28]. For example, genomic information could indicate not only that an individual is more likely to develop a specific illness in the future [31], but also that the individual would not be responsive to standard medications [28], that is, treating people differently based on information collected about them.

It has been argued in respect of enhancement technologies that too much information about individuals' health risks and status can undermine solidarity by depriving people of the very uncertainty about their own and others' fates on which a commitment to sharing those fates depends [6]. Personalized medicine also entails the risk of exacerbating health inequalities, in particular between racial and ethnic groups [32]. The fact that personalized medicine has a participatory component requires that different racial and ethnic groups trust and actively engage in personalized medicine initiatives [32], which can be extremely challenging. Kahn argues that "constructions of race as genetic are not only scientifically flawed, they are socially dangerous, opening the door to new forms of discrimination or the misallocation of scarce resources needed to address real health disparities" [33]. This idea is the real danger of personalized medicine, the fear of a new racial segmentation[4] of medicine likely to result from testing will exacerbate existing inequalities in the society [14]. Fundamentally, the beauty of genetic diversity should be studied and understood, but we should protect the universality of our human heritage.

Personalized medicine gives the impression that healthcare should be "all about me." It is the individual who becomes essential as opposed to society, which even leads back to the idea that one race is better than another. However, the COVID-19 pandemic has created unprecedented uncertainty and widespread vulnerability; it has further highlighted the tension between individual and collective discretion. From this point of view, personalized medicine raises a further dilemma and also raises the question of equity [6]. If I am in a low-risk category, should I pay higher taxes for the entirely predictable illnesses of those at high risk—or should I opt out and insure myself, taking advantage of low rates on account of my good genetic fortune? If I know, or could know, that I am at high risk, should I disclose this information or disguise it—leaving others to take responsibility for the costs of my failure to disclose [14]? This individualist perspective to medicine challenges the ethical obligation of those who are committed to promoting the *"common good."* However, we cannot deny the fact that genetic variations in different populations probably cause many common diseases; it is essential to acknowledge that nothing is more variable than the facts in medicine. On the other hand, pharmaceutical companies could invest in products for the most expensive markets, and not in the medical needs of those who suffer from the most prevalent diseases [34].

We argue that prioritizing equity and inclusion should be a clearly stated goal when developing and deploying personalized medicine in healthcare. There are widely recognized inequities in health outcomes due to the variety of social determinants of health and perverse incentives in the existing healthcare system. Unfortunately, consumer-facing technologies have often worsened historical inequities in other fields and are at risk of doing so in personalized healthcare as well.

There is also a more positive side; we are looking at the beginnings of new forms of solidarity, social networking of people afflicted by similar conditions. Indeed, some personal genomic sites explicitly seek to foster such communities, notably '23andMe' [35, 36], although it is less clear whether this attention to community is for genuine ethical reasons or those of commercial ambition.[5] Through websites such as "Patients Like Me",[6] people try to develop new kinds of collectives, linked by a common condition, and by collective concern [37]. They share information ranging from the latest scientific research to the mundane details of the day-to-day management of illness, campaigning for research into their disease, but such social networks among active patient communities are confined mainly to the developed world. The most uncomfortable question that follows is: Is personalized medicine inherently discriminatory? In our view, personal medicine, if it is optimized to its outcomes, is a positive effort, but if it is optimized to its values, then the answer will be yes.[7] Some people will suffer under the new system because they will not receive the treatments they previously had. However, the system is already limited by resources—the distribution of those limited resources is a zero-sum game; the denial of treatment will just now be going somewhere else, and hopefully, those denials will make more sense.

10.4 THE POWER OF DATA IN MEDICINE

There is yet no single definition of big data analytics, but there seems to be some consensus on its components. One definition is that big data analytics consists of large amounts of data produced from different types of sources, such as people, machines and sensors (the "big" component of the data).

In personalized medicine, it is not just about generating large datasets ("big data"), it is also about finding meaningful insights from combining different datasets and converting long-term longitudinal datasets ("long data") into "actionable big data" which can be used to improve health outcomes and establish effective and efficient healthcare systems.

The advancement of personalized medicine relies on the ability to mine, analyse and derive new insights from the enormous volumes of data generated by digital technologies [1]. This new field unlocks the value of patient data so that individual differences in a person's genes, environment and lifestyle can be considered. Combining these abundant and intricate health data with innovative analysis strategies in a multidisciplinary setting can generate powerful models of complex diseases, and lead to new forms of diagnosis, treatment and prevention [38, 39]. This generation of strategies from data will allow researchers to take the guesswork out of healthcare. If we manage to analyse large datasets of genetic and health information, it is possible to uncover previously unknown connections between patient characteristics, symptoms and medical conditions [40].

Indeed, it seems inevitable that optimized and individualized health products will form one element of personal "whole-life management" [41]. Genomic data acquired at the beginning of life will be supplemented throughout life by findings from continuous supplies of additional data as well as from aggregated data gleaned from the whole population [42]. Both the volume and variety of data stand to increase tremendously in the coming years [43]. As it is, due to personalization and the sheer amount of molecular data being generated, modern-day healthcare is becoming increasingly information intensive [44]. Much of these data are collected, stored and analysed in digital form. Widespread data sharing will radically accelerate personalized medicine, making discovery and treatment more efficient [45].

Although the role of drugs is still central to a great deal of patient care, prescribing a drug with a generalized instruction as to how much to take and when is becoming insufficient [46]. There is an expansion in the kinds of data in digital form that exist and that are health-relevant. This expansion is contextualized by the so-called digital era of bioinformatics and "big data," which is enabling the collation of, and application of predictive modelling methods to, unprecedented quantities of biomedical data [18]. Dutfield argues that AI could extract knowledge in ways not possible before. "Significantly, the technology can uncover patterns in large and complex datasets that would not easily be apparent or perceivable to humans, helping to lead to new insights and greater stratification of patients for disease prediction and prognosis" [1].

Social media platforms amass individual data that may well have health relevance when integrated with genomic data and personal medical records. Furthermore, machine learning can massively accelerate the identification of patterns and make health-relevant "context-jumping" inferences. However, digital collections and biobanks are many, highly dispersed and subject to different rules, regulations, ownership and control norms depending on various factors, including whether they are private or public. We are witnessing the emergence of a range of miniaturized and portable medical and non-medical devices that can be connected to data capture and analysis systems via the Internet [20]. In principle, these devices could radically transform the landscape of when, where and how healthcare activities take place [47].

Moreover, the widespread diffusion of mobile technology, mHealth and wearables will provide a rich source of health-related data to catalyse the development of personalized health approaches by commercial and research entities [48]. The latter includes those of genetic testing companies like Myriad but also direct-to-consumer DNA testing kit providers like 23andMe, and wearable health monitoring technology firms like Fitbit. However, this implies circulating and sharing personal health data among data experts and medical specialists who can, together, derive the most apt interpretation and extend understanding [49]. The extent to which privacy protection inhibits or promotes the adoption of new technologies is a contentious issue [50–52].

In an age of data compiling and sharing across academic, industry and healthcare settings, the most important considerations are patient confidentiality and protection of information [53]. Hence a society conscious of the importance of personal rights as well as of the importance of personal health legitimately demands a balance between the sharing of data and data privacy [54]. Consequently, without adequate resolution of this inherent tension, the benefits of personalized medicine will be delayed and perhaps lost [53].

10.5 PRIVACY AND PERSONALIZED MEDICINE

The concept of privacy stands for a diverse set of interests [55]. It is a surprisingly difficult concept to define, as there are many different definitions within the literature generated by different academic disciplines that examine privacy [23]. Researchers[8] recognize that the definition of privacy is multi-dimensional, [41] potentially including information, activities, decisions, thoughts, bodies and communication, and is shaped by complex social, economic and political processes [56]. A full theory of privacy would need to consider all these dimensions, even if, eventually, it asserted theoretically grounded exclusions [57]. However, a detailed exploration of privacy theory is beyond the scope of this chapter, which aims not for a full theory of privacy, but only the right to privacy as it applies to information about individuals.

It is imperative to distinguish between privacy principles that are voluntary and unenforceable on the one hand and actual privacy law that has enforceable rights and procedures. The concept of "privacy as control" embeds the main points of this concept [58]. Individuals' consent to the processing of information concerning them lies at the heart of these opinions. In other words, consent is closely linked to the concept of informational self-determination.[9] From this perspective, ensuring an individual's consent to their data processing is crucial for the realization of privacy. The expression of "individual autonomy" continuously requires making choices and decisions [59]. Often assumed to contribute to a just healthcare system where all members of society benefit equally from scientific discovery, these technologies nevertheless raise the question as to whether their processing of data may ignore or undermine the autonomy-based rights of individuals to decide with whom to share their data.

While we accept that personalized medicine will provide significant benefits to society, it can also raise privacy concerns. For example, the healthcare system may use data that are personally and potentially identifiable, and correlations of that data can also produce or generate new personal data. In the context of big data and personalized medicine, it is helpful to think not just in terms of privacy in general, but in terms of specific privacy threats. The critical question is: How could this go wrong? We argue that there are at least two broad categories of threats: Unintended disclosure and discrimination. The further question is, if harm is caused because of such action—who should be held responsible? Also, it would not be wrong to argue that a lack of transparency can, in some ways, constitute a third category of threats. Hence an adequate legal framework must be developed to ensure data privacy in personalized medicine. While we acknowledge the vigorous debate over almost every aspect of the problem of genomic privacy and personalized medicine, in this section, we focus on consent in the development of trust and transparency in personalized medicine.

There has been a long-standing assertion that a genome constitutes de-identified [60] information, the disclosure of which poses no significant privacy risk. Medical researchers have been debating whether subjects of genomic research can expect to remain anonymous. However, new studies suggest that future re-identification is increasingly possible [60], if not probable. As we understand, a de-identified file can contain both genomic data and traditional medical data, including demographic information on the patient. An individual can be re-identified [61].

Even before the advent of personalized medicine, there has been a long-standing struggle to design personal data systems to support application developers who want to provide rich, personalized experiences without compromising end-user privacy [62, 63]. Big data analytics and personalized medicine have managed to make it worse. For example, gene sequencing is often carried out without specific consent from the individual whose DNA is sequenced, while the protection of genetic privacy is essential for minimizing genetic discrimination [64].

The EU, based on the argument that safeguarding privacy must be a legal imperative, has taken an active initiative towards a top-down approach to data protection [65]. The "regulation model" proffered by the EU holds that standardized data protection regulations (eventually on a global scale) are necessary [66]. "General Data Protection Regulation (GDPR) is premised on the aim to balance the protection of individual privacy, and it is informed by principles and values such as privacy, accountability, transparency, and fairness" [67]. It aims to avoid unduly restricting or prohibiting the "free movement of personal data"[10] and to make the EU legal framework in this area work with new scientific concepts.

Data protection laws apply when personal data, i.e., any information relating to an identified or identifiable natural person, are being processed. The health data of an individual are inherently personal data[11] and a "special category" of personal data,[12] often called "sensitive personal data".[13] The GDPR introduces a broad definition of health data:

> Personal data concerning health should include all data pertaining to the health status of a data subject which reveal information relating to the past, current or future physical or mental health status of the data subject. This includes information about the natural person collected in the course of the registration form or the provision of, healthcare services.[14]
>
> [67]

There was a substantial policy debate about whether genetic health data are distinct and different from regular health data and therefore need a special class of protection [51, 52, 68]. Health data are distinguished from genetic and biometric data[15] as any data "which reveal information about [the data subject's] health status",[16] about the data subject's "physical or mental health or condition," and is thus not limited to "ill-health" [23].

Sensitive data now specifically include genetic data and biometric data, processed "to uniquely identify a person." Article 9(2) sets out the circumstances in which the processing of "special categories of personal data," otherwise prohibited, may occur. Article 9(4) GDPR maintains or imposes further conditions (including limitations) in respect of genetic, biometric or health data. This prohibition stems from the need to specially protect data subjects against "significant risks to a person's fundamental rights and freedoms," such as privacy and discrimination, that the processing of sensitive personal data can bring [23].[17] The prohibition has a wide scope, in that its processing comprises the collection and all further uses of the data, including the process of anonymizing personal data [23]. Viewed in this light, even the continuous collection of health data for medical records and their sharing within the medical team in the direct care of a patient are prohibited unless the collection and sharing of the records can be justified and meet the specific requirements set out in the law.

Finally, at the heart of this issue lies perhaps the most important area of concern, the misunderstandings over the consent model. According to the GDPR, consent[18] is "any freely given, specific, informed, and unambiguous indication of the data subject's wishes by which he or she, by a statement or by clear affirmative action, signifies agreement to the processing of personal data relating to him or her." First of all, there are significant doubts about whether consent, when required because there is no other legitimate ground, is meaningful. Informed consent is a concept first adopted in codes of medical ethics concerning treatment and participation in research. The same principles, however, apply in both areas (data protection and medical treatment and research) since the principle of autonomy underpins both contexts. It must be made clear that in data protection legislation, consent is not necessary for legitimizing the processing of data by healthcare professionals.[19] However, the opaque nature of data analytics hinders meaningful consent. Since specific consent must also be intelligible and refer clearly and precisely to the purpose and means of data processing, for personalized medicine, the traditional concept of one-off consent to a specific purpose[20] appears to be inadequate.

The prevalent views of meaningful autonomy in medical ethics can enhance this idea about the utmost importance of the way information is provided about data processing. Bowman et al. [9] argue that autonomy gains more value when the exchange of information facilitates it. This argument would also be valid even when processing is based on grounds other than consent, and the principle of transparency still applies. Recital 56 of the GDPR suggests that the principle of transparency entails that the data controller should provide information about the processing of the data in a concise, easily accessible and comprehensible way in clear and understandable language. It is also suggested that visualization can be used and that such information could be provided in electronic form, for example, when addressed to the public, through a website. According to the Recital, attention should be paid to cases of complex practices that enhance informational asymmetries between the data controller and the data subject. It could be suggested that this approach could also be followed when informed consent is given to the processing of medical data.

Ensuring trust of patients in data processing is a key factor for promoting data sharing and data linkage. Indeed, research shows that the level of trust individuals place in research organizations, oversight bodies or government affects their level of support for research uses of data. More trust in the public sector than the private sector was reported, due to the greater accountability and data protection mechanisms within the public sector. Exceptions for public sector organizations cast doubt on the actual respect for privacy. More private organizations legitimize their data processing based on consent, while the public sector can invoke a list of various exceptions. In general, there is evidence of a high level of public trust in primary healthcare providers. This trust may be explained by the close relationship between the first-line doctor and the patients. It is the GP who bears the responsibility for how their data will be used because a relationship of confidentiality and fidelity has been established. Certification mechanisms[21] can play a significant role in enhancing trust, especially in the private sector [69].

Transparency about data practices is essential not just as a fundamental element of privacy, but it is also key to engendering trust, which in turn is critical to the adoption of personalized medicine. Research[22] has shown that when people are informed about processing activities, they tend to be more supportive of data-sharing projects. It has also been demonstrated that a quite high percentage of people are not aware of how patients' data can contribute to medical research. GDPR has put much emphasis on transparency. The principle of transparency[23] has been recognized as a central principle in the data protection framework. This principle, which is further analysed in Article 12, justifies the imposing of an obligation to provide information to data subjects, foreseen in Article 13 and 14. Many stakeholders complain about the information requirements, asserting that they are extremely burdensome, especially concerning highly sophisticated genomic projects.

Nevertheless, considering the needs of the data subjects and their fundamental right to autonomy, the legal framework has provided for conditions that facilitate the provision of information to data subjects in a way that is not too complicated for the data controller. Most crucially, transparency and provision of information are an obligation binding the data controller even if informed consent is not the legal ground for the processing. This obligation is key for the empowerment of patients as data subjects. The information provided will enable them to exercise their right and actively participate in the digital health environment.

It can be observed that there is a tendency for the empowerment of weaker parties in contractual relationships in the EU context. Starting from patient empowerment, which put limits on medical paternalism, to consumer empowerment and the data subject's empowerment, it seems that social relationships, as well as digital health initiatives, will thrive if individuals trust and engage in the system. If they trust the system, their doctors and data controllers will be happy to share their data to be used for social benefit. In the context of health data, informational asymmetry requires the empowerment of data subjects through clear, intelligible information. Taking into account that respect for confidentiality constitutes a necessary element of a trust relationship between the physician and the patient and has a positive impact in the treatment, it is aptly mentioned in Recital 75 of the GDPR that loss of confidentiality of personal data protected by professional secrecy constitutes a significant risk to the rights and interests of the individual. However, it is also argued that respect for and protection of confidentiality are also an ~~demonstration~~indication of public interest. Respect for doctors is a decisive factor for high-quality care.

Transparency seems to satisfy the essence of privacy as a right to self-determination. Even if informed consent is not required, the data subjects must be aware of the data processing. Transparency also protects the sense of confidentiality because transparent information can make clear the reasons behind any disclosure in favour of the others' rights or public interest and form the relevant expectations. While consent seems to be a relevant factor, studies do not indicate that it is a fundamental requirement for public acceptability. What counts more is not which consent mechanisms are preferable, but how relationships of trust can be developed [70].

Evidence suggests that patients are becoming more alert to the possibilities that allowing the sharing of their data will make it possible to put data to use for the benefit of healthcare in general as well as for individual patients (European Alliance for Personalised Medicine, [71]). It further shows that societal benefits anticipated to come from the research overcome any potential negative impact on privacy. Spencer et al. found that when people were informed about the aims of research projects, they were more willing to share their data but noted a lack of transparency and awareness around the use of data. This view makes it difficult to secure public trust, so for the majority of the people, the research should have a precise, practical application or real-world value [56, 72].

Although GDPR prescribes methods to provide people with control over their personal information, it does not provide a model of consent that accurately reflects behaviour in different contexts and particularly in the context of healthcare and its various sub-contexts [73]. Birnhack argues that the current legal framework implies that patients become data subjects without their consent for medical progress [58]. Birnhack maintains that data protection law materializes the protection of human dignity, a demonstration of which is privacy, in the sense that the right to privacy involves the power to choose a state of privacy or not [58]. Therefore, consent enhances subjects' autonomy by giving them the right to determine who will process their personal data and for what purpose. The process-based approach that involves the assessment of privacy risk and the implementation of safeguards at each stage of processing can safeguard the human dignity of data subjects by equipping them with control over their data in the context of data-driven medical innovation.

With information privacy, a capacious claim of right to all personal information undermines legal enforcement because the consequences of a lack of privacy are too often ill-defined and misunderstood [74]. All developed countries have grappled with the trade-offs between open access to information, which enables economic efficiency, and an individual's right to privacy [75]. There is the argument that market-oriented mechanisms based on individual ownership of personal data may enhance personal data protection [76]. Hence, an adequate amount of information sharing will occur up to the point where the economic benefits of information sharing are balanced against associated costs. Specifically, if the economic value created by information sharing exceeds the value derived from privacy, the theory maintains that the economically efficient outcome would be to share information [77].

In contrast, if the economic value generated by private parties from access to information does not exceed the benefit from privacy, then economic efficiency dictates that information is not shared [78]. Simultaneously, disclosure or non-disclosure of personal information is also subject to what is called the "calculus of behaviour" [79], which means an individual considers future consequences a critical determinant when considering the disclosure of personal information [80]. An individual who perceives potential future (negative) consequences to be minimal will be more willing to disclose personal information [80]. In other words, individuals will exchange personal information as long as they perceive that adequate benefits will be received in return—that is, benefits which exceed the perceived risks (economic or social benefit outweighs the risks) [81] of information disclosure as they view them [82]. At present, there is not enough transparency around the benefits of sharing, so people are naturally suspicious. If patients knew how many lives had been saved via research, some might feel differently.

10.6 CONCLUSION

There is no doubt that personalized medicine can transform the healthcare system by providing effective, tailored therapeutic strategies based on the genomic, epigenomic and proteomic profile of an individual [3]. These strategies would improve the quality of patient care and eventually reduce increasing healthcare costs and drug-development costs for which data collection and sharing are essential. Unnecessarily complex data protection rules would impede innovation in healthcare, and personalized medicine will not work without the initial sharing of data (something that cannot be avoided).

Reinforcing privacy as control by providing more control to data subjects can be an enabler for healthcare innovation. At the same time, GDPR is a step in the right direction to ensure the free flow of data within the EU. However, beyond the EU, some of the barriers to data sharing are cultural, some are regulatory and some are simply the consequence of insufficient technical methods for obtaining consent [71]. It is problematic to seek explicit consent as the purpose of using the data is not always clear at the time of collection of the data, and the informed consent requirement of GDPR makes the process far more complicated; at the time of consent, participants cannot know every exact potential use of their genetic data or the information they reveal about not just the individual but their families.

The GDPR promoted a risk-based approach in the data protection legislation. This approach is more flexible and permits review and monitoring of risks at each stage of the processing of healthcare data. Depending on the risks, data controllers are expected to implement appropriate safeguards. This approach seems to be more suitable for the digital health environment. However, fundamental rights will always play a role. Legal rules intersect and interact, and human rights legislation takes precedence over the secondary EU legislation. Therefore, the right to private life, as enshrined in the ECHR, and the right to data protection, as enshrined in the EU Charter, must always be taken into consideration, and their interpretation by the European Courts will guide the interpretation of GDPR. Their respect and the specific procedural and substantive safeguards for their protection cannot be considered unnecessary. Of course, they are not absolute and need to be balanced with other rights and public interests such as the right to healthcare and the public interest in better treatments and more effective and efficient healthcare systems [83]. We argue that non-discrimination, transparency, trust and empowerment of the individual have to be central for the protection of human dignity, and they are critical prerequisites for innovation in healthcare.

NOTES

1. National Information Board is responsible for setting out strategies for data and technology in healthcare in the UK.
2. DeepMind, a British AI company, now absorbed in Google Health UK.
3. The clinical trials regulation aims to simplify the conduct of clinical trials and consequently to facilitate research in therapies using personalized medicine.
4. 23andMe and similar companies have faced criticism over a lack of representation of people of colour in their genetic databases. See https://www.advisory.com/daily-briefing/2019/03/13/23andme-diabetes.
5. For example, in 2019 concerns were raised that 23andMe's diabetes risk assessment, which calculated consumers' polygenic risk scores, or a person's chance of developing a certain disease, was not broadly applicable because the genetic database that the company relies on to determine a person's polygenic risk score was predominantly made up of data from white participants. See https://www.advisory.com/daily-briefing/2020/06/15/race-genetics.
6. https://www.patientslikeme.com/.
7. The Genetic Information Non-discrimination Act in the USA provides some protection against such discrimination; however, law needs to develop further.
8. See David Lyon, *Surveillance Society: Monitoring Everyday Life* (Philiadelphia, Pa: Open University Press, 2001); James R. Beniger, *The Control Revolution: Technological and Economic Origins of the Information Society* (Cambridge, Mass.: Harvard University Press, 1986); Judith Wagner DeCew, *In Pursuit of Privacy: Law, Ethics and the Rise of Technology* (Ithaca: Cornell University Press, 1997).
9. Data Protection Working Party 29, Opinion 15/2011 on the definition of consent (adopted on July 13, 2011) 01197/11/EN WP187 8.
10. Article 1(3) GDPR.
11. *Campbell v Mirror Group newspapers* [2004] UKHL 22 [145] per Lady Hale; *R (on the application of W, X, Y and Z) v Secretary of State for Health and Secretary of State for the Home Department, the British Medical Association* [2015] EWCA Civ. 1034 [3434].
12. Article 9 GDPR; Article 8 Directive.
13. Article 6 of the GDPR and a separate condition for processing under Article 9.
14. Recital 35 GDPR.
15. Articles 4(13) and (14) GDPR. Under the GDPR, but not under the Directive, these two types of data are sensitive data (Article 9 GDPR).
16. Article 4(15) GDPR. Recital 35 lists examples of health data. The Directive and the DPA 1998 did not define "health data," but Article 29 WP did in "Letter to the Director of Sustainable and Secure Society Directorate of the European Commission," published February 5, 2015.
17. Recital 51 GDPR.
18. Conditions for valid consent under the GDPR can be found in Article 4(11) and Article 7. Furthermore Recitals 32, 33, 42, 43.
19. General Data Protection Regulation Article 9(2) (h).
20. Article 5(1) (b).

21. General Data Protection Regulation (n 1) Article 42.
22. https://understandingpatientdata.org.uk/how-do-people-feel-about-use-data.
23. GDPR Article 5(1) (a).

REFERENCES

1. Dutfield, D. (2020). *That High Design of Purest Gold: A Critical History of the Pharmaceutical Industry, 1880-2020*. World Scientific.
2. NHS England. (2016). *Improving Outcomes through Personalised Medicine: Working at the Cutting Edge of Science to Improve Patient's Lives*. NHS England. https://www.england.nhs.uk/wp-content/uploads/2016/09/improving-outcomes-personalised-medicine.pdf.
3. Mathur, S., & Sutton, J. (2017). Personalized medicine could transform healthcare. *Biomedical Reports*, 7(1), 3–5. https://doi.org/10.3892/br.2017.922.
4. Hunt, S. (2008). Pharmacogenetics, personalized medicine, and race. *Nature Education*, 1(1), 212.
5. Flores, M., Glusman, G., Brogaard, K., Price, N. D., & Hood, L. (2013). P4 medicine: How systems medicine will transform the healthcare sector and society. *Personalized Medicine*, 10(6), 565–576.
6. Rose, N. (2007). *The Politics of Life Itself: Biomedicine, Power, and Subjectivity in the Twenty-First Century*. Oxford: Princeton University Press.
7. García, J. C., & Bustos, R. H. (2018). The genetic diagnosis of neurodegenerative diseases and therapeutic perspectives. *Brain Sciences*, 8(12), 222.
8. Bresnick, J. (2018, January 11). What are precision medicine and personalized medicine? *Health I.T. Analytics: Xtelligent Healthcare Media*. https://healthitanalytics.com/features/what-are-precision-medicine-and-personalized-medicine.
9. Bowman, D., Spicer, J., & Iqbal, R. (2012). *Informed Consent: A Primer for Clinical Practice*. Cambridge: Cambridge University Press.
10. Vicente, A. M., Ballensiefen, W. & Jönsson, J. (2020). How personalised medicine will transform healthcare by 2030: The ICPerMed vision. *Journal of Translational Medicine*, 18, 180.
11. Meyer, S. L. (2020). Toward precision public health. *Journal of Public Health Dentistry*, 80, S7–S13.
12. Baiardini, I., & Heffler. E. (2019). The patient-centered decision system as per the 4Ps of precision medicine. In I. Agache & P. Hellings (Eds.), *Implementing Precision Medicine in Best Practices of Chronic Airway Diseases* (pp. 147–151). Academic Press.
13. Paul, N. W. (2009). Medicine studies: Exploring the interplays of medicine, science and societies beyond disciplinary boundaries. *Medicine Studies*, 1, 3–10.
14. Rose, N. (2013). Personalized medicine: Promises, problems and perils of a new paradigm for healthcare. *Procedia—Social and Behavioural Sciences*, 77, 341–352.
15. Goetz, L. H., & Schork, N. J. (2018). Personalized medicine: Motivation, challenges, and progress. *Fertility and Sterility*, 109(6), 952–963.
16. Cesuroglu, T., Syurina, E., Feron, F., & Krumeich, A. (2016). Other side of the coin for personalised medicine and healthcare: Content analysis of 'personalised' practices in the literature. *BMJ Open*, 6(7), e010243. https://doi:10.1136/bmjopen-2015-010243.
17. Council of the European Union (2015). *Personalised Medicine for Patients – Council Conclusions* (Document Number 15054/15). http://data.consilium.europa.eu/doc/document/ST-15054-2015-INIT/en/pdf.
18. Erikainen, S., & Chan, S. (2019). Contested futures: Envisioning "Personalized," "Stratified," and "Precision" medicine. *New Genetics and Society*, 38(3), 308–330.

19. De Grandis, G., & Halgunset, V. (2016). Conceptual and terminological confusion around personalised medicine: A coping strategy. *BMC Medical Ethics*, 17, 43. https://doi.org/10.1186/s12910-016-0122-4.
20. Raza, S. et al. (2018). *The Personalised Medicine Technology Landscape*. PHG Foundation. https://www.phgfoundation.org/documents/phgf-personalised-medicine-technology-landscape-report-50918.pdf.
21. National Information Board. (2014). *Personalised Health and Care 2020: Using Data and Technology to Transform Outcomes for Patients and Citizens*. H.M. Government. https://assets.publishing.service.gov.uk/government/uploads/system/uploads/attachment_data/file/384650/NIB_Report.pdf.
22. Chen, Y., Elenee Argentinis, J. D., & Weber, G. (2016). IBM Watson: How cognitive computing can be applied to big data challenges in life sciences research. *Clinical therapeutics*, 38(4), 688–701.
23. Basu, S., & Guinchard, A. (2020). Restoring trust into the NHS: Promoting data protection as an 'architecture of custody' for the sharing of data in direct care. *International Journal of Law and Information Technology*, 28(3), 243–272.
24. Gardner, S. (2016). Delivering precision medicine: Personalization at scale. *Digital Medicine*, 2(4),140–143.
25. Ho, D., Quake, S. R., McCabe, E. R. B., Chng, W. J., Chow, E. K., Ding, X., Gelb, B. D., Ginsburg, G. S., Hassenstab, J., Ho, C. M., Mobley, W. C., Nolan, G. P., Rosen, S. T., Tan, P., Yen, Y., & Zarrinpar, A. (2020). Enabling technologies for personalized and precision medicine. *Trends in Biotechnology*, 38(5), 497–518.
26. Lo, C. (2020). *Precision Medicine: What Barriers Remain?* Pharmaceutical Technology. https://www.pharmaceutical-technology.com/features/precision-medicine-2020/.
27. Kazzazi, F., Pollard, C., Tern, P. et al. (2017). Evaluating the impact of Brexit on the pharmaceutical industry. *Journal of Pharmaceutical Policy and Practice*, 10, 32. https://doi.org/10.1186/s40545-017-0120-z.
28. Brothers, K. B., & Rothstein, M. A. (2015). Ethical, legal and social implications of incorporating personalized medicine into healthcare. *Personalized Medicine*, 12(1), 43–51.
29. Nuffield Council on Bioethics. (2010). *Medical Profiling and Online Medicine: The Ethics of "Personalised Healthcare" in a Consumer Age*. London, Nuffield Council on Bioethics. https://www.nuffieldbioethics.org/assets/pdfs/Medical-profiling-and-online-medicine-the-ethics-of-personalised-healthcare-in-a-consumer-age.pdf.
30. Oster, E., Shoulson, I., Quaid, K., & Dorsey, E. R. (2010). Genetic adverse selection: Evidence from long-term care insurance and Huntington disease. *Journal of Public Economics*, 94 (11–12), 1041–1050.
31. Savitz, J. B., & Ramesar, R. S. (2004). Genetic variants implicated in personality: A review of the more promising candidates. *American Journal of Medical Genetics Part B: Neuropsychiatric Genetics*, 131(1), 20–32.
32. Geneviève, L. D., Martani, A., Shaw, D., Elger, B. S., & Wangmo, T. (2020). Structural racism in precision medicine: Leaving no one behind. *BMC Medical Ethics*, 21(1), 17.
33. Kahn, J. (2011). Mandating race: How the USPTO is forcing race into biotech patents. *Nature Biotechnology*. 29(5), 401–403.
34. Taylor, D. (2015). The pharmaceutical industry and the future of drug development. In R. E. Hester & R. M. Harrison (Eds.), *Pharmaceuticals in the Environment* (pp. 1–33). DOI: 10.1039/9781782622345-00001.
35. Stoeklé, H., Mamzer-Bruneel, M., Vogt, G. et al. (2016). 23andMe: A new two-sided data-banking market model. *BMC Medical Ethics*, 17, 19. https://doi.org/10.1186/s12910-016-0101-9.
36. Vayena, E. (2015). Direct-to-consumer genomics on the scales of autonomy *Journal of Medical Ethics*, 41,310–314.

37. Ham, C., Charles, A., & Wellings, D. (2018). Shared responsibility for health: The cultural change we need, The King's Fund. https://www.kingsfund.org.uk/publications/shared-responsibility-health.
38. Sandel, M. J. (2004). The case against perfection: What's wrong with designer children, bionic athletes, and genetic engineering. *The Atlantic*: Technology. https://www.theatlantic.com/magazine/archive/2004/04/the-case-against-perfection/302927/.
39. Soukup, T., Lamb, B. W., Arora, S., Darzi, A., Sevdalis, N., & Green, J. S. (2018). Successful strategies in implementing a multidisciplinary team working in the care of patients with cancer: An overview and synthesis of the available literature. *Journal of Multidisciplinary Healthcare*, 11, 49–61.
40. Kaba, R., & Sooriakumaran, P. (2007). The evolution of the doctor-patient relationship. *International Journal of Surgery*, 5(1), 57–65.
41. Basu, S., & Omotubora, A. (2018). Beyond the present: Privacy and personalised medicine. In Proceedings of 33rd Annual BILETA Conference, University of Aberdeen, Aberdeen, U.K.
42. Craig, D. W., Goor, R. M., Wang, Z., Paschall, J., Ostell, J., Feolo, M., Sherry, S. T., & Manolio, T. A. (2011). Assessing and managing risk when sharing aggregate genetic variant data. *Nature Reviews Genetics*, 12(10), 730–736. https://doi.org/10.1038/nrg3067
43. Raghupathi, W., & Raghupathi, V. (2014). Big data analytics in healthcare: Promise and potential. *Health Information Science and Systems*, 2, 3. https://doi.org/10.1186/2047-2501-2-3.
44. Hulsen, T., Jamuar, S. S., Moody, A. R., Karnes, J. H., Varga, O., Hedensted, S., Spreafico, R., Hafler, D. A., & McKinney, E. F. (2019). From big data to precision medicine. *Frontiers in Medicine*, 6, 34.
45. Shoaib, M., Rameez, M., Hussain, S. A., Madadin, M., & Menezes, R. G. (2017). Personalized medicine in a new genomic era: Ethical and legal aspects. *Science and Engineering Ethics*, 23(4), 1207–1212.
46. Velo, G. P., & Minuz, P. (2009). Medication errors: Prescribing faults and prescription errors. *British Journal of Clinical Pharmacology*, 67(6), 624–628.
47. Dimitrov D. V. (2016). Medical internet of things and big data in healthcare. *Healthcare Informatics Research*, 22(3), 156–163.
48. Kotz, D., Gunter, C. A., Kumar, S., & Weiner, J. P. (2016). Privacy and security in mobile health: A research agenda. *Computer*, 49(6), 22–30.
49. Evans R. S. (2016). Electronic health records: Then, now, and in the future. *Yearbook of Medical Informatics*, 25(Suppl 1), S48–S61. https://doi.org/10.15265/IYS-2016-s006.
50. Miller, A. R., & Tucker, C. E. (2009). Privacy protection and technology diffusion: The case of electronic medical records. *Management Science*, 55(7), 1077–1093.
51. Miller, A. R., & Tucker, C.E. (2011). Encryption and the loss of patient data. *Journal of Policy Analysis and Management*, 30(3), 534–556.
52. Miller, A. R., & Tucker, C. E. (2018). Privacy protection, personalized medicine, and genetic testing. *Management Science*, 64(10), 4648–4668.
53. Parkin, E., & Loft, P. (2020). Patient health records: Access, sharing and confidentiality, Briefing Paper, Number 07103.
54. Vogenberg, F. R., Isaacson Barash, C., & Pursel, M. (2010). Personalized medicine: Part 1: Evolution and development into theranostics. *P & T: A Peer-Reviewed Journal for Formulary Management*, 35(10), 560–576.
55. Basu, S. (2012). Privacy protection: A tale of two cultures. *Masaryk University Journal of Law and Technology*, 6(1), 1–34.
56. Westin, A. F. (2003). Social and political dimensions of privacy. *Journal of Social Issues*, 59, 431.

57. Munns, C., & Basu, S. (2015). *Privacy and Healthcare Data: Choice of Control to Choose and Control*. London: Routledge.
58. Birnhack, M. (2019). Process-based approach to informational privacy and the case of big medical data. *Theoretical Inquiries in Law*, 20(1), 5.
59. Kaye, J., Whitley, E. A., Lund, D., Morrison, M., Teare, H., & Melham, K. (2014). Dynamic consent: A patient interface for twenty-first-century research networks. *European Journal of Human Genetics*, 23(2), 141–146.
60. Kulynych, J., & Greely, H. T. (2017). Clinical genomics, big data, and electronic medical records: Reconciling patient rights with research when privacy and science collide. *Journal of law and the biosciences*, 4(1), 94–132.
61. Armstrong, S. (2017). Data, data everywhere: The challenges of personalised medicine, *BMJ*, 359, j4546.
62. Hong, J. I., & Landay, J. A. (2004). An architecture for privacy-sensitive ubiquitous computing. In Proceedings of the 2nd International Conference on Mobile Systems, Applications, and Services, Boston, MA.
63. Wiese, J., Das, S., Hong, J. I., & Zimmerman, J. (2017). Evolving the ecosystem of personal behavioral data. *Human-Computer Interaction*, 32(5–6), 447–510.
64. Mifsud, J., & Gavrilovici, C. (2018). Big data in healthcare and the life sciences. *Ethics and Integrity in Health and Life Sciences Research* (*Advances in Research Ethics and Integrity, Vol. 4*) (pp. 63–83). UK: Emerald Publications.
65. Omotubora, A., & Basu, S. (2020). Next generation privacy. *Information & Communications Technology Law*, 29(2), 151–173.
66. Greenleaf, G. (2011). Global data privacy laws: 40 years of acceleration. *Privacy Laws & Business International Report*, 112, 11–17.
67. Marelli, L., Lievevrouw, E., & Hoyweghen, I. V. (2020). Fit for purpose? The GDPR and the governance of European digital health, *Policy Studies*. DOI: 10.1080/01442872.2020.1724929.
68. Yesley, M. S. (1998). Protecting genetic difference. *Berkeley Technology Law Journal*, 13, 653.
69. Lachaud, E. (2018). The general data protection regulation and the rise of certification as a regulatory instrument. *Computer Law & Security Review*, 34(2), 244–256.
70. Aitken, M., de St. Jorre, J., Pagliari, C. et al. (2016). Public responses to the sharing and linkage of health data for research purposes: A systematic review and thematic synthesis of qualitative studies. *BMC Medical Ethics*, 17, 73.
71. European Alliance for Personalised Medicine. (2013). *Innovation and Patient Access to Personalised Medicine*. http://euapm.eu/pdf/EAPM_REPORT_on_Innovation_and_Patient_Access_to_Personalised_Medicine.pdf.
72. Spencer, K., Sanders, C., Whitley, E. A., Lund, D., Kaye, J., & Dixon, W. G. (2016). Patient perspectives on sharing anonymized personal health data using a digital system for dynamic consent and research feedback: A qualitative study. *Journal of Medical Internet Research*, 18(4), e66. https://doi.org/10.2196/jmir.501.
73. Policy and Research Group of the Office of the Privacy Commissioner of Canada. (2016.). Consent and Privacy—A discussion paper exploring potential enhancements to consent under the Personal Information Protection and Electronic Documents Act. https://www.priv.gc.ca/en/opc-actions-and-decisions/research/explore-privacy-res.
74. Cunningham, M. (2014). Next generation privacy: The internet of things, data exhaust, and reforming regulation by risk of harm. *Groningen Journal of International Law*, 2(2), 115–144.
75. Milberg, S. J., Smith, H. J., & Burke, S. J. (2000). Information privacy: Corporate management and national regulation. *Organization Science*, 11(1), 35–57.
76. Laudon, K. C. (1996). Markets and privacy. *Communications of the ACM*. 39(9), 103.

77. Nadeem, W., Juntunen, M., Shirazi, F., & Hajli, N. (2020). Consumers' value co-creation in sharing economy: The role of social support, consumers' ethical perceptions and relationship quality. *Technological Forecasting and Social Change*, 151, 119786. https://www.sciencedirect.com/science/article/pii/S0040162519305943.
78. Varian, H. R. (1997). Theory of markets and privacy. In *Privacy and Self-Regulation in the Information Age*, Washington, DC: U.S. Department of Commerce. www.ntia.doc.gov/reports/privacy/privacy_rpt.htm.
79. Laufer, R. S., & Wolfe, M. (1977). Privacy as a concept and a social issue: A multidimensional development theory. *Journal of Social Issues*, 33(3), 22–42.
80. Lwin, M. O., & Williams, J.D. (2003). A model integrating the multidimensional developmental theory of privacy and theory of planned behaviour to examine fabrication of information online. *Marketing Letters*, 14 (4), 257–272.
81. Milne, G. R., & Gordon, M. E. (1993). Direct mail privacy-efficiency trade-offs within an implied social contract framework. *Journal of Public Policy and Marketing*, 12(Fall), 206–215.
82. Acquisti, A., & Grossklags. J. (2004). Privacy attitudes and privacy behavior. In L Jean Camp and Stephen Lewis (Eds.), *The Economics of Information Security*, Chapter 1. Dordrecht: Kluwer. http://www.heinz.cmu.edu/~acquisti/papers/acquisti_grossklags_eis_refs.pdf.
83. Gellert, R. (2016). We have always managed risks in data protection law: Understanding the similarities and differences between the rights-based and the risk-based approaches to data protection. *European Data Protection Law*, 2(4), 481–492.

11 Legislation Comparison in the Sphere of Health Protection in Selected European Countries

Yuriy Yu. Shvets

CONTENTS

11.1 Problem Statement: The Nexus of Medical Secrecy 199
11.2 Preview of Medical Confidentiality 200
11.3 Legislative Stipulations 202
11.4 Legal Protection of Confidentiality Worldwide 203
11.5 Safeguards to Medical Confidentiality 205
11.6 Conclusion 208
References 208

11.1 PROBLEM STATEMENT: THE NEXUS OF MEDICAL SECRECY

The protection of human rights and legitimate interests has occupied mankind as a significant aspect of public life. The most important tasks of the modern state include protection of the citizen's life and health, as well as ensuring the inviolability of private life. One of the institutions that is supposed to protect the relevant legal rights and interests is the institution of secrecy, in particular, doctor's secrecy or confidentiality, as health protection is ensured through it.

Confidentiality as a rule should protect the doctor and the patient from unauthorized "outside intrusions" into the privacy of the individual and the treatment process. This rule guards information about the patient, which the physician receives either from the patient's mouth or as a result of examination. It cannot be shared with third parties without the patient's permission. This rule bears the sanctity of medical secrecy in most countries' civil or criminal codes, starting with the Hippocratic Oath. It applies not only to physicians, but also to all health professionals who have access to medical information.

An analysis of the studies and publications available shows that the emergence and development of medical secrecy has been studied by scientists like F. Walter, A. Ferguson, P. Chesnokov, E. Baluchi, T. Katashina, Yu. Sergeev, A. Makhnik, D. Berg and Yu. Among the scientists who have worked on the legal regulation of medical confidentiality are Yuliya Argunova, V. Golovchenko, L. Dembo, N. Korobtsova, O. Makhnik, S. Stetsenko, J. Chevichalova, I. Shatkovskaya and others. It must be noted that the comparative aspects of the functioning and maintenance of confidentiality need further exploration, as they have not yet been sufficiently investigated.

The purpose of the chapter is to study the legislation of foreign countries regulating the provision of confidentiality in the field of health protection, including its comparative aspects.

11.2 PREVIEW OF MEDICAL CONFIDENTIALITY

The maintenance of confidentiality of information in the field of health protection is monitored medical secrecy. It concerns a kind of professional confidentiality and is an independent form of information with limited access that concerns information that is confidential and protected by law. The segregation of medical secrecy into an independent group contributes to the establishment of a unified legal regime of protection of information and its components. It is not identical to any other legal regime of information with limited access [1].

Medical secrecy has emerged and existed for a long time as an absolute phenomenon. It pertains to the secrecy from both the authorities and those close to the patient. Gradually it began to take on a partial character because the legislation of many countries at different times tended to gradually move to a system of legal provisions regarding the situations when medical information could be accessible to the public.

The subject of medical secrecy is usually the data on the health status of a patient—the diagnosis as well as the prognosis. It also considers all the information which is made available to the doctor as a result of the examination or the patient's own words. The law defines a narrow range of situations in which a medical worker has the right to pass on medical information known to him to a third party in particular. This especially in cases where the patient is unable to express his will independently. The situation is even more critical in the presence of a threat of the spread of any infectious disease or mass poisoning, etc.

According to the British scientist and medical ethics specialist R. Edwards, there are seven factors that ensure the essentiality of confidentiality in many areas of professional activity, especially in medicine [2, 3]. These have been listed as:

1. Confidentiality between a professional and a client (doctor and patient) is desirable because it is the confirmation of a fundamental value like privacy. In the process of communication, some of the patient's information may become known to the physician as he or she may sometimes need intimate information about the patient's privacy for effective diagnosis and treatment. Ensuring that the doctor unconditionally observes confidentiality encourages the patient to be honest and the doctor ensures that the patient's privacy is not compromised.
2. Confidentiality is a condition for the protection of the patient's social status as medical diagnosis and other medical information may stigmatize an individual. This can significantly limit the possibility of social self-assertion

especially when talking about the mentally sick, people suffering sometimes from venereal diseases, genetic defects, acquired immunodeficiency syndrome (AIDS), etc. Sometimes such information tends to provoke a negative reaction and can lead to social isolation of the patient. Thus, violation of confidentiality poses a direct threat to the social status of the patient.
3. Confidentiality protects the economic interests of the patient also because information about the patient's disease can severely impair and limit the economic, social and political opportunities. It can negatively affect the patient's business activities, promotions, etc.
4. Confidentiality ensures openness in communication which is very significant between the patient and the doctor. When the patient opens up to the doctor, he or she is confident that this will not have undesirable consequences for the patient. Strict confidentiality is a guarantee for the patient's openness given among normal professional healthcare workers. This confidentiality determines not only interests of the patients, but also of the doctors because professional success is realized not only in terms of financial compensation, but also personal self-realization of the medical personnel.
5. The doctors' ability to ensure the confidentiality of their patients' information depends, to an extent, on their popularity and prestige. The right to choose a doctor and a medical institution rests with the patient and tends to provide an advantage to those professionals who, in addition to their professional qualities and capabilities, also meet high moral standards in terms of confidentiality.
6. Effectively implementing the requirement of confidentiality ensures the trust of the patient in their relationship with their doctor which inherently is more important than honesty. Often a seriously ill person is completely dependent on the doctors and therefore must trust them and believe that they will always be guided by the patient's interests.
7. Confidentiality is therefore essential for the realization of the patient's right to autonomy and effective control over events of his life. It coincides with the protection of privacy to guarantee the patient's social status and economic interests. It guarantees personal freedom and minimal dependence on external forces that may be seeking to manipulate his behaviour [3].

Compliance with the rule of confidentiality is often difficult in situations of widespread threat of infectious diseases. It is vital when medical information about a patient keeps salient interests of third parties (relatives, employees) as well as in the genetic testing of an individual or when there is a threat to the health and maybe even lives of others if the silence of the doctor is breached with the information about a patient. For example, when dozens of health workers are coming in contact with a patient in a treatment facility or when relatives of a terminally ill person are informed about the patient's state of health in an attempt to prevent speculation and rumours concerning the patient's health.

11.3 LEGISLATIVE STIPULATIONS

The guidelines for the national legislation on the confidentiality of health information, healthcare and the functioning of the institution of medical confidentiality are mandated by international regulations in this area. The 17th International Covenant on Civil and Political Rights has made provisions stipulating that "arbitrary or unlawful interference or unlawful attacks" on the patients by countermanding the secrecy and confidentiality clause will be considered unlawful attacks on the individuals' honour and reputation [4].

Article 6 of the European Charter of Patients' Rights has ensured that information about their health status and possible diagnostic or therapeutic procedures, and the protection of their privacy during diagnostic examination, are governed by the right to privacy of personal information.

According to Article 8 of the Charter on the Right to Health, medical personnel should practice confidentiality (medical secrecy), which ensures respect for the privacy of their patients to guarantee the best treatment in an unbiased manner. Any dilution or breach of secrecies can only be justified for protecting the health safety and hygiene of the community. In case they become aware of an infringement of human dignity, doctors must automatically be exempt from this confidentiality.

The "right to confidentiality" is also Principle 8 of the Lisbon Declaration on Patients' Rights. According to the content of this principle, all information that identifies a patient's state of health, illness and diagnosis that pertains to treatment is confidential, extending even up to the time of patient's death. In emergency the right to information can be exercised by the patient's kin. This is largely concerning the risk of inherited diseases. Direct consent can facilitate disclosure under law. Unless the patient has explicitly consented to the disclosure, the information can be shared with the health functionaries only when it is essential. All patient identification information should be preserved and protected, as should human substances that may be a source of identification information [5].

Article 8 of the European Convention on Human Rights (ECHR) Part-1 states, "everyone has the right to respect his private and family life, his home and correspondence" [6]. In this regard, the European Court of Human Rights (ECHR) has held that

> the protection of personal data—not in the least, medical data—is fundamental to the exercise by a person of his right to respect for private and family life ... Respect for the confidentiality of human health information is an essential principle of the legal systems that are parties to the ECHR ... It is necessary not only to respect the privacy of the patient, but also to maintain confidence in the medical profession and in the medical services in general.
>
> [7]

The ECHR also notes that the disclosure of medical information "may significantly affect an individual's private and family life, social status and employment, subjecting him to public condemnation and risk of ostracism" [8]. The ECHR judgement in the case of "I.F. against Turkey" (24209/94) noted that a person's body is an intimate aspect of his private life. It mandates that "there is a clear connection between the right to privacy and the right to physical integrity" [9].

According to Part 1 of Article 10 of the Convention of Human Rights and Biomedicine, "everyone has the right to respect for his private life regarding information about his health" [10].

Article Recommendation №. R (2004) 10 Part-1 The Council of Europe provides that "all personal data of any individual affected by mental ailments shall be considered confidential. Such data should be collected, processed and transmitted in accordance with the rules concerning professional secrecy and the collection of personal data" [11].

Within the meaning of Part 1, Part 8, Article 4 of the <u>The Declaration on the Promotion of Patients' Rights in Europe</u>, the patient's health information should remain confidential even after the patient's death. Patients entering a treatment and preventive care institution are entitled to expect the material conditions necessary to guarantee medical confidentiality [12].

The Convention for Protection of Individuals pertaining to Automatic Processing of Personal Data introduces additional safeguards to protect the privacy of communications regarding all forms of personal data. Thus, the following requirements are imposed on the data: Personal data are automatically processed, must be obtained and processed in good faith and legally and must be collected for purely medical and research purposes. They must be used only for the purpose for which they have been collected. They must be accurate, constantly updated and must be kept in a form that allows the ethical use of the data only. Personal data relating to health may be automatically processed only if national law provides adequate safeguards for their protection under Article 6. [13].

The Resolution №1165 (1998) of the Parliamentary Assembly of the Council of Europe stipulates public persons to be aware that the special status they have in society automatically increases the level of pressure on their privacy [14]. Therefore, a person's presence in a position related to the execution of state or local government functions provides not only guarantees for the protection of that person's rights, but also additional legal burdens, including in the area of health information confidentiality. In the decision "Von Hannover v. Germany," the ECHR states: The distinction established between outstanding contemporary figures and "relatively public figures" must be clear and obvious so that in a state where the rule of law is respected, a particular person has specific instructions as to how to behave. First of all, such persons must necessarily know where and when they are protected and, conversely, where and when interference by others is possible (para. 73) [15]. Accordingly, when establishing a balance at the national level, great care must be taken in identifying the subject of medical information [16].

11.4 LEGAL PROTECTION OF CONFIDENTIALITY WORLDWIDE

Turning to the national specifics of the legal protection of confidentiality, it should be noted that, in Germany, medical legislation, both at the federal and state levels, includes rules governing measures against particularly dangerous infections, access to medical activities, the circulation of drugs and narcotic drugs, etc. [17]. Analysing the history of German legislation on medical confidentiality, O. Mechnik notes that:

> German law prohibited doctors from providing information entrusted to them in the performance of their professional duties. If a doctor is invited as a witness, he has the right to refuse to testify if the patient whom he treated has not given him permission to do so.
>
> [18]

At present, according to Section 53 of the German Criminal Procedure Code, persons to whom the law grants the right to refuse to testify as witnesses may not be questioned as witnesses. This right is enjoyed in particular by doctors, dentists, pharmacists and obstetricians [19].

It should be noted that after a crash of a German plane, in which 150 people died, there was an active public discussion in Germany regarding the possibility of mitigation of the rule of non-disclosure of medical confidentiality, in particular, with regard to representatives of professions associated with risk. At the same time, the Chairman of the Federal Association of Psychotherapists, R. Richter, opposed the relaxation of patient confidentiality obligations, because doctors and psychotherapists already have the right to derogate from this principle if they can thus prevent damage to third parties [20].

In a similar way, Article 378 of the French Penal Code establishes criminal liability for the disclosure of medical information by doctors and other health professionals, except where the law permits or obliges disclosure [19].

The United Kingdom and Northern Ireland have a well-established healthcare system: The National Health Service of England (NHS) as well as the Health Service of Wales, Scotland and Northern Ireland. The NHS of England is one of the most efficient and powerful health systems in the world—its principles and operations are supported by around 90% of its citizens. The NHS England is also ranked 18th out of 190 in the world's health systems ranking [21]. However, in the context of the study of the legal regime of medical secrecy, British jurisprudence is interesting on the awarding of compensation for moral damages in connection with the disclosure of confidential information, or unauthorized processing of such information. Thus, in the UK, for a long time, compensation for moral damages in these cases was impossible in the absence of property damage (losses). After all, in accordance with paragraph 13.2 of the Data Protection Act 1998, the individual had the "right to compensation for moral damages only if there is property damage" [22].

Thus, one English pound of property damage opened the possibility for the plaintiff to claim compensation for moral damages. In addition, the concept of "moral harm" as such is not used by the English legislator; the more common term, as has already been noted, is "compensation for distress." However, the March 2015 appeal decision in Google Inc. v Vidal-Hall and Ors [23] was historic for the UK in the context of protecting personal data from unauthorized processing and then compensating for moral harm (compensation for distress) for violations related to the processing of personal data. Analysing the circumstances of the case and referring to Directive 95/46/EC of the European Parliament and of the Council on the protection of individuals with regard to the processing of personal data and on the free movement of such data, namely Article 23 ("Liability"), lays down that any person who has suffered harm as a result of the unlawful processing of his personal data is entitled to compensation for the damage [24]. The Court of Appeal of England and Wales interpreted the above provision of the National Data Protection Act, noting that "compensation for suffering as a result of the unauthorized processing or use of personal data does not require property damage" [22].

As for the USA, it should be noted that, according to J.V. Berg:

> The protection of confidentiality in the states differs significantly. Several states have comprehensive privacy laws, some control the disclosure of health information by developing detailed rules on everything from disease specific information to autopsy records. Some states refrain from establishing rules requiring general confidentiality and simply legislate on the basis that the protection of health information by common law is sufficient.
>
> [25]

The US has a Health Insurance Act that provides for confidentiality in healthcare. At the same time, the Act sets out a number of exceptions, including the possibility of disclosure without the consent of the mass media in particular to persons who are at risk of falling ill or spreading the disease if the law authorizes a legal entity to do so, as necessary to carry out public health interventions or investigations (Code of Federal Rules, arts. 45, 164.512(b)(1)(iv)). As I. Shatkovskaya notes, the US experience in the field of medical confidentiality should be taken into account for the following reasons: the phenomenon of "full information," when a patient is given full truthful information about his condition and prospects; the expediency of forming jurisprudence on court decisions on disclosure of information that is subject to medical confidentiality; the high level of legal culture and legal consciousness of both doctors and patients [26].

However, a vivid example of violation of the principle of medical information confidentiality in the US was a data leak in 2008, when a clinical trial manager left unattended a computer that stored unencrypted data on clinical trials conducted by the then National Heart, Lung and Blood Institute (NHLBI). The total number of victims—participants in clinical trials in cardiology—was 2,500 people. All participants in the clinical study were informed about the information leak, which included their personal and health information and examination indicators. The material equivalent of damage could have been significant if the computer thief had known about the value of the stolen information and had been able to use it [27]. Currently, the disclosing of medical records without the consent of the carrier is likely to require changes to existing legislations, eliciting a rapid response from state power as well as the judiciary [16].

11.5 SAFEGUARDS TO MEDICAL CONFIDENTIALITY

According to the legislation of the Russian Federation, the following information is subject to medical secrecy: The fact of seeking medical assistance; and a citizen's health status, examination and treatment, including data transmitted by the patient, for example, about his/her personal family history. As per the Fundamentals of Legislation of the Russian Federation on health protection, providing any data or information comprising medical secrecy in the absence of the individual's or a legal representative's consent is strictly stipulated in such cases, for example, in cases where the individual cannot express his will due to his condition (being in an unconscious, life- and health-threatening condition and in a situation when his representative is unavailable); in cases of widespread contagion and community spread at the request of the bodies conducting the initial inquiry and investigation, the procurator and the proceedings of the court; in cases of assistance to a minor under 15 years of age to inform his or her parents or legal representatives. This is also true for cases where there is estimated harm to an individual's health that may have been caused by unlawful acts [28].

Art. 46 of the Law of the Republic of Belarus "On Public Health" [29] has provisions wherein the information on the fact of the patient's need for treatment in, and the provision of medical assistance to the patient, and in the event of death, information on the results of the pathological and anatomical examination is medically confidential. Providing information that constitutes medical secrecy where the consent of the patient or other authority is not available has been allowed upon request in writing and/or as an electronic document executed according to the Republic of Belarus's legislation on electronic documents and electronic digital signature. The Ministry of Health, Republic of Belarus, main departments and offices (divisions) as also the Health Care Committee of Minsk City designated an Executive Committee for the purpose of organization of medical care provision to the patient, control over correctness of its provision or in case of threat of infectious diseases spread within their competence, as well as in case of state sanitary supervision; healthcare organizations in order to organize healthcare delivery in cases of the spread of infectious diseases; criminal prosecution bodies and courts in connection with investigation or court proceedings; internal affairs bodies on the appearance (non-appearance) of a person obliged to reimburse expenses spent by the state on the maintenance of children under state care to a state healthcare organization for a medical examination, and also on the passing or (not passing) of a medical examination by that person; bodies engaged in operative search activity ; insurance companies; the Belarusian Bureau of Transport Insurance in order to resolve the issue of insurance payments; local military authorities for medical examination of citizens conscripted to military service and bodies conducting initial inquiries in connection with the conduct of expert examinations in order to decide whether to initiate criminal proceedings; internal affairs agencies for the medical re-examination of drivers of motor vehicles and self-propelled vehicles, and for the presence of a disease or contra-indications that prevent the driving of motor vehicles or self-propelled vehicles; and employers in connection with the investigation of industrial accidents and occupational disease, according to the legislation of the Republic of Belarus [29].

Under Article 178, Chapter 21, "Crimes against the organization of family relations and the interests of minors," of the Criminal Code, disclosure of medical confidentiality is punishable. In particular, this article establishes criminal liability for the deliberate disclosure by medical or pharmaceutical personnel having any case-related exigency pertaining to any health condition or treatment and examination output of a patient as well as for the disclosure of medical secrecy consisting in the "disclosure of information about a person's HIV infection or AIDS" [30]. Part 1 of Article 8 of the Law of the Republic of Belarus "On Assisted Reproductive Technologies" states that medical secrecy also includes information about the usage of specific reproductive technologies involving patient or donor [31].

According to the Fundamentals of Health Legislation (Article 39-1) the patient has the right to seek confidentiality on his or her health status seeking treatment, diagnosis and medical examination information. Information about the patient's diagnosis and treatment methods may not be required or submitted at their place of work or study. In accordance with Article 40 of the Basic Principles, medical secrecy covers information about an illness, a medical examination, an examination and its results, and about the intimate and family side of a citizen's life, which has become known to medical workers and other persons in connection with the performance of their professional or official duties and who have no right to divulge such information, except in cases provided for in legislation. In uses of information constituting a medical secret, in the educational process or research work, "that include its publication in the special literature, anonymity of the patient should be provided" [32]. Doctors and other medical personnel cannot be questioned as witnesses either in civil or criminal proceedings on the basis of information constituting medical secrecy in the Civil Procedural Code of Ukraine (para-2, Article 51) [33] and Criminal Procedural Code of Ukraine (Article 65, para 4 of Part2) [34]). At the same time, there are cases when medical information can be disclosed. Medical documentation about an individual can be obtained only directly by the person concerned (The Civil Code of Ukraine—Part 1, Article 285 [35]), or his representative on the basis of power of attorney or an agreement on legal assistance (provided that copies of these documents are attached to the request), as well as parents (adoptive parents, guardian or tutor) as legal representatives of a child (under 18 years) or a ward (incompetent person).

The temporary access to documents containing medical information can be granted by an investigating judge or court within the framework of criminal proceedings, if it is established that there are no other ways to obtain the necessary "information for the investigation" according to the Criminal Procedure Code of Ukraine (Part-6, Article 163) [34]). Cases of legislative acts include the request of the court to provide a certificate of attending physicians' consultations; the healthcare institution has the right to provide such a certificate, as well as any other medical documentation required by the court. In all other cases, including requests by lawyers, if the lawyer is not the representative of the person in respect of whom the information is requested, the healthcare institution has not only the right but also the obligation to refuse to give any data or documents.

There is an urgent need worldwide to have strict legislations in place to ensure that patients' and doctors' confidentiality is protected at all times. It is also essential that in case of life-threatening situations that may affect large sections of the population, the data concerning the patients' health status are made available.

The Criminal Code of Ukraine Article 145 provides for "criminal liability for intentional disclosure of medical secrecy by a person to whom it has become known in connection with the performance of professional or official duties," if such an act has entailed serious consequences. Under the Criminal Code, Article 32- a medical establishment's auxiliary employees which receive information from authorization or a medical worker who must disclose information about the medical examination of a person to detect infection, which became known to them "in connection with the performance of their official or professional duties".

11.6 CONCLUSION

To summarize, it should be noted that the general trend in national legislation in many countries is to strike a balance between the rule of confidentiality of patient information and measures "to protect the health and safety of the patient" and allied third parties. The key benchmarks, which, in our opinion, must necessarily be taken into account when further improving national legislation to ensure the confidentiality of health information are the priority rights. Various forms of freedom in information exchange and person legitimate interests with an attempt to make the healthcare high quality, high-tech and consistent with international standards. The current COVID-19 virus pandemic has brought these considerations sharply into focus.

REFERENCES

1. Zhigalov A. F. (2000). Commercial and banking secrecy in Russian criminal legislation. PhD thesis in law: 12.00.08. Nizhny Novgorod: Criminal Law and Criminology; Penal Enforcement Law. 257 p.
2. Shchastny E., et al. (ed.). (2018). Biomedical ethics and communications in public health: Educational and methodical manual (in Russian) (p. 310) / A.T. Shchastny, et al.; under edition of A. T. Shchastny. Vitsebsk
3. Rule of confidentiality. URL: https://dt.ua/HEALTH/likarska-tayemnicya-ta-bezpeka-suspilstva-.html (date of address by reference: 23.03.20).
4. International Covenant on Civil and Political Rights (adopted by General Assembly resolution 2200 A (XXI) of 16 December 1966). URL: https://www.un.org/ru/documents/decl_conv/conventions/pactpol.shtml (date of address by reference: 23.03.20).
5. Declaration of Lisbon on the Rights of the Patient (adopted by the 34th World Medical Assembly). Lisbon, Portugal, September-October 1981 (as amended and supplemented by the 47th General Assembly. Bali, Indonesia, September 1995). URL: http://www.e-stomatology.ru/ star/info/2010/lissabon_declaration.htm (date of address by reference: 20.03.20).
6. The European Convention on Human Rights (as amended and supplemented by Protocol №11, accompanied by the texts of Protocols №№1, 4) Rome, 04.11.1950). URL: https://old.irs.in.ua/index.php?option=com_%20content&view=article&id=276%3A1&catid=43%3Aeu&Itemid=70&lang=ru (date of address by reference: 20.03.20).
7. Decision in "M.S. against Sweden" (27/08/1997) / European Court of Human Rights Decision on Access to Information. https://rm.coe.int/CoERMPublicCommonSearchServices/DisplayDCTMContent?documentId=090000168044e84d (date of address by reference: 18.03.20).

8. Decision in "Z against Finland" (25 EHRR 371) / Decision of the European Court of Human Rights on access to information. URL: https://rm.coe.int/CoERMPublic CommonSearchServices/DisplayDCTMContent?documentId=090000168044e84d (date of address by reference: 18.03.20).
9. ECHR. Decision in "I. F. against Turkey" judgment (24209/94) European Court of Human Rights decision on access to information. URL: https://rm.coe.int/CoERMP ublicCommonSearchServices/DisplayDCTMContent?documentId=090000168044e8 4d (date of address by reference: 18.03.20).
10. Convention on Human Rights and Biomedicine. URL: https://rm.coe.int/168007d004 (date of address by reference: 17.03.20).
11. Recommendation №Rec. (2004). 10 of the Committee of Ministers of the Council of Europe to member States on the protection of the rights and dignity of persons suffering from mental disorders and explanatory report (adopted by the Committee of Ministers on 22.09.2004 at the 896th meeting of the Deputy Ministers). URL: https://rm.coe.int/ rec-2004-10-psy-ru/168066caa8#_ftn1 (date of address by reference: 17.03.20).
12. Declaration on Patient Rights Policy in Europe (European Meeting on Patient Rights, Amsterdam, Netherlands, March 1994). URL: http://samlib.ru/s/stonogin_s_w/europe .shtml.
13. Convention for the Protection of Persons with regard to Automatic Processing of Personal Data (Strasbourg, 28.01.1981). URL: http:// conventions. coe.int/Treaty/en/ Treaties/Word/108.doc (date of address by reference: 17.03.20).
14. Resolution of the Parliamentary Assembly of the Council of Europe №. 1165 (1998). URL: http://cedem.org.ua/library/rezolyutsiya-1165-1998-pravo-na-pryvatnist/ (date of address by reference: 17.03.20).
15. Case of von Hannover v. Germany (Application no. 59320/00). URL: https://hudoc.e chr.coe.int/tur#{%22itemid%22:[%22001-61853%22]} (date of address by reference: 17.03.20).
16. Senuta I. Y. Medical secrecy under COVID-19. URL: https://medcom.unba.org.ua/pub lications/5362-likars-ka-taemnicya-v-umovah-covid-19.html (date of address by reference: 17.03.20).
17. Beske F., Hallauer I. (2000). *Health Care Germany. System—Achievements—Prospects of Development: Per. with him* (p. 288). / Scientific Ed. by O. P. Szczepin. - Moscow: OOO "Labpress."
18. Makhnik, O. P. (2005). From the history of medical secrecy / O. P. Makhnik // Scientific Proceedings of the II All-Russian Congress (National Congress) on Medical Law (pp. 124–129). Russia (Moscow, April 13–15, 2005). M.: NAMP.
19. Moldavan, V. V. (1999). Comparative-Procedural Law: Ukraine, Germany, France, England, USA: [Educational manual] / V. V. Moldovan, A. B. Moldovan (p. 289). K. K.: Jurinkom Inter.
20. In Germany, pilots and doctors are called upon to soften medical secrecy after the disaster in the Alps: URL: https://www.unian.ua/world/1062192-u-nimechchini-zaklik ayut-pomyakshiti-likarskutaemnitsyu-pislya-katastrofi-v-alpah-piloti-ta-likari-proti. html (date of address by reference: 19.03.20).
21. How England's health care system works. URL: https://moz.gov.ua/article/health/jak -pracjuesistema-ohoroni-zdorovja-anglii (date of address by reference: 21.03.20).
22. Data Protection Act. 1998. URL: http://www.legislation.gov.uk/ukpga/1998/29/conten ts (date of address by reference: 23.03.20).
23. Google Inc. v Vidal-Hall & Ors. URL: http://www.bailii.org/ew/ cases/EWCA/ Civ/2015/311.html (date of address by reference: 21.03.20).
24. Directive 95/46/EC of the European Parliament & of the Council of 24 October 1995 on the protection of individuals with regard to the processing of personal data

and on the free movement of such data. URL: http://eur-lex.europa.eu/legal-content/EN/TXT/?uri=celex:31995L0046 (date of address by reference: 21.03.20).
25. Berg, J. V. (2003). "To speak or not to speak": ethics and the law on confidentiality of the medical information (in Russian) / J. V. Berg // Modern medical law in Russia and abroad: A collection of scientific articles / edited by A. A. Bezh. INION. Centre of social scientific-informational research; Department of law; IGP Centre of ecological legal research. Center for Social Science-Information Research; Department of Law; IGP Center for Environmental Legal Studies (pp. 162–180). Editor: Dubovik O. L., Pivovarov Y. S. Moscow: INION.
26. Shatkovsky, I. V. Legal Regulation of the Institute of Medical Secrecy (Ukrainian History and International Experience). URL: http://nbuv.gov.ua/ UJRN/FP_index.htm_2009_3_105 (date of address by reference: 22.03.20).
27. Kiev hosted a round table on "Protection of personal data of persons participating in clinical trials of medicines." URL: https://uba.ua/ukr/news/1844/print/ (date of address by reference: 21.03.20).
28. Federal Law "On the Fundamentals of Health Protection of Citizens in the Russian Federation" of 21.11.2011 N 323-FL. URL: http://www.consultant.ru/document/ cons_doc_LAW_121895/ (date of address by reference: 25.03.20).
29. Law of the Republic of Belarus "On Healthcare" of 18.06.1993, 2435-XII. URL: https://kodeksy-by.com/zakon_rb_o_zdravoohranenii/46.htm (date of address by reference: 24.03.20).
30. Criminal Code of the Republic of Belarus. URL: http://уголовный-кодекс.бел/ (date of address by reference: 24.03.20).
31. Law of the Republic of Belarus "On assisted reproductive technologies" from 07.01.2012 № 341-3. URL: https://kodeksy-by.com/zakon_ rb_o_vspomogatel_nyh_reproduktivnyh_tehnologiyah.htm (date of address by reference: 24.03.20).
32. The Law of Ukraine "Fundamentals of the Legislation of Ukraine on Healthcare" of 19.11.1992. URL: https://zakon.rada.gov.ua/laws/show/2801-12 (date of address by reference: 14.03.20).
33. The Civil Procedure Code of Ukraine. URL: https://zakon.rada.gov.ua/laws/show/1618-15 (date of address by reference: 14.03.20).
34. Criminal Procedure Code of Ukraine. URL: https://zakon.rada.gov.ua/laws/show/4651-17 (date of address by reference: 16.03.20).
35. Civil Code of Ukraine. URL: https://zakon.rada.gov.ua/laws/show/43515 (date of address by reference: 17.03.20).

12 Challenges of Implementing Privacy Policies Across the Globe

Tanvi Garg and Navid Kagalwalla

CONTENTS

12.1 Introduction 212
12.2 Importance of Privacy Policies in Healthcare 213
12.3 Privacy Policies in the World 213
    12.3.1 United States of America (HIPAA) 214
    12.3.2 Europe (GDPR) 214
    12.3.3 Australia 215
    12.3.4 Nigeria (NHA) 215
    12.3.5 Russia 216
    12.3.6 Japan 217
    12.3.7 China 217
    12.3.8 Canada 217
    12.3.9 Korea 218
12.4 Challenges Faced by Developing Countries 219
    12.4.1 Data Storage and Management 219
    12.4.2 Data Sharing 220
    12.4.3 Prevalent Indifference and Red-Tape 220
    12.4.4 Infrastructure 221
    12.4.5 Population 221
    12.4.6 Budgetary Constraints 221
    12.4.7 Culture and Literacy Rate 222
    12.4.8 Cyber-Attacks 222
    12.4.9 State-Sponsored Surveillance 223
    12.4.10 Privacy as a Constitutional Right 223
    12.4.11 Internal and External Threats 223
    12.4.12 Data Breaching 223
    12.4.13 Consent Management 224
    12.4.14 Trusting the Third Party 224
    12.4.15 Improper Human Resource Management 224
12.5 Conclusion 224
References 225

12.1 INTRODUCTION

In the 21st century, cybercrimes focusing on healthcare systems are as prolific as they are versatile, targeting individuals from all walks of life ranging from heads of nations to executives of top companies to the common people. These crimes focus on ransomware, identity theft, sensitive data exposure, scams and the list goes on. With the prevalence of diseases and viruses taking the world by storm and the advent of new technologies in healthcare such as EHRs, pharmacogenomics and genome sequencing, etc., to combat these growing threats to human health and wellbeing, the focus on preventing the exploitation of a patient's records and identity hasn't been given as much importance in developing and underdeveloped countries [1–3]. The reason for substandard healthcare privacy policies boils down to the fact that every developing country suffers from overpopulation, lack of security establishment in healthcare systems, budget constraints and politics [4–6]. Developing and underdeveloped countries face a health crisis where tuberculosis and HIV/AIDS threaten millions. Privacy policies in these countries become merely a case of building trust between the government and its people for the betterment of the people. Insufficient testing facilities and patient history of past illnesses lead to many avoidable deaths. A robust, scalable system set in place, which could provide insight into the spread of diseases among citizens by analysing patient data specific to a region, could help stem diseases in their infancy. The absence of a healthcare privacy policy which secures patient data leaves room for exploitation by hackers.

Healthcare data management is the secure storing of personal data using various technologies like encryption, access control, monitoring and logging use, data use policies and risk assessment, preventing attacks and exploits which could expose personally identifiable information. Reliable storage and management allow health systems to create holistic views of patients, personalize treatments, improve communication and enhance the quality of life through the early detection and prevention of diseases [7]. The data you provide for a normal health check-up, ranging from your address to your emergency contact to even your eating habits, can give so much insight about your personal life, putting your privacy at risk.

Various countries in the world have put in place laws to protect healthcare data, with developed countries leading the charge, e.g., the United States of America has the Health Insurance Portability and Accountability Act (HIPAA), the United Kingdom has the Data Protection Act and the European Union has the General Data Protection Regulation (GDPR). Developing and underdeveloped countries face a tough battle when it comes to the privacy of personal data. To successfully implement a privacy policy requires substantial funding, technological know-how and a concrete plan on how to integrate the country's full population into a secure, well-structured, scalable system.

In this chapter, we will focus on the following topics:

- Importance of privacy policies in healthcare
- Privacy policies of countries with key takeaways

- Challenges faced by developing countries in implementing a privacy policy
- Possible solutions/models to the challenges faced

12.2 IMPORTANCE OF PRIVACY POLICIES IN HEALTHCARE

Cambridge Dictionary defines privacy as "someone's right to keep their matters and relationships secret." Some depict privacy as a basic human need to protect oneself and one's personal space, and a very important component of human development and wellbeing. As written in the chapter "The Value and Importance of Health Information Privacy" of the book *Beyond the HIPAA Privacy Rule: Enhancing Privacy, Improving Health Through Research* [8, 9], privacy consists of the most fundamental views and ideas of personhood; they are:

- Personal autonomy (the ability to make personal decisions)
- Individuality
- Respect
- Dignity and worth as human beings

Security permits us to settle on our own choices liberated from compulsion, to thoroughly act naturally and possibly take part in conduct that may digress from normal practices. Privacy gives people power to decide who may access various pieces of their data. It permits individuals to keep some part of their life to themselves and conduct themselves in an independent manner which isn't governed by the thinking that it would be humiliating for others to view it. Privacy additionally permits individuals to abstain from offering data to other people who might utilize it against them, for example, segregation by businesses, teachers or safety net providers. Security is additionally required for creating relational associations with others. While some underline the requirement for security to set up close connections, others take a more extensive perspective on protection as being important to keep up an assortment of social connections. By enabling us to control who views, comprehends and shares our personal data, security permits us to modify our conduct with various individuals so we may keep up and control our different social connections. For instance, individuals may impart different data to their employer than they would with their doctor, as proper with their various connections. Therefore, an individual needs to control the flow of their information. Privacy is also accompanied by the confidentiality of the parties involved and the security of data through authorization mechanisms and protection from data breaches. This is ensured by various countries as a constitutional right as discussed in Section 12.3, whereas some countries are still to take measures.

12.3 PRIVACY POLICIES IN THE WORLD

We discuss the privacy policies of some countries to get an idea of the implementation, budgetary requirements and gaps in execution. Using these privacy policies as a baseline, we establish the points which any healthcare privacy policy must cover.

12.3.1 UNITED STATES OF AMERICA (HIPAA)

The Health Insurance Portability and Accountability Act (HIPAA) was signed into effect in 1996. The main purpose of HIPAA was to ensure patients' healthcare data privacy, the security of electronic records, administrative ease and insurance portability [8]. It provides detailed instructions for handling and protecting personally identifiable data. These instructions may include access control mechanisms in the form of passwords and PINs, encrypting the stored information which ensures that only users who have the "key" can decrypt it, and an audit trail feature which can record who accessed the data, what changes were made and when. HIPAA provides the users rights over their healthcare information, including the right to get a copy of their information, make sure it is correct and know who has seen it [10]. HIPAA regulations must be followed by certain covered entities which include health insurance companies, HMOs, company health plans and healthcare providers such as doctors, clinics, hospitals, psychologists, chiropractors, nursing homes, pharmacies and dentists and business associates of covered entities such as people like outside lawyers, accountants and IT specialists and companies that store or destroy medical records. HIPAA includes the following key points related to healthcare data protection:

The HIPAA Security Rule: It sets rules and standards for the physical, administrative and technical handling of patient data. It emphasizes securing the creation, use, receipt and maintenance of personal healthcare information.

The HIPAA Privacy Rule: It limits the data which can be disclosed to third parties without patient consent and defines how these data can be used by them. It provides safeguards to protect the privacy of healthcare data including medical records, insurance information and other private data.

Even though HIPAA has been around 20+ years, its implementation has been far from perfect. At the time of implementation, the Department of Human and Health Services (HHS) estimated that HIPAA would initially cost healthcare systems approximately $113 million with subsequent maintenance costs of $14.5 million per year. The actual costs of HIPAA compliance are estimated at closer to $8.3 billion a year, with each physician on average spending $35,000 annually for health information technology upkeep. It increased the administrative requirements, and instead of providing the entire medical file of a patient, HIPAA requires that only the relevant data be offered which affects specific diagnosis. However, the pros of HIPAA outweigh the cons since it prevents any form of discrimination, assigns role-based security of information based on a person's role and was the foremost policy on healthcare privacy for many years, based on which other countries have developed their policies.

12.3.2 EUROPE (GDPR)

The General Data Protection Regulation (GDPR) is a regulation in EU law on data protection and privacy in the European Union and the European Economic Area. It also addresses the transfer of personal data outside the EU and EEA areas. GDPR in terms of healthcare follows certain principles such as lawfulness, fairness,

Challenges of Implementing Privacy Policies 215

transparency, purpose limitation, data minimization, accuracy, integrity, confidentiality, accountability and limited storage. It defines certain circumstances in which a patient's health and genetic data can be processed, the rules for consent and the rights provided to patients regarding their data. GDPR makes a special clause which ensures a patient's voice is heard in data protection debates. While GDPR helps ensure trust between companies who handle personally identifiable data and patients, there are some drawbacks present. The one-time cost for companies to get their data affairs in order was huge which affected many businesses. Also, the cost of violating GDPR could lead to a fine up to $23.5 million, or 4% of the global annual revenue of a business.

12.3.3 Australia

The Australian Healthcare and Hospitals Association (AHHA) is bound by the Australian Privacy Principles in the Privacy Act of 1988. The policy defines how healthcare information is to be collected and how personal information is used, along with access control and authorization mechanisms and the security of personally identifiable information using encryption. People are given the right to access the personal information that the AHHA holds and can ask to correct the information if incorrect. The Privacy Act establishes 13 principles (APP) and they are:

1. Open and transparent management of personal information
2. Anonymity and pseudonymity
3. Collection of solicited personal information
4. Unsolicited personal information
5. Notification of collecting personal information
6. Uses or disclosures of personal information
7. Direct marketing
8. Cross-border disclosure of personal information
9. Adoption, use or disclosure of government-related identifiers
10. Quality of personal information
11. Security of personal information
12. Access to personal information
13. Correction of personal information

12.3.4 Nigeria (NHA)

Nigeria doesn't have a widely inclusive healthcare security structure. Rather, it has a few excerpts in its laws and legislations which refer to healthcare privacy. This arrangement is counterproductive and often applied in an ad hoc manner creating confusion. There are several loopholes present in the application of the national healthcare services framework which can leave the insurance services overburdened and leave the people of Nigeria helpless [11]. As of now, laws and arrangements from other sectors of industry not directly related to healthcare provide more security than the healthcare laws themselves. This cannot be a lasting solution. A legitimate structure that oversees the privacy concerns, establishes rules and directs security strategy must be established to ensure patient data privacy in Nigeria. The constitution guarantees the privilege of security in Nigeria and, alongside the National Health Act (NHA), Health Records Officers Act and Code of Medical Ethics, serves to guarantee the protection of each patient in Nigeria. The NHA provides recommendations which make hospital services liable for collection of data and has established rules which define methods of sharing of healthcare data. The NHA of Nigeria is based upon the standards of the HIPAA of the USA. However, in terms of implementation the NHA lags severely with most patient privacy laws only lingering on paper. This is because of the absence of financing, the enormous populace and the absence of trust among patients and medicinal service providers. In any case, Nigeria has a long way to go before they can ensure patient privacy and security.

12.3.5 Russia

Russia adopted the Personal Data Law that defines the special legal status of patients in the Russian Federation [12]. This law defines the responsibilities of healthcare personnel, ensures the legitimacy of healthcare data and provides means for redressal in case of violation of rights by way of exposing confidential information. "On the fundamentals of protection of the health of citizens in the Russian Federation." The patient has the right to:

1. The choice of which doctor and medical organization provides him/her treatment
2. The prevention, diagnosis, treatment and medical rehabilitation in medical institutions in conditions that meet the sanitary-hygienic requirements
3. Receive consultations with doctors and specialists
4. The relief of pain associated with disease and/or medical intervention through available methods and medicines
5. Receive information about his rights and duties, the state of his health and the selection of people to whom can be transferred information about his state of health, in his best interests
6. Receive therapeutic feeding during treatment in stationary conditions
7. Protection of information classified as "medical confidence"
8. Refusal of medical intervention
9. Compensation for harm caused to health consequent to the provision of medical care
10. Access to his lawyer or legal representative for the protection of his rights
11. Access to a clergyman, as well as provision to perform religious rites if they do not violate the rules of the medical institution

In case these rights are violated, an individual can complain to higher authorities like professional medical associates, the head of the institution, the prosecutor's office and the legislative committee or can even go to the court directly. Information is subject to "medical secrecy," and the disclosure of any information stored under this is prohibited for every person from colleagues to medical and nonmedical professionals.

12.3.6 Japan

Japan uses the Protection of Personal Information Acts to protect its citizens that include the concept of anonymously processed information. A separate act was enacted to cover healthcare data: Act on Anonymously Processed Medical Information to Contribute to Medical Research and Development, which aims at processing a patient's data anonymously and securely for research purposes. The act provides for the security of patient records and allows redressal in case of violation. The Act to Promote Healthcare and Medical Strategy offers guidance regarding genetic testing and diagnosis which must also be conducted securely.

12.3.7 China

In China, the Network Security Law regulates that network providers must not disclose, falsify or destroy any personal information they have collected [13]. A network provider cannot divulge personally identifiable information to any third party without getting consent from data owners. However, data of users which cannot be used to re-identify a specific individual can be shared without consent.

The Chinese government later formally released a new regulation called the Information Security Technology and Personal Information Security Specification, referred to as the Specification. The security requirements, from collecting to storing, transferring and displaying the data, are defined in the Specification, though the Specification is a recommended standard, not compulsory. Even though the Specification has defined privacy and security with its phases, it has also added a few situations as exceptions:

1. Academic institutions can act as a personal information controller to perform statistical and academic research which is in the interest of the public. Academic institutions are exempted from obtaining consent for data use from every individual if the results of their research are such that they cannot be used to re-identify a specific person. The results of the statistical and academic research must be de-identified.
2. There is no need to obtain every individual's consent for data use if the utility of data is directly related to public safety or public health.
3. There is no need to obtain consent from the data owner if certain difficulties are present and the data use is to safeguard major legal rights such as the life and property of another individual.

12.3.8 Canada

Privacy breach notification in Canada is covered under the Personal Information Protection and Electronic Documents Act (PIPEDA) that states that private sector organizations are now required to notify affected individuals of any kind of security breach that may be a threat to the individual and report it to the privacy commissioner of Canada. This act stated that the customers should be given control of their data, and the data mobility rights, de-indexing and transparency should be maintained. It asks the firms to use tools for safer and protected data sharing. PIPEDA applies to federally regulated organizations like railways, banks, etc. Provinces like Alberta, British Columbia and Quebec have similar policies. The PIPEDA has incorporated the Canadian Standards Association Model Code (CSA Model Code) into the text of PIPEDA for the Protection of Personal Information. The CSA Model Code establishes ten principles:

1. Accountability
2. Identifying purposes
3. Consent
4. Limiting collection
5. Limiting use, disclosure and retention
6. Accuracy
7. Safeguards
8. Openness
9. Individual access
10. Challenging compliance

These principles are followed by all the firms under the act, protecting all information of the individual received through notes, conversations, videos, etc. If any such breaches occur that have a real risk of significant harm (RROSH) and the company fails to comply with the guidelines, a penalty of around $100,000 (Canadian) will be charged.

12.3.9 Korea

As written in Ref. [14], the Personal Information Protection Act (PIPA) serves as a general statute covering data privacy issues in Korea. This act defines the right to information privacy and includes the right to be informed of the processing of personal information and the right to claim damages that result from personal information processing. A patient's healthcare data are termed as sensitive and confidential information since they can be used to identify a patient's ideology, belief, political opinions, health and sexual life [15]. Healthcare data processing requires consent from data owners. The transfer and collection of these sensitive data can be done only after consent from the data owner on a separate consent form from the one which gives consent to only processing. The PIPA makes exceptions in a few cases: Personal genome data can be accessed for a criminal investigation, or to provide data to a foreign government to make extradition deals. The controller of healthcare information can use or share data for research purposes only if the data cannot be used to re-identify a specific individual.

Challenges of Implementing Privacy Policies

No privacy policy is perfect, with each one being a work in progress towards a more robust, scalable and efficient system. Every healthcare privacy policy must have the following characteristics:

- Enforce a strict access control policy to help limit access to only a set of qualified authorized individuals [16]
- Encrypting healthcare data which are at rest, in transit or in use
- Utilizing multi-factor authentication for people wishing to access the data [17]
- Maintaining and updating logs of who is accessing the data [18]
- Establishing a data trail feature to keep track who the data have been shared with and who has modified the data
- The signing of a data use agreement between third parties and patients to ensure the patient's data are not exploited
- Ensuring the patient has the right to access his/her personal data and appeal to the authority in case any personal information about the patient is wrong
- Allowing the patient to file complaints and seek redressal in case of violation of data use agreements
- Allow the patient to direct healthcare providers and insurance companies to not divulge certain information

To ensure any privacy policy enforces the above points, implementation and administrative expertise is required. It is essential to include researchers and scholars from the security and healthcare field to ensure every scenario is considered. While the above privacy policy defines the major points to be enforced, it is important to remember that every country is different in terms of the population, the spending and purchasing power of the people, the economy and the literacy present. There can be no uniform privacy policy solution for all countries. The budget allocated to developing a healthcare privacy system also plays a major role.

12.4 CHALLENGES FACED BY DEVELOPING COUNTRIES

Tremendous technological advancements have been made in the healthcare field in the last ten years. While most developing countries have now acquired the technological know-how which was first only reserved for the developed countries, unfortunately developing countries still lag far behind in the race of securing the privacy of patients [19]. Due to a myriad of challenges present in developing countries, the personally identifiable information of patients is not secure. The lack of a coherent healthcare system which ensures the privacy of an individual affects the level of treatment meted out to patients. Protecting the integrity of a patient's data ensures that a patient is comfortable to reveal accurate information. The challenges faced by developing countries are:

12.4.1 Data Storage and Management

The papers [20–24] state that the establishment of a healthcare privacy system entails secure data storage and management. Healthcare data must be encrypted to ensure confidentiality. The management of and access to data should be restricted and logs must be maintained. The secure management of information entails significant administrative overhead for which qualified individuals must be employed. Healthcare information needs to be constantly updated and maintained. The type of data storage used, centralized or distributed, should also be taken into consideration. In huge countries which are split into states for better management, should healthcare data be stored centrally or stored locally? Many times, data would need to be shared between states to combat a ubiquitous disease in real-time. The management of such a data repository requires considerable overhead. The type of data storage employed must be carefully worked out. Healthcare data management is a sensitive task. The leakage of personally identifiable information can be devastating for a patient. Should a third-party company be employed to transfer the risk of leakage or should the government of the country itself oversee the data management? In most cases, developing countries don't have the resources to employ all the mechanisms and technologies needed to make storage and management secure. The establishment of a privacy policy in writing but without any implementation results in more confusion and chaos which inevitably leads to the leakage of information.

12.4.2 Data Sharing

In Refs. [20, 25], the secure sharing of healthcare data between patients and healthcare providers or insurance companies must be facilitated by a nation's healthcare privacy policy. A system must be set in place to ensure data shared does not lead to the identification of the patient. A data use agreement must be enforced, and the patient's consent must be taken before data can be shared. Data which are shared must be encrypted and anonymized. The access to these data must be restricted. To ensure secure data sharing and exchange, a policy must be set in place which specifically points out the penalty for the violation of any clause of the policy. To ensure secure data sharing there must be a harmonization of guidelines and regulations enforced by the country. In most developing countries, the establishment of a clear, coherent law which enables the sharing of healthcare data is absent, instead having multiple contractual obligations in its place which only serve to alleviate issues on paper and not in reality.

12.4.3 Prevalent Indifference and Red-Tape

In Ref. [26], complacency and indifference towards bringing in legislation which establishes a robust healthcare system are widespread. While healthcare is given importance, the privacy of the individual takes a backseat. However, with identity theft and cybercrime at an all-time high, the privacy and security of healthcare records must be focused on. Politics and red-tape almost always succeed, which leaves progress faltering for years on end. Politicians make promises to win elections but do absolutely nothing to fulfil them once elected. The work, planning, cooperation and communication required amongst multiple departments to make the privacy and security of healthcare in developing countries a success are gargantuan.

However, due to negligence, the likelihood of a privacy model being implemented is poor. Red-tape must be removed to ensure an efficient, scalable and secure healthcare system.

12.4.4 Infrastructure

As suggested in Refs. [27, 28], infrastructure plays a critical role in the security of the healthcare system. The defence-in-depth concept should be utilized instead of a single security control while developing the healthcare system to prevent unauthorized access. Developing countries must be ready to completely overhaul their healthcare system to integrate security and privacy mechanisms. In some cases where integration is not possible, the infrastructure would have to be built from the ground up. The infrastructure must be scalable, easily accessible and dynamic. A proper healthcare privacy protocol and structure must be defined, taking into consideration the urban and rural population. The infrastructure should be easy to use but at the same time secure. The sharing, storage and management of data hinge on a secure infrastructure. The development and integration of a new privacy healthcare infrastructure in a developing country require inputs from the top minds in various fields, viz. security, healthcare, privacy, all working together to ensure that the system is robust. This may require international experts as well. The cost of planning the infrastructure is also significant which must be taken into consideration. The infrastructure must support interoperability and availability to ensure privacy is maintained for every patient.

12.4.5 Population

The population plays a significant role in the efficiency of healthcare privacy in a country. The larger the population, the harder it is to implement a policy which effectively secures privacy for all. With almost every developing country suffering from population explosion, ensuring the privacy of every citizen becomes a hard task. Errors in data entry where the healthcare information of one individual is stored under another person's name or multiple people having the same name lead to confusion, data inconsistency and affects the level of treatment meted out. Establishing a privacy policy on paper and implementing a policy which is scalable and dynamic enough to provide reliable security is immensely hard.

12.4.6 Budgetary Constraints

The cost of implementing a privacy system is huge and requires continuous funding from the government for upkeep, maintenance and upgrades against new-age cyber-attacks. The development and planning require specialists in the fields of healthcare, security, privacy and architecture to help implement a model which effectively secures the privacy of personally identifiable information. Building the actual infrastructure may have to be outsourced to third-party companies. The management, storage and exchange of data may be facilitated by companies overseas. The unseen costs while implementing a privacy model for a whole country are huge. Most developing countries don't possess the adequate budget necessary to implement a healthcare privacy system [29]. The lending of money by other countries to facilitate development leads to huge debt which affects the country's long-term growth. Taking the help of another country's physical resources, such as servers, may lead to the leakage of information and the threat of snooping. Thus developing countries find it immensely onerous to implement a privacy system.

12.4.7 CULTURE AND LITERACY RATE

The culture prevalent in every country is unique [30, 31]. A country like India has a vast number of dialects, with each region speaking a different language. Thus the implementation of a privacy model in one language or dialect would not suffice. Automating the conversion of healthcare reports from one language to another may lead to discrepancies and incorrect information. In many cultures, the disclosure of sensitive personal information is looked down upon. This may be due to tradition, insufficient trust between patients and healthcare providers or fear of ostracization. Eliminating the stigma associated with the disclosure of sensitive healthcare information to healthcare providers would improve the level of treatment meted out and reduce fatalities. Due to inaccurate disclosure, research and statistics of treatment given then don't match the records. The literacy rate present in a region also plays an immense role in the success of a healthcare system. The literate realize the need for a reliable and efficient healthcare system. Strong health literacy enables people to develop the skills and confidence to make informed decisions about their health and the health of their families, to be active partners in their care, to effectively navigate healthcare systems and to advocate effectively to their political leaders and policy-makers.

12.4.8 CYBER-ATTACKS

Cyber-attacks against healthcare systems are increasing at an alarming rate. Attacks are increasing not only in number but also in sophistication [32, 33]. Hackers target healthcare data due to easy access because of insufficient security controls. Comprehensive medical records can sell on the black market for huge sums since they can be used to create fake IDs to buy drugs or file fake insurance claims. The prevalence of identity theft is also worrisome. In many cases, healthcare providers share data with third parties who aren't as secure as the providers themselves. Hackers target these third parties to steal and modify sensitive data. In some cases, hackers pose as legitimate healthcare providers to trick patients into revealing their healthcare data. Social engineering is widespread and can only be prevented by user awareness. Denial of service (DOS) attacks and distributed denial of service (DDOS) attacks exhaust the network resources available and prevent legitimate healthcare providers from accessing, sending, receiving and entering medical records. Implementing a healthcare system which can resist such attacks is extremely hard and requires constant maintenance, upgrades and monitoring. The development and execution of such a system require substantial money, resources and manpower.

12.4.9 STATE-SPONSORED SURVEILLANCE

Surveillance and abuse of privacy are quickly climbing the policy agendas of developing countries [34]. National identification systems, DNA databases and biometric systems have all given rise to significant political debates, with activists up in arms. Due to this opposition, laws are tweaked, regulators and third parties are brought in to oversee the system and courts are called upon to judge compliance with constitutional provisions. However, all of this rarely affects the real intention of state-sponsored snooping and surveillance. Advocacy groups, media organizations, regulators and judiciaries, where they exist, are less equipped to engage in these complex technology privacy policy discussions. Even the policy-makers themselves may be unable to cope with the complexities. Developing countries are usually associated with the weak economic status tag, but when it comes to the adoption of surveillance policies, many developing countries are implementing vastly more sophisticated surveillance systems than exist in the developed world. One might then ask, how can a government hell-bent on snooping into every activity of its citizens be trusted with handling sensitive healthcare information? By ignoring privacy and security concerns, new risks are being introduced to already vulnerable patients, potentially leading to increased stigma, social exclusion or persecution. In some developing countries, practices and systems are being overhauled but with little importance given to security and privacy. It seems that privacy of healthcare data is a luxury only present in developed countries.

12.4.10 PRIVACY AS A CONSTITUTIONAL RIGHT

The majority of developing countries have privacy stated as a fundamental right in their constitutions. Article 12 of the Universal Declaration of Human Rights states that no one shall be subjected to arbitrary interference with his privacy. Yet, the privacy and security of an individual's personally identifiable information are constantly undermined and shared without consent. The absence of a strategy and framework, however, to enforce the privacy of healthcare data is worrying and must be focused on.

12.4.11 INTERNAL AND EXTERNAL THREATS

Most of the healthcare systems in the world partner with various external centres such as diagnostics, insurance and laboratories for the smooth working of the entire system, but involving so many layers can lead to many built-in flaws, making the system vulnerable to attacks and giving various actors in play a chance to access the data for misuse. Different centres that get involved during the course many times fail to flawlessly integrate their security systems, therefore leading to many security loopholes which can be easily noticed and exploited by anybody who accesses the system.

12.4.12 DATA BREACHING

In Ref. [35], data breaching refers to the intentional or unintentional release of private information to an untrusted environment. Because all the healthcare dataset has now been shifted to cloud servers and is accessible on the Internet, the data have become less secure and are prone to more threats through the server, allowing third parties to access the data and misusing them, like copying them and sending to someone or making unauthorized changes.

12.4.13 Consent Management

To access the records of any individual, one person needs to have the consent of the patient as well as that of the doctor treating the patient. This ensures that the private records are available to only those who have been authorized and authenticated. The challenge to act out this procedure is to ensure that the consent is not being faked and has been given by the patient and doctor. In cases like these, it is very easy to impersonate a member involved, jeopardizing the patient's privacy. Proper methods and tools need to be used to incorporate this without any security threat.

12.4.14 Trusting the Third Party

In Ref. [31], hospitals use third parties to authorize the user and authenticate the data; as to who can access the data and how much, it needs to be guaranteed that the third party is operating without any bias and that, even with the authority to control the data, it does not get the power to manipulate them and exploit them.

12.4.15 Improper Human Resource Management

As written in an article in Home Business titled "8 Challenges Faced by Healthcare in India," in a country like India, the difference between the healthcare structure of the rural and urban areas is massive. The management to train employees and provide services is lacking in rural areas; nonetheless even the doctors and nurses from these areas wish to move to bigger and more developed areas for better career exposure. Another point lacking in human resource management is the education system. With the Internet taking over the world and all the hospitals shifting to cloud server databases, there needs to be proper protocol followed while accessing the data; one step gone wrong can put every user's privacy at risk. Therefore, the management needs to educate their employees on the accurate use of the system.

12.5 CONCLUSION

Privacy in healthcare is an absolute necessity to keep the patient's healthcare data confidential and secure. Strict policies and robust systems are the need of the hour to protect patient data from exploitation and misuse. Healthcare inventions and technologies which help improve patient care and improve longevity and standard of life are emerging at breakneck speed. However, in most of these advancements, the security and privacy of patient information are compromised. The security of patient data ensures hackers can't steal identities or manipulate healthcare records and builds trust between the patient and the system. This chapter explores the privacy policies present in countries along with the pros and cons of their policies. It further explores the challenges and problems faced by developing countries while trying to establish a uniform, robust policy throughout the country and, finally, searches for possible models which may serve as a solution to the patient privacy issues in developing countries.

REFERENCES

1. Vora, J., DevMurari, P., Tanwar, S., Tyagi, S., Kumar, N., & Obaidat, M. S. (2018). Blind signatures based secured e-healthcare system. In 2018 International Conference on Computer, Information and Telecommunication Systems (CITS) (pp. 1–5). IEEE. https://doi.org/10.1109/CITS.2018.8440186.
2. Pussewalage, H. S. G., & Oleshchuk, V. A. (2016). Privacy preserving mechanisms for enforcing security and privacy requirements in E-health solutions. *International Journal of Information Management*, 36(6), 1161–1173. https://doi.org/10.1016/j.ijinfomgt.2016.07.006.
3. Senthilkumar, S. A., Rai, B. K., Meshram, A. A., Gunasekaran, A., & Chandrakumarmangalam, S. (2018). Big data in healthcare management: A review of literature. *American Journal of Theoretical and Applied Business*, 4, 57–69. https://doi.org/10.11648/j.ajtab.20180402.14.
4. L. Sweeney. (2002). k-anonymity: A model for protecting privacy. *International Journal on Uncertainty, Fuzziness and Knowledge-based Systems*, 10(5), 557–570. https://doi.org/10.1142/S0218488502001648.
5. Sweeney, L.. (2018). Simple demographics often identify people uniquely. Carnegie Mellon University. Journal contribution. https://doi.org/10.1184/R1/6625769.v1.
6. Xu, L., Jiang, C., Chen, Y., Ren, Y., & Liu, K. R. (2015). Privacy or utility in data collection? A contract theoretic approach. *IEEE Journal of Selected Topics in Signal Processing*, 9(7), 1256–1269. https://doi.org/10.1109/JSTSP.2015.2425798.
7. Chiauzzi, E., Rodarte, C. & DasMahapatra, P. (2015). Patient-centered activity monitoring in the self-management of chronic health conditions. *BMC Medicine*, 13, 77. https://doi.org/10.1186/s12916-015-0319-2.
8. Pritts, J. (2008). The importance and value of protecting the privacy of health information: Roles of HIPAA privacy rule and the common rule in health research. Institute of Medicine.
9. Institute of Medicine (US) Committee on Health Research and the Privacy of Health Information: The HIPAA Privacy Rule; Nass SJ, Levit LA, Gostin LO, editors. (2009). *Beyond the HIPAA Privacy Rule: Enhancing Privacy, Improving Health Through Research*. Washington, DC: National Academies Press. 2, The Value and Importance of Health Information Privacy. Available from: https://www.ncbi.nlm.nih.gov/books/NBK9579/.
10. U.S. Department of Health & Human Services Office for Civil Rights. Privacy, security, and electronic health records. https://www.hhs.gov/sites/default/files/ocr/privacy/hipaa/understanding/consumers/privacy-security-electronic-records.pdf?language=en.
11. Nigeria Health Ict Phase 2 Field Assessment Findings. http://ict4somlnigeria.info/wp-content/uploads/2016/03/Nigeria-Health-Data-Security-Guide.pdf.
12. Pishchita A. N. (2013). Legal maintenance of patient data confidentiality in the Russian federation. In Beran R. (eds.), *Legal and Forensic Medicine*. Berlin, Heidelberg: Springer.

13. Gong, M., Wang, S., Wang, L., Liu, C., Wang, J., Guo, Q., Zheng, H., Xie, K., Wang, C., & Hui, Z. (2020). Evaluation of privacy risks of patients' data in China: Case study. *JMIR Medical Informatics*, 8(2), e13046. https://doi.org/10.2196/13046.
14. Kim, H., Kim, S. Y., & Joly, Y. (2018). South Korea: In the midst of a privacy reform centered on data sharing. *Human Genetics*, 137(8), 627–635. https://doi.org/10.1007/s00439-018-1920-1.
15. Lee, D., Park, M., Chang, S., & Ko, H. (2019). Protecting and utilizing health and medical big data: Policy perspectives from Korea. *Healthcare Informatics Research*, 25(4), 239–247.
16. A. Salehi Shahraki, C. Rudolph and M. Grobler.(2019). A dynamic access control policy model for sharing of healthcare data in multiple domains. In 18th IEEE International Conference on Trust, Security and Privacy in Computing and Communications/13th IEEE International Conference on Big Data Science and Engineering (TrustCom/BigDataSE), Rotorua, New Zealand (pp. 618–625), doi: 10.1109/TrustCom/BigDataSE.2019.00088.
17. T. Bhattasali and K. Saeed. (2014). Two factor remote authentication in healthcare. In International Conference on Advances in Computing, Communications and Informatics (ICACCI), New Delhi (pp. 380–386), doi: 10.1109/ICACCI.2014.6968594.
18. L. Rostad and O. Edsberg. (2006). A study of access control requirements for healthcare systems based on audit trails from access logs. In 22nd Annual Computer Security Applications Conference (ACSAC'06), Miami Beach, FL (pp. 175–186), doi: 10.1109/ACSAC.2006.8.
19. Raul, A. C. (Ed.). (2018). *The Privacy, Data Protection and Cybersecurity Law Review*. Law Business Research Limited.
20. Wadhwa, R., Mehra, A., Singh, P., & Singh, M. (2015). A pub/sub based architecture to support public healthcare data exchange. In 2015 7th International Conference on Communication Systems and Networks (COMSNETS) (pp. 1–6). IEEE.
21. Manogaran G., Thota C., Lopez D., Vijayakumar V., Abbas K. M., & Sundarsekar R. (2017). Big data knowledge system in healthcare. In Bhatt C., Dey N., & Ashour A. (eds.), *Internet of Things and Big Data Technologies for Next Generation Healthcare. Studies in Big Data* (vol. 23). Cham: Springer.
22. Deshmukh, P. (2017). Design of cloud security in the EHR for Indian healthcare services. *Journal of King Saud University-Computer and Information Sciences*, 29(3), 281–287.https://doi.org/10.1016/j.jksuci.2016.01.002.
23. Manogaran, G., Thota, C., Lopez, D., & Sundarasekar, R. (2017). Big data security intelligence for healthcare industry 4.0. In *Cybersecurity for Industry 4.0* (pp. 103–126). Cham: Springer. https://doi.org/10.1007/978-3-319-50660-9_5.
24. Senthilkumar S. A., Bharatendara K Rai, Amruta A Meshram, Angappa Gunasekaran, Chandrakumarmangalam S. Big data in healthcare management: A review of literature. *American Journal of Theoretical and Applied Business*, 4(2), 57–69. doi: 10.11648/j.ajtab.20180402.14.
25. C. Esposito, A. De Santis, G. Tortora, H. Chang and K. R. Choo. (2018). Blockchain: A panacea for healthcare cloud-based data security and privacy?. *IEEE Cloud Computing*, 5(1), 31–37, doi: 10.1109/MCC.2018.011791712.
26. Kagalwalla, N., Garg, T., Churi, P., & Pawar, A. (2019). A survey on implementing privacy in healthcare: An indian perspective. *International Journal of Advanced Trends in Computer Science and Engineering*, 8(3), 963–682.
27. Sreenu, N. (2019). Healthcare infrastructure development in rural India: A critical analysis of its status and future challenges. *British Journal of Healthcare Management*, 25(12), 1–9.

28. Mittal, Y. K., Paul, V. K., Rostami, A., Riley, M., & Sawhney, A. (2020). Delay factors in construction of healthcare infrastructure projects: A comparison amongst developing countries. *Asian Journal of Civil Engineering*, 21, 649–661.
29. Roger Strasser, Sophia M. Kam, & Sophie M. Regalado. (2016). Rural health care access and policy in developing Countries. *Annual Review of Public Health*, 37(1), 395–412.
30. Kiyomu Ishikawa. (2001). Health data use and protection policy; based on differences by cultural and social environment. *International Journal of Medical Informatics*, 60(2), 119–125.
31. Shrestha, N. M., Alsadoon, A., Prasad, P. W. C., Hourany, L., & Elchouemi, A. (2016). Enhanced e-health framework for security and privacy in healthcare system. In 6th International Conference on Digital Information Processing and Communications (ICDIPC) (pp. 75–79). IEEE.
32. Sun, Z., Strang, K. D., & Pambel, F. (2018). Privacy and security in the big data paradigm. *Journal of Computer Information Systems*, 60(2), 146–155.
33. Martin Guy, Martin Paul, Hankin Chris, Darzi Ara, & Kinross James. Cybersecurity and healthcare: How safe are we? *BMJ*, 358, j3179.
34. Office of the Privacy Commissioner of Canada. https://www.priv.gc.ca/en/opc-actions-and-decisions/research/explore-privacy-research/2011/hosein_201109/#archived.
35. Rana, M. E., Kubbo, M., & Jayabalan, M. (2017). Privacy and security challenge towards cloud-based access control. *Asian Journal of Information Technology*, 16(2–5), 274–281.

13 The Role of Law in Protecting Medical Data in India

S. P. Chakrabarty, S. Mukherjee and A. Rodricks

CONTENTS

13.1 Introduction 229
13.2 International Instruments Regulating Medical Data Privacy......................231
    13.2.1 Convention 108 232
    13.2.2 Oviedo Convention 232
    13.2.3 Declarations on Promotion of Patients' Rights in Europe...............233
    13.2.4 Opinion of the European Group on Ethics in Science and New Technologies 234
    13.2.5 Directives by European Parliament..235
    13.2.6 Big Data and Convention 108 235
    13.2.7 Regulation on General Data Protection by European Parliament....236
13.3 Jurisdictional Challenge to Laws on Medical Data Privacy.........................236
    13.3.1 Conservative Approach..237
    13.3.2 Liberal Approach..237
    13.3.3 Supervisory Approach 238
13.4 Shaping up of Laws Pertaining to Genetic Testing: An Illustration.............238
    13.4.1 Europe...238
    13.4.2 USA...239
13.5 The Laws Prevailing in India to Address Medical Data Privacy 240
    13.5.1 Understanding Privacy Rights as a Fundamental Right...................240
    13.5.2 Right to Information Act, 2000 (RTI Act) 241
    13.5.3 The Information Technology Act, 2000 (IT Act).............................241
    13.5.4 Indian Council of Medical Research (ICMR) 241
13.6 Conclusion 242
References..243

13.1 INTRODUCTION

Quantum physics, with its theory of relativity, has made staggering developments in the area of telecommunication and satellite technology. In turn, today, people have become more dependent on GPS than their brains to find a new place. Technology today is dominating major aspects of human life. Significant jurisdictions consider the right to access the Internet today as a fundamental right. This technological inclusion eliminates those limitations that time, distance and money would have otherwise imposed. Virtual reality has enrooted and challenged the concept of nationality and traditional ways of life, and given us a new global village called cyberspace. This growth in the technological sector has touched all the areas humans interact with in the general course of life, and the healthcare sector is no stranger to this evolution. This change has brought a lot of people, and with them their thoughts, under an umbrella. With the major players in the world health sector coming closer, the three Vs which have proven to be of much significance come as a consequence. Volume, variety and velocity: The volume of medical records available is increasing at a staggering pace, and almost all counties have started relying on it. The variety of medical data is also huge, as multiple areas need to be diagnosed and identified for choosing the right course of action for the patient. The velocities at which these medical records are increasing are phenomenal and unprecedented, as major developing countries are now transitioning to digitalization [1, 2]. As tech giants like "Fitbit" and "Apple Health" are collecting an enormous amount of data from all parts of the world from various users and patients [3, 4], data management becomes a key area of concern.

These modern technological marvels have replaced a plethora of outdated, unscientific thoughts and notions, including *lex loci* (laws of the land). The biggest challenge that the law needs to address today is the jurisdictional challenges inherent in colonial laws where the concept of state and formation of the government has always been based on territoriality.

In cyberspace, there is no territoriality. The laws fit for a specific jurisdiction with its implementational machinery are suddenly outdated today. The question of privacy, amidst this technological evolution, has challenged all regulatory mechanisms searching for an answer. Medical data privacy, being a species of the genus privacy, is also struggling for a static regulatory mechanism. In a highly globalized world, healthcare issues are no longer limited to a specific jurisdiction. This global issue, prior to its resolution, requires retrospection from a global standpoint.

There are certain normative aspects involved in multidisciplinary research. Caution must be exercised while dealing with technical and medical data concerning privacy, ethics and similar other normative issues. Informed consent plays a significant role as patients should be aware that the said data are subject to commercial availability and that they form a part of big data [5, 6].

In this chapter, the authors intend to unravel the struggle developed countries have undergone to formulate laws and frame policies to prevent the misuse of data of patients. The importance of this global issue, as has been addressed by the world community through various international instruments, is also highlighted. The collective approach of European nations, the US and Asian countries, including India, in regulating the issue of medical privacy has been analysed and grey areas unravelled. The absence of adequate literature in this area of research was noticed; hence primary sources like international instruments, enactments and judgements of the apex courts have largely been relied upon. The study proposes to bridge the gaps that have not been addressed by the existing laws and what should be the best way forward from the regulatory and legal standpoint.

13.2 INTERNATIONAL INSTRUMENTS REGULATING MEDICAL DATA PRIVACY

The fundamental source of data is the society we live in, and said data are used and applied to people living in that society. Medical data privacy is multifaceted, including, but not limited to, cybersecurity, cyber frauds, etc. Laws and regulations pertaining to this area of discourse require scrutiny. Significant development in the process of law-making for a subject matter of international concern certainly requires international law to play a vital role. International laws and international instruments, as reflected in Table 13.1, are connected to the people through domestic legislation. The primary modes by which this process materializes are through three theories: Specific adoption theory, the delegation theory and the transformation theory. Laws and regulations of medical records have to be managed. Hence, the proper classification of medical, non-medical and non-healthcare medical data is to be developed. Specific laws need to be made on accessing and using those data diligently.

The "Universal Declaration of Human Rights" was intended to recognize individuals' privacy and dignity [3]. Article 12 therein prohibited "*arbitrary interference*" in the privacy and dignity of individuals and their families. At that juncture, i.e., post-Second World War, the potential threat of interference was primarily anticipated from the state machinery [3]. A similar position is reiterated in Article 17 in 1966 in the "International Covenant on Civil and Political Rights" [7]. "The Convention for the Protection of Human Rights and Fundamental Freedom," popularly known as "European Convention on Human Rights," also respects the privacy

TABLE 13.1
Collective Measures for Medical Data Privacy

S. No.	Year	Instrument	Key provision(s)
1	1948	UDHR	Article 12
2	1976	ICCPR	Article 17
3	1950	ECHR	Article 8
4	1981	Convention 108	Preamble, Article 1,2, 8,9,12,13
5	1995	"Directive 95/46/EC of the European Parliament"	Article 1,9, 13, 25, 26
6	1997	Oviedo Convention	Article 10
7	1994	"Declaration on the Promotion of Patients' Rights in Europe"	Guiding Principles, Clause 1, 4
8	1995, 2005, 2015	"Lisbon Declaration on Rights of Patient"	Clause 7, 8, 10
9	1999	EGE Opinion	–
10	2017	"Consultative Committee of the Convention for the Protection of Individuals with Regard to Automatic Processing of Personal Data, 2017"	–
11	2018	GDPR, European Parliament	Chapter III

of every individual; however, it also provides that this right can be interfered with, if issues pertaining to public safety, national security, the economic well-being of the state, crime prevention, protection of health or the moral state or rights and freedom of others demand such interference; albeit such intervention should be done in accordance with the law [8]. In the initial stage, the law of privacy was concerned with the protection of individual privacy, from arbitrary interference of the state, and is considered one of the most significant human rights. The authors have made a comprehensive study of almost all international instruments pertaining to medical data privacy along with laws in various jurisdictions and have identified some very crucial missing areas that have to be bridged in the upcoming laws of data privacy in India.

13.2.1 Convention 108

With technological evolution, reforms needed to be brought in the law of privacy irrespective of jurisdictions. The European nations acknowledged the need to address the issue of protection of data privacy as a collective. The member nations of the European Council, with a view of protecting fundamental rights, especially the right to privacy and a significant rise in automated personal data processing ("data protection"), came up with the "Convention for Protection of Individuals with regard to Automatic Processing of Personal Data, 1981" also known as "Convention 108" [9].

As per the Convention,

> "The automatic processing meant storage of data, carrying out of logical and/or arithmetic operation on those data, alteration, erasure, retrieval or dissemination."

The member states were under obligation to take appropriate measures to legislate domestic laws based on the fundamental principles laid by the Convention. The Convention explicitly places the responsibility on the parties prohibiting automatic processing of data relating to race, political or religious belief, health and sexual life. However, the parties may bypass such prohibitions through enactment of domestic legislations. This very Convention could be considered as the first international instrument which explicitly addressed the issue of potential risks associated with the abuse of privacy law involving medical data. The Convention further provided for guidelines on additional safeguards that entail rectifying or erasing such data which were obtained or processed violating or ignoring the domestic legislations, by effecting the provisions of Article 6 drafted precisely to safeguard sensitive information including restrictions on the flowing of personal data across borders. Furthermore, a specific exception was made to the basic principles for the protection of data reflecting similar provisions as provided in the "European Treaty on Human Rights" [8].

13.2.2 Oviedo Convention

In 1995, the European Parliament took another significant step by issuing a directive addressing personal data processing and its free movement. The directive's very objective was to protect the right to privacy of personal data and allied processes involved in handling such data. The directive clarifies personal data as that information related to a natural person, whether directly or indirectly. These data may include information relating to the physical, mental or physiological features as well as the social, economic or cultural characteristics of an individual [10].

The European Council followed up Convention 108 with the "Convention for the Protection of Human Rights and Dignity of the Human Being" concerning the "Application of Biology and Medicine: Convention on Human Rights and Biomedicine of 1997" (Oviedo Convention). This Convention was drafted in the wake of accelerated development in biology and medicine and the realization that the potential misuse of biology and medicine could endanger human dignity. The Convention primarily dealt with human rights, biology and medicine. The Convention further bestows the right to the individual of not receiving health-related information [11].

13.2.3 DECLARATIONS ON PROMOTION OF PATIENTS' RIGHTS IN EUROPE

With technological advancement, it became imperative for European nations to pay significant attention to patients' rights. The "Declaration on Promotion of Patient's Right" in Europe (1994) laid down the principles of patients' rights. Clause 4 of the declaration lays down the principle on the confidentiality and privacy of the patients. Perusals of the clause reflect that that patients' health status, diagnosis or prognosis, and all other private information are paramount, and confidentiality must be maintained, not only during the lifetime but also after death. The confidentiality of a patient's information is considered so crucial that it can be disclosed only if explicit consent is received from the patient or if the law provides for it; however, the consent of the patient could be presumed in such circumstances where another healthcare facility is jointly involved in the process of treatment. The clause also gives the patient the right to access and receive medical and technical details concerning them but does not extend to third-party data; furthermore, the patient has the right to correct, complete, delete and update such personal medical data which are inaccurate, outdated, incomplete or irrelevant for the treatment and diagnosis of the individual. In addition to the rights of the patients, the healthcare facilities also had specific duties concerning the maintenance of confidentiality and privacy of the patient, such as protection of identifiable data in an appropriate manner of storing; no intrusion in the patient's private life without the consent of the patient, and even after receiving consent any such intrusion must be justifiable for treatment, diagnosis and requisite care; catering to the expectation of the patient of aforementioned facilities dealing with privacy [12]. After the 1994 "Declaration of Patient's Health," the "World Medical Association" came up with a "Revised Declaration of Lisbon on the Rights of the Patient" in 1995, 2005 and 2015. In the 1995 revision, there was a significant shift from the design of the declaration of 1994. The 1995 "Revised Declaration of on Rights of Patient" had moved away from the comprehensive clause on confidentiality and privacy, and incorporated a separate clause on the "Right to Confidentiality" which remains identical in principle to the 1995 declaration. However, specific and significant alterations were introduced, such as providing for the rights of the descendants to access the information, to enable them to be informed about potential health risks they may face; healthcare facilities which are engaged in joint treatment with the parent facility, such additional facility can be given information on a "need to know" basis unless the patient grants explicit consent for the sharing of information. The provisions relating to the privacy of individual also could be found as sub-clauses under the clauses titled "Right to Dignity" and "Right to Information," wherein the existing rights of the patients regarding privacy are supplemented with due consideration given to the cultural aspect of the patient; and choice of such individuals, relatives, etc. who can be made aware of the medical condition of the patient. However, certain limitations on the rights of patients regarding privacy were incorporated, which provide for the withholding of information from the patient if there is a reasonable belief that such information may be hazardous to the patient's life. The declaration also gives the patient liberty to refuse participation in research and the teaching of medicine [13]. The declaration was subsequently revised in the years 2005 [14] and 2015 [15]; the clause addressing the confidentiality and privacy relating to patient information remained similar to 1995's revised declaration.

13.2.4 OPINION OF THE EUROPEAN GROUP ON ETHICS IN SCIENCE AND NEW TECHNOLOGIES

In 1999, "The European Group on Ethics in Science and New Technologies to the European Commission" opined on issues of ethics in healthcare in the information society after taking due consideration of the actual progress in medical data-related international instruments and the practical aspects intertwined with technology and society. After considering the social, technological, legal and medical factors, the group opined that the medical data of an individual are part of his/her personality and must not be converted into commercial objects. Informed consent is non-derogable for collecting and accessing these data; collection of such data must be limited to the treating medical professional and to such other parties who can justify their role in the treatment process; the authorized users of such data should treat the information as part and parcel of medical secrecy, the only exception being existence of a law in operation providing for digression from the rule; the confidentiality of medical data should be respected even after the death of the individual; citizens have the right to know about the data collected, their purpose and who will be using them and to correct the data; furthermore, the citizen also have the right to oppose secondary use of the data which is not regulated by law; feature of accountability was established over all the parties who engage in medical data; the standard of such accountability must be similar to the accountability of health professionals; the act of collection of the medical data must strictly be premised upon a legitimate purpose and entities who are connected to the healthcare industry but operate independently; a state-of-the-art security system must be provided for safety in the storing and transfer of medical data; accountability of the health information providers over new "Information and Communication Technology" was established; information sought over the Internet regarding drugs and medicine are to be considered as part of personal health data;

health-related consultation over the Internet or the creation of profiles is not to be traded with a third party; health cards are to be dealt with extreme care and caution, as no such data are to be included without consent of that individual (and some not even with the consent of the individual) and the card holder must have the liberty to restrict partial or complete data on the card, including the right to restrain the use of such data; the participatory element of decision making, with regard to medical data, is essential and must be encouraged; education and training of individuals on the aspects of medical data and technology must be undertaken by the healthcare professionals even without any explicit request [16].

13.2.5 Directives by European Parliament

With the rising dependency on technology, and more importantly IT, the European Parliament issued several directives. "Directive 2002/58/EC," for example, addresses the privacy and safety of personal data in e-communication, and "Directive 2004/23/EC" addresses processing of privacy-related data, safety, standards of quality, procurement and testing of human tissues and cells. Furthermore, the European Parliament issued a specific regulation addressing the processing and free movement of personal data. However, the regulation governed data protection in the general sense; nonetheless, the "data concerning health," "genetic data" and "biometric data" were addressed within the ambit of general data protection regulation. The continued development in technology led to the formulation of Opinion of the European Group in Ethics in Science and New Technology concerning the ethical implications of new health technologies and citizen participation in 2015. Therein, the "European Group on Ethics" (EGE) *inter-alia* recommended that fundamental rights considerations should be integral to EU policy on health data, including big data. Observing that data are deemed to be the new currency of the 21st century, bringing considerable opportunities for economic activity and R&D, and because health data have become both a sensitive and a strategic object of attention, the EGE recommends the EU institutions to clarify the concept of ownership concerning data. Weighing in on the debate of private ownership and public good, the EGE recommends the setting up of measures in order to protect individuals against overreach by third parties with regard to health data [12].

13.2.6 Big Data and Convention 108

The challenge of the protection of data got only more severe with the introduction of artificial intelligence and big data. The Consultative Committee of the Convention, in order to protect automated data privacy rights, laid down comprehensive guidelines wherein the significance of human rights, fundamental freedoms and a necessity for compliance with data protection obligations are laid down. The impacts of big data processing were acknowledged, and the privacy concerns addressed in Convention 108 are reiterated in the wake of the potential implications of big data processing and artificial intelligence. The guidelines laid down specific clauses limiting the use of personal data, consent and education [17].

13.2.7 REGULATION ON GENERAL DATA PROTECTION BY EUROPEAN PARLIAMENT

In 2018, the "European Parliament and Council of European Council" implemented "Regulation (EU) 2016/679," which deals with protecting medical data concerning natural persons. This regulation repealed the earlier Directive 95/46/EC [18]. The regulation establishes specific principles on personal data processing and is based on transparency, fairness and lawfulness, purpose limitation and limiting data collection; the accuracy of data; temporal limitations on storage; integrity and confidentiality. Chapter III of the regulation provided detailed provisions on transparency, information and access, rectification and the right to be forgotten, the right to object and restriction under different heads, titled as "sections".

Even though the regulation at present is applicable in the member countries of the European Union, nonetheless the standards have found acceptability in individual other nations beyond Europe, and it is expected that in due course of time they will have a broader impact in shaping accepted international standards on medical data protection with requisite contextualization. Furthermore, the trend of accepting the standards of nations other than European countries may lead to the creation of customary international law, albeit with specific modifications, exceptions and reservations, and successfully remove the void in international law specifically addressing the concerns of medical data protection.

While the EU acted as a collective, some of the major jurisdictions also took significant steps towards data protection law through legislations as reflected in Table 13.2 [4]; though they may not be considered as international law, nonetheless, they can definitely act as inspiration to the nations without such legislation.

13.3 JURISDICTIONAL CHALLENGE TO LAWS ON MEDICAL DATA PRIVACY

Would it be legal for a state to collect medical data from its citizens and use it to improve public health? If the trend (data analysis) reflects that a major section of the population is tending towards diabetes, and consequently, the state takes necessary action to prevent such a foreseeable health crisis (the state acts as a guardian) would

TABLE 13.2
Legislative Measures by Major Jurisdictions

S. No.	Country	Legislation(s)
1.	USA	HIPAA Act, 1996; Patient Safety and Quality Improvement Act, 2005; HITECH Act, 2009
2.	Canada	Personal Information Protection and Electronic Documents Act, 2007
3.	UK	Data Protection Act, 2018
4.	Russia	Russian Federal Law on Personal Data, 2006
5.	Brazil	Constitutional Provisions
6.	Angola	Data Protection Law, 2011

the state be considered as violating the jurisdiction vested upon it? This position, however, is not absolute and is subject to certain restrictions. There are certain rights (of the people) with which the state cannot interfere. Fundamental rights *per se* fall within the purview of those restrictions. In law, these rights are called inalienable rights, as these cannot be suspended nor surrendered. These rights are protected by specific checks and balances including ethical, moral and legal precepts.

From the policy perspective, one of the major challenges that India needs to address is the adoption of a policy that would be capable of addressing the data privacy rights of its citizens without compromising its economic development in the IT and data management sector [19].

13.3.1 Conservative Approach

The EU laws can at best be nomenclated as conservative. The primary reason for this policy is the experience the people had with their rulers. Prior to the end of WWII, the Nazi Germans violated the people's rights to such an extent that the people of that country and its surroundings fear similar misuse of power by state machinery. Thus, the laws in these developed economies are conservative, and their approach towards the challenge of data privacy is conservative and restrictive. Privacy rights and data protection are included in Article 7 and 8(1) of the "Charter of Fundamental Rights 2000" [18].

13.3.2 Liberal Approach

The USA had its laws on privacy, which *per se* were very old and were limited in their application to private places (and do not extend to public places) [20]. With the advent of the Internet and the booming US economy, including the success of Silicon Valley, the country opted to go slow on the issue of data privacy rights and approached the issue on a "case by case" basis. In other words, they developed the laws on data privacy on a "selected issue" basis. This liberal policy convinced the IT industries to make a permanent address in various parts of the USA. These sector-specific laws are also federal and state-specific. Recent examples of state-specific data protection legislation are the "California Online Privacy Protection Act, 2003" and the "California Consumer Privacy Act of 2018" (on consumer privacy).

Though this liberal policy was an economic success, the ethical challenges were exposed with the 9/11 disaster, when it was revealed that the federal government had been accessing a lot of private data. This complicated the relationship with the EU, leading to the revocation of the "access to data" agreement. Technically, certain specific differences may be noted between the two [21], from the political perspective; the US is a federal republic comprising of 50 states with 1 common language, whereas the EU is not a state but an economic and political union comprising 28 member states having a diversity of cultures and languages. (There are 24 languages popularly used in the EU.) From the legal perspective, there are two types of laws, the federal and the state. Federal laws are made by central government and states make laws for respective states. The EU has regulations and directives. Regulations are basically stronger laws and they are made applicable to its formation by the EU. The directives are also strong laws as they are also made by the EU but are made to be developed by the member states according to their setup. Hence, the directives lead to a multilingual and multiple legislation passed by different EU members for specific jurisdictional applications. Because of the diversity involved typically amongst the EU members, it is tough to have uniformity in the law. Thus, it is not difficult to conclude that the legal position of the EU with regard to data privacy laws is far more complicated than the US.

13.3.3 Supervisory Approach

In Asia, China is playing an interesting role in big data and AI [22]. Privacy rights have always been debated in democracies, but the situation is not so in a non-democratic jurisdiction. The Chinese government's social credit system has also raised questions from human rights activists about the vulnerability of individuals in China [23]. Instances of measures taken against civilians by applying AI in social media platforms are commonly reported in China. Another important strategy by China to control big data was to keep the data within the territorial limits to allow jurisdiction to be invoked [24]. This practice can also be seen in use in India due to the weak law enforcement mechanism.

13.4 SHAPING UP OF LAWS PERTAINING TO GENETIC TESTING: AN ILLUSTRATION

With the advent of technology in medical science, especially genetic science, there has been a noticeable demand for the regulation and management of these data. There have been multiple legal procedures with each national developing their individual approach, but what would be best for India is yet to be implemented.

13.4.1 Europe

Even though there has been a rise in the availability of direct-to-consumer (DTC) genetic testing in recent times across the EU, it is presently not clear as to how such tests are regulated within Europe, as there is still an absence of law either formulated nationally or by the union in this accord.

The guidelines and laws are usually placed to suit provisions relating to the highlighted concepts such as medical supervision and genetic counselling, which revolve around the legal compliance through the process of gaining the informed consent of the patient before the commencement of the procedure. There are specific national laws regarding genetic testing in Europe, which conflict with the laws of some other jurisdictions; for example, some countries like France and Germany have banned DTC genetic testing. In contrast, in some jurisdictions such as Luxembourg and Poland, the practice of DTC genetic testing is, to a considerable extent, regulated by general laws addressing the healthcare services and patients' rights.

Within the European Union, biotechnological inventions involving genetic material are protected through Directive 98/44/EC, Legal Protection of Biotechnological Inventions and the European Patent Convention [25], whereas, within the international domain, these inventions are regulated through the "Agreement on Trade-Related Aspects of Intellectual Property Rights." The "TRIPs Agreement" puts forth specific minimum standards of operation that member states are expected to follow when regulating IPRs within their municipal jurisdictions. Most of the EU usually regulate their respective IPR legislations in terms of the provisions of Directive 98/44/EC [26].

A brilliant example of such a genetic study being carried out in Europe is "The Cooperative Health Research in South Tyrol" (CHRIS). This quantified macro research across the union was initiated in 2011 with the object of investigating the genetic-basis faculties related to human ageing, and their relation to the lifestyle of humans and other environmental factors prevalent within the general population. In addition, the CHRIS study has also contributed to the creation of a "comprehensive ethical, legal, and social implication" (ELSI) framework which targets long-lasting trust along with participation.

The testing system is absolutely in legal and policy compliance with the Italian and EU guidelines coupled with the "Helsinki Declaration." The protection and security of data collected and shared are carefully upheld. The code directs how information and tests can be mutually utilized by the testing agencies keeping in mind the privacy norms, as information criteria are potentially dependent on data transfer agreements. The whole regulatory and governance model based upon ethical and legal regulation is transparent and thus available for review by the community and stakeholders.

13.4.2 USA

The security of genome data is ensured through research in biobanks in the US, which derives their powers through the "Health Insurance Portability and Accountability Act, 1996" [27] and the "Privacy Rule, and the Federal Policy for Protection of Human Subjects" (Common Rule). Neither of the regulations was however formulated for biobank regulation, and in this manner, neither applies in totality to biobank-based research across America. In addition to the fact that it is difficult to decide when the Privacy Rule and Common Rules relating to HIPAA would apply, these laws apply various guidelines to ensure privacy and protection. Likewise, numerous other government and state laws also might be relevant to a specific biobank, analyst or undertaking, i.e., the stakeholders within the US setup of biobanks [27].

US laws do not legitimately address the worldwide sharing of information outside of the "EU–US Safe Harbour Agreement," which *per se* applies to the receipt of information by certain US elements from EU nations [28, 29]. Although new principles would help explain biobanking security assurances, any actualized changes ought to be concentrated to decide the adequacy of the insurances.

13.5 THE LAWS PREVAILING IN INDIA TO ADDRESS MEDICAL DATA PRIVACY

Laws are not limited to statutes, rule books (positive laws) or courts' determination in specific cases (precedents). Other law sources prevent a person from wrongdoing—for instance, morality, ethics, equity or religion. Understanding the laws relating to medical data privacy requires following a set of independent laws unless the Personal Data Protection Bill, 2019, comes into force as a separate enactment. Till then, the formal laws as provided in Table 13.3 related to medical data privacy in India call for independent scrutiny of interrelated laws. A much more complicated approach is involved in unravelling medical privacy laws today, than a simplistic solution like *pari materia* to HIPAA of US.

The existing legal system, in the absence of a comprehensive data privacy law, is vulnerable in many dimensions. The multiplicity of redressal mechanisms caused by this vacuum calls for some selective legal analysis.

13.5.1 UNDERSTANDING PRIVACY RIGHTS AS A FUNDAMENTAL RIGHT

In India, where a significant number of the child populace suffers from malnutrition and goes to school primarily for mid-day-meal or has to queue up for hours in a government hospital for affordable medical advice or travel hundreds of kilometres to the local government healthcare facilities, which doctors believe to be a punishment posting, protecting privacy rights seems to be a misnomer.

TABLE 13.3
Available Legislations to Protect Medical Data Privacy in India

S. No.	Legislations (Selective)	Provisions (Selective)
1	Indian Telegraph Act, 1885 and Indian Telegraph Rules	Sections 4 and 5 Rule 419A of the IT Rules
2	Indian Post Office Act, 1898	Section 26
3	The Indian Wireless Telegraphy Act, 1933	Sections 3 and 4 vesting the power on the Government to regulate data
4	Information Technology Act, 2000 and Information Technology Rules	Section 69
5	Unlawful Activities Prevention Act, 1967	Section 4
6	Code of Criminal Procedure, 1973	Section 91
7	Consumer Protection Act, 2019	Unfair Trade Practice to disclose the data of the consumers
8	Right to Information Act, 2005	Section 8 (including related provisions)
9	Personal Data Protection Bill, 2018	Yet to be enacted

Privacy is a fundamental right in India, however, but a "privacy right" *per se* is not included in Part III of the constitution and needs to rely upon an expanded notion of Article 21's interpretation.

> "No person shall be deprived of his life or personal liberty except according to procedure established by law."

The Supreme Court has time and again stated that the term

> "life in its wholesome meaning, under a beneficial interpretation, should include all those aspects of life that are essential to make a person's life more meaningful and worth living" [30].

The apex court, while including the right to privacy within the scope of Article 21, must have considered Article 12 and Article 17 of UDHR ICCPR respectively.

13.5.2 RIGHT TO INFORMATION ACT, 2000 (RTI ACT)

RTI Act plays a very significant role in protecting individuals' rights, mandating the state to share relevant records. In the case of Mr. Surup Singh Hrya Naik v. the State of Maharashtra, the Bombay High Court decided that the RTI Act would override and prevail over the Code of Ethics of the Medical Council of India [31]. The responsibility of the hospital to retain medical records is not explicit in any statute prevailing in India. However, in this case, the said record may be sought by an application under the RTI Act [32].

The RTI Act would, therefore, override a patient's privacy right to prioritize public interest. However, the concept of public interest is not static, and it may vary from case to case [33].

13.5.3 THE INFORMATION TECHNOLOGY ACT, 2000 (IT ACT)

The territorial challenge of data privacy has been addressed in Sections 1 and 75 of the "IT Act, 2000." The Act requires a computer, computer system or a computer network within India to bring any extraterritorial issues within its scope.

The IT Act came up *inter alia* to legitimize online agreements and regulate certain acts of online offences and civil wrongs. Data privacy is also covered under this Act but not distinctively for medical data. Thus, the general rules that apply to data apply for medical data as well. Unauthorized access to data would lead to both criminal charges and civil remedies. (Chapter IX and XI of the Act.)

13.5.4 INDIAN COUNCIL OF MEDICAL RESEARCH (ICMR)

In India, ICMR formulates, regulates and coordinates biomedical research. It is the national organization responsible for the formulation of ethical frameworks and guidelines and coordination with international organizations and other research institutes

[34]. In the past few years, India has experienced a rise in "contract research organizations" (CRO). Their emergence as organized entities conducting clinical trials, the development of stem cell therapy and commercial surrogacy are also on the rise. This significant rise in biotechnological endeavour in India today calls for guidelines governing research ethics in matters of technology-assisted reproduction, therapies through stem cells and allied activities which require compliance with ICMR's "Ethical Guidelines for Biomedical Research on Human Participants and the Good Clinical Practices, 2001," guidelines framed by the CDSCO. Similarly, the Ministry of Health is to be adhered to while formulating research proposals involving human subjects along with approval from the Institutional Ethics Committee with prior consent from the patient or the person whose sample has to be collected for testing purposes [35].

ICMR guidelines also include an important aspect of consent, "informed consent." First, the informed consent of all the human participants for all biomedical must be obtained. The "informed consent form" must be detailed and signed by the participants [20]. Only after the participants approve the form, are specific alphanumeric codes allotted to the samples.

In 2010, this process was revised, leading to the Biomedical Ethics Bill's submission in 2014. After passing the proposed Ethics Bill, a "Biomedical Research Authority" is expected to be set up to regulate and implement the various facets of biomedical research. This would, *inter alia*, include multiple aspects of biobanks as well. While ICMR has been playing an essential role in biobank guidelines, an authority created through the law (with representatives from stakeholders and having comprehensive powers) thus would be in a better position for regulation and governance in this sector, rather than the already existing guidelines which only have substantial value under Indian municipal laws. The new law *inter alia* would encourage bioethical standards.

13.6 CONCLUSION

Medical data is an emerging market for economic dominance. Personalized healthcare systems will slowly and steadily bridge the gap between clinical and real-world data. Controlling the health conditions of every individual and application of AI is going to be the order of the day and big data (or relevant data) will play a very significant role. As this transformation takes place, the possibilities for the misuse of data become a reality. The vulnerability of the state in regulating big data has been exposed and highlighted by the apex court in many cases. Where laws pertaining to medical data are going to be a reality, anticipating what is around the corner would eventually put the state in an advantageous position.

The state must play the role of a guardian to the people and ward off the misuse of data access, storage and transfer by private operators for mere financial gains. The market in medical data in India is at its nascent stage, and so are the related challenges. But the situation will be more complicated by the next decade. For India, the first step is surely the passing of the Data Privacy Bill of 2019. In its absence, a significant number of grey areas will keep on cropping up, with regard to medical data privacy in India.

Issues like linking *Aadhar* with healthcare databases, developing a uniform standard for e-health records, the regulation of health insurance records, maintaining data concerning the medical termination of pregnancy cases, regulations of DNA-based technology, etc., should be properly addressed at this juncture. India has a long way to go when it comes to data protection and more importantly medical data protection. A dedicated team of experts must be set up which would, *inter alia*, raise and address those issues democratically to achieve a balance between data availability, its regulation and the protecting of privacy rights. Said authority should also be empowered with adequate powers to impose sanctions. The proposed legislation and regulations must incorporate global standards of data management in both the public and private domains. As the world becomes a global village, Indian data privacy laws must adequately serve the need of the hour; unfortunately, they are insufficient today.

REFERENCES

1. Bellazzi, R. 2014. Big data and biomedical informatics: A challenging opportunity. *Yearbook of Medical Informatics*, 9(1), 8.
2. Vora, J., Italiya, P., Tanwar, S., Tyagi, S., Kumar, N., Obaidat, M. S., & Hsiao, K. F. 2018. Ensuring privacy and security in E-health records. In International Conference on Computer, Information and Telecommunication Systems (CITS) (pp. 1–5). IEEE.
3. 1948. *Universal Declaration of Human Rights*. https://www.un.org/en/universal-declaration-human-rights/.
4. Abouelmehdi K., Beni-Hessane A., and Khaloufi H. 2018. Big healthcare data: Preserving security and privacy. *Journal of Big Data*, 5:1.
5. Barrows Jr, Randolph C., and Paul D. Clayton. 1996. Privacy, confidentiality, and electronic medical records. *Journal of the American Medical Informatics Association*, 3(2): 139–148.
6. Borry, P., Bentzen, H. B., Budin-Ljøsne, I., Cornel, M. C., Howard, H. C., Feeney, O., ... & Riso, B. 2018. The challenges of the expanded availability of genomic information: An agenda-setting paper. *Journal of Community Genetics*, 3: 103–116.
7. 1976. *International Covenant on Civil and Political Rights*. https://treaties.un.org/doc/publication/unts/volume%20999/volume-999-i-14668-english.pdf.
8. 1950. European Convention on Human Rights. https://www.echr.coe.int/Documents/Convention_ENG.pdf.
9. 1981. Convention for the Protection of Individuals with Regard to Automatic Processing. https://rm.coe.int/16808ade9d.
10. 1995. *Directive 95/46/EC of the European Parliament*. https://eur-lex.europa.eu/legal-content/EN/TXT/?uri=celex%3A31995L0046.
11. 1997. Oviedo Convention. https://rm.coe.int/168007cf98.
12. European Group on Ethics in Science and New Technologies. 2016. *The Ethical Implications of New Health Technologies and Citizen Participation*. https://op.europa.eu/en/publication-detail/-/publication/e86c21fa-ef2f-11e5-8529-01aa75ed71a1/language-en/format-PDF/source-77404221.
13. 1995. *World Medical Association Declaration of Lisbon on Rights of the Patient*. https://www.wma.net/wp-content/uploads/2005/09/Declaration-of-Lisbon-1995.pdf.
14. 2005. *WMA Declaration of Lisbon on the Rights of the Patient*. https://www.wma.net/wp-content/uploads/2005/09/Declaration-of-Lisbon-2005.pdf.
15. 2015. *WMA Declaration of Lisbon on the Rights of Patient*. https://www.wma.net/policies-post/wma-declaration-of-lisbon-on-the-rights-of-the-patient/.

16. European Group on Ethics in Science and Technologies; European Commission, 1999. https://ec.europa.eu/info/publications/ege-opinions_en.
17. 2017. *Consultative Committee of the Convention for the Protection of Individuals with Regard to Automatic Processing of Personal Data*. https://www.coe.int/en/web/data-protection/home/-/asset_publisher/RMbj8Pk1ApgJ/content/the-bureau-of-the-consultative-committee-of-the-convention-for-the-protection-of-individuals-with-regard-to-automatic-processing-of-personal-data-t-pd.
18. 2000. *Charter of Fundamental Rights of the European Union*. https://www.europarl.europa.eu/charter/pdf/text_en.pdf.
19. Wright, A. 2017. *8 Things You Need to Know about India's Economy*. https://www.weforum.org/agenda/2017/10/eight-key-facts-about-indias-economy-in-2017.
20. Karegar, Farzaneh, Gerber, N., Volkamer, M., & Fischer-Hübner, S. 2018. Helping john to make informed decisions on using social login. In Proceedings of the 33rd Annual ACM Symposium on Applied Computing (pp. 1165–1174).
21. Coos, A. 2018. *EU vs US: How Do Their Data Privacy Regulations Square Off?* https://www.endpointprotector.com/blog/eu-vs-us-how-do-their-data-protection-regulations-square-off/.
22. Pernot-Leplay, E. 2020. *Data Privacy Law in China: Comparison with the EU and U.S. Approaches*. https://pernot-leplay.com/data-privacy-law-china-comparison-europe-usa/.
23. Kobie, N. 2019. *The Complicated Truth about China's Social Credit System*. https://www.wired.co.uk/article/china-social-credit-system-explained.
24. Walters, R. 2018. *China and US Compete to Dominate Big Data*. https://www.ft.com/content/e33a6994-447e-11e8-93cf-67ac3a6482fd.
25. Ghidini, G. 2006. *Intellectual Property and Competition Law*. https://epdf.pub/intellectual-property-and-competition-law-the-innovation-nexus.html.
26. WTO. *Agreement on Trade Related Aspects of Intellectual Property*. https://www.wto.org/english/docs_e/legal_e/27-trips.pdf.
27. 1996. *Health Insurance Portability and Accountability Act (HIPAA)*. https://www.cdc.gov/phlp/publications/topic/hipaa.html.
28. Dove, E. S., & Phillips, M. 2015. Privacy law, data sharing policies, and medical data: A comparative perspective. In *Medical Data Privacy Handbook*, 639–678. Cham: Springer.
29. *U.S.-EU Safe Harbor Framework*. https://www.ftc.gov/tips-advice/business-center/privacy-and-security/u.s.-eu-safe-harbor-framework.
30. Olga Tellis and ors. v. Bombay Municipal Corporation and ors, 1985 SCC (3) 545 (Supreme Court of India July 10, 1985).
31. Mr. Surupsingh Hrya Naik vs State Of Maharashtra, AIR 2007 Bom 121 (Bombay High Court March 23, 2007).
32. Arjesh Kumar Madhok v. Centre for Fingerprinting & Diagnostics (CDFD) 2007, Decision_26102007_06 (RTI Commissioner 2007).
33. Wetzels, M., Broers, E., Peters, P., Feijs, L., Widdershoven, J., & Habibovic, M. 2018. Patient perspectives on health data privacy and management: "Where is my data and whose is it?". *International Journal of Telemedicine and Applications*, 2018.
34. *The Indian Council of Medical Research*. https://main.icmr.nic.in/content/about-us.
35. 2006. *Ethical Guidelines for Biomedical Research on Human Participants*. https://ethics.ncdirindia.org//asset/pdf/ICMR_ethical_guidelines_for_biomedical_research_for_human_participants_2006.pdf.

Index

4IR, *see* Fourth Industrial Revolution

A

AAA, *see* Authentication, authorization and auditing
Aam Aadmi Mohallas Clinics, 137
AAMCs, *see* Aam Aadmi Mohallas Clinics
ABAC, *see* Attribute-based access control
Advanced encryption standard, 15, 41, 82, 90, 102, 103
AES, *see* Advanced encryption standard
AHHA, *see* The Australian Healthcare and Hospitals Association
Ambiguous data, 71
Anonymization, 6, 7, 10, 51, 53, 54, 58–60, 61, 117, 151, 152
Apple watch, 94
Arbitrary interference, 223, 231, 232
Asthma attacks, 68, 70
Attribute-based access control, 117
The Australian Healthcare and Hospitals Association, 215
Authentication, authorization and auditing, 33
Authentication phase, 42–44, 46–48
Automated Validation of Internet Security Protocols, 79, 90
AVISPA, *see* Automated Validation of Internet Security Protocols

B

Backward secrecy, 73
BAN, *see* Burrows–Abadi–Needham
Big data, 1, 8–10, 26, 110, 113, 132, 133, 146, 154, 156, 157, 167, 175, 184–187, 194, 230, 235, 238
Biohashing function, 78
Blockchain-based HIS, 125, 128
Blockchain-based infrastructure, 109, 124, 128
Bluesnarfing, 95
Bluetooth Low Energy, 93, 95, 101
BTLE, *see* Bluetooth Low Energy
Burrows–Abadi–Needham, 77

C

California Consumer Privacy Act, 32, 237
Canadian Standards Association, 218
CBC, *see* Cipher block chaining
CCPA, *see* California Consumer Privacy Act
Chaotic map, 41, 42, 46, 47, 57, 76
Cipher block chaining, 15
Clinical information, 2, 13, 52
Cloud healthcare data, 23
Cloud servers, 22, 25, 29, 67, 68, 71–73, 92, 224
Cloud service provider, 23, 27, 33
CMS, *see* Cryptographic message syntax
Consent management, 211, 224
Convention, 108–233, 235
Crossroads, 147–150
Cross-site scripting, 92
Cryptographic message syntax, 59
CSP, *see* Cloud service provider
CSS, *see* Cross-site scripting
Cyber-attacks, 9, 102, 211, 222
Cybersecurity, 4, 8 9, 59, 60, 231

D

Data anonymity, 6
Data anonymization, *see* Data anonymity
Data at rest, 7, 8 26, 71, 72
Data consistency, 55
Data defocusing, 7
Data modelling, 115
Data processing, 1, 10, 32, 109, 167, 186, 188–190, 218, 232, 235, 236
Data Protection Act, 118, 204, 205, 209, 212, 236
Data provenance, 21, 29, 30, 118, 119
Data quality, 30
Data revolution, 178
Data transformation, 115
Database attack, 75
DDoS, *see* Distributed denial of service
Decision support systems, 112, 113
Decryption algorithm, 76
DICOM, *see* Digital Imaging and Communications in Medicine
Differential privacy, 27, 84
Diffie–Hellman key exchange, 83, 84
Digital collection, 14, 151
Digital Imaging and Communications in Medicine, 51–53
Digital privacy, 3, 6 8, 10, 11, 15, 16
Digital risk, 2, 9
Digital signature, 2 3, 8 10, 12, 14, 16, 26, 60, 77, 83, 103, 119, 121, 206
Digitization, 2, 14, 55, 113, 137
Distributed denial of service, 40, 222

DNA, 142, 144, 185, 187, 223, 243
DNN, 60
Doctor–patient relationship, 30
Dolev-Yao (DY) threat model, 71
DPA, *see* Data Protection Act

E

Eavesdropping, 33, 95, 100–102, 116
ECHR, *see* European Convention on Human Rights
EGE, *see* European Group on Ethics
EHR, *see* Electronic Health Records
Elasticity, 22, 23
Electronic Healthcare Records, 4, 5, 14, 51, 110, 146, 151, 167, 182, 195, 225, 244
Encryption algorithm, 56, 60, 71, 76, 83
Encryption, 2, 3 6, 7 8, 12, 15, 25, 28, 29, 33, 41, 46, 51, 53, 56, 57, 59–61, 71, 74–76, 82, 83, 93, 94, 99, 100, 102, 103, 116, 128, 151, 152, 162, 175, 212, 215
European Convention on Human Rights, 202, 208, 231
European Group on Ethics, 209, 234, 235, 243
Execution cost, 46
Existential inference, 55, 56
Eyewear device, 93, 97

F

Facebook, 31, 32, 55
Facial features, 56
Firewall, 2, 9
Fitbit, 91–98, 101, 104
Fitbit tracker, 94
Fitness, 102, 104, 105
Fog-based architecture, 67
Fog servers, 67, 68
Forward secrecy, 73
Fourth Industrial Revolution, 132
Fuzzy extractor, 78

G

GDPR, *see* General Data Protection Regulation
General Data Protection Regulation, 93, 187
Google Glass, 91, 93, 97–101
GPS, 58, 101, 229

H

Hardware security modules, 15, 20
Health Information System, 109–114, 124, 128, 135, 137, 150
Health Insurance Portability and Accountability Act, 58, 59, 212, 214, 239, 243

Healthcare Organizations, 4, 25, 117, 151, 177, 206, 218
Healthcare professionals, 15, 150, 151
HIPPA, *see* Health Insurance Portability and Accountability Act
HIS, *see* Health Information System
HITECH Act, 118, 236
Homomorphic encryption, 27, 28, 60, 82
Hospitalization, 2, 5, 69, 136, 151
HPV, *see* Human papillomavirus
HSBlox, 168
HSM, *see* Hardware security modules
HTTPS connection, 59
Human development report, 133, 158
Human papillomavirus, 134
Human rights, 12, 31, 148, 191, 199, 202, 203, 208, 223, 231–233, 235, 238
HybrEx, *see* Hybrid execution
Hybrid execution, 117

I

IaaS, *see* Infrastructure as a service
IBM Watson, 182
ICMR, *see* Indian Council of Medical Research
Identity-based anonymization, 117
Image segmentation, 57
Immutability, 119, 120
Impersonation, 42, 71, 72, 74
Indian Council of Medical Research, 138, 139, 159, 229, 241, 244
Information Technology, 109, 146, 147, 150, 214, 240
Infrastructure as a service, 24
Instagram, 55
International Covenant on Civil and Political Rights, 202, 208, 231
Internet of Healthcare Things, 65, 67, 69, 71, 73, 75, 77, 79, 81, 83, 85, 87, 89
Internet of Things, 65, 92, 104
IoHT, *see* Internet of Healthcare Things
IoT, *see* Internet of Things
IT, *see* Information Technology
IT Act and IT (Amendment) Act, 118
ITreatU, 165, 173

J

Japanese encephalitis virus, 134
Jawbone, 91–101
JEV, *see* Japanese encephalitis virus
JPEG, 58

K

Knowledge creation, 115

Index

L

Low-frequency coefficients, 57

M

MAC address, 97, 102–105
Malware attack, 74
Man-in-the-middle, 33, 40, 74, 80, 84, 93, 99, 100, 102, 103
Marketing Development Assistance, 137
Masking, 7, 116
Master patient index, 111
MDA, *see* Marketing development assistance
MEC, *see* Medical ethics committee
Medical claim management system, 166
Medical confidentiality, 199, 202–206
Medical ethics committee, 55
Medical images, 51–57, 61
Medical keyframes, 57, 76
Medical tourism service providers, 137
Metadata, 29, 30, 55–61, 169
MTSPs, *see* Medical tourism service providers

N

Nanotechnology, 154
National Digital Health Ecosystem, 137
National Family Health Survey, 136
National Health Act, 216
National Health Service of England, 204
National Heart, Lung and Blood Institute, 205
National Institute of Mental Health and Neurosciences, 137
National Research Council, 181
NDHE, *see* National Digital Health Ecosystem
Nehru-Mahalanobis strategy, 135
NHA, *see* National Health Act
NHLBI, *see* National Heart, Lung and Blood Institute
NHS, *see* National Health Service of England
NIMHANS, *see* National Institute of Mental Health and Neurosciences
Non-repudiation, 73
NRC, *see* National Research Council

O

OCR, 59, 61
Oviedo Convention, 232, 233, 243

P

P2P, *see* Peer-to-peer
PaaS, *see* Platform as a service
Password-guessing, 41, 42
Patient Safety and Quality Improvement Act, 118, 236
PBFT, *see* Practical Byzantine fault tolerance
Peer-to-peer, 125, 129, 166
Personal digital information, 3
Personal Information Protection and Electronic Documents Act, 118, 196, 236
Personalized anonymization, 7
Pharmaceutical companies, 27, 113, 127, 183
PHI, *see* Protected health information
PIPEDA, *see* Personal Information Protection and Electronic Documents Act
PKI, *see* Public Key Encryption
Platform as a service, 24
PNG, 58
PoB, *see* Proof of Burn
PoC, *see* Proof of capacity
PoET, *see* Proof of elapsed time
PoS, *see* Proof of stake
PoW, *see* Proof of work
Powerful servers, 26, 68
Practical Byzantine fault tolerance, 123
Precision Medicine, 181
Privileged-insider attack, 75
PRNG, *see* Pseudorandom number generator
Proof of Burn, 124
Proof of capacity, 124
Proof of elapsed time, 124
Proof of stake, 123
Proof of work, 123, 170
Protected health information, 31, 53, 62
Pseudorandom number generator, 76
PSQIA, *see* Patient Safety and Quality Improvement Act
Public Key Encryption, 103

Q

QR photo-bombing malware, 101

R

Radio frequency identification, 70
RAFT, 169
Ransomware, 4, 9 14, 15, 74, 212
RBAC, *see* Role based access control
Red-tape, 211, 220, 221
Region of interest, 57
Registration phase, 42–44, 46
Re-linkage, 55, 56
Remote patient monitoring, 111
Replay, 47, 71, 74, 80, 84
REST methods, 104, 105
RFID, *see* Radio frequency identification
Right to Confidentiality, 202, 233
Right to information, 202, 218, 219, 234, 240

ROI, *see* Region of interest
Role based access control, 117
Russian Federal Law on Personal Data, 118, 236

S

SaaS, *see* Software as a service
Samsung Galaxy Watch, 91, 93, 99
Scrambling, 6
Smart city, 37, 38
Smart healthcare, 37–40, 67, 68, 70, 72–75
Smart tags, 70
Social networks, 1, 5 13, 184
Software as a service, 24
State-sponsored surveillance, 211, 223
Substitution, 6
Supply chain management, 70, 168

T

Technology-enabled healthcare, 179
Telecare medicine information systems, 41
Third party, 53, 73, 92, 117, 121, 147, 200, 211, 217, 220, 221, 224, 233, 235
Third-party protection, 73
Threat Model, 65, 71, 75, 80, 86
TIFF, 58
TMIS, *see* Telecare medicine information systems

Traffic analysis, 40, 73
Trojan, 74
Twitter, 55

U

Unauthorized parties, 72
Universal Declaration of Human Rights, 223, 231, 243

V

Velocity, 2, 230
Veracity, 2, 10
VISCERAL project, 54
Von Willebrand disease, 139
VPN, 60
VWD, *see* Von Willebrand disease

W

Wearable healthcare devices, 69, 105
Wellness Tourism Service Providers, 137
World Happiness Ranking, 134
World Health Organization, 135, 147, 149
World Medical Association, 233
WTSPs, *see* Wellness Tourism Service Providers

Printed in the United States
By Bookmasters